Medical Music Therapy: A Model Program for Clinical Practice, Education, Training, and Research

Medical Music Therapy: A Model Program for Clinical Practice, Education, Training, and Research

Jayne M. Standley
Dianne Gregory
Jennifer Whipple
Darcy Walworth
Judy Nguyen
Jennifer Jarred
Kristen Adams
Danielle Procelli
Andrea Cevasco

American Music Therapy Association, Inc.

The American Music Therapy Association is a non-profit association dedicated to increasing access to quality music therapy services for individuals with disabilities or illnesses or for those who are interested in personal growth and wellness. AMTA provides extensive educational and research information about the music therapy profession. Referrals for qualified music therapists are also provided to consumers and parents. AMTA holds an annual conference every autumn and its eight regions hold conferences every spring.

For up-to-date information, please access the AMTA website at www.musictherapy.org

ISBN: 1-884914-14-4

The American Music Therapy Association, Inc.
8455 Colesville Road, Suite 1000
Silver Spring, MD 20910

Phone: (301) 589-3300
Fax: (301) 589-5175
Email: info@musictherapy.org
Website: www.musictherapy.org

Printed in The United States of America

Dedication

This book is dedicated to the medical staff of Tallahassee Memorial HealthCare, the caring people who facilitate and support music therapy interventions for their patients on a daily basis; to the many FSU students who have returned so much to the community during their thousands of hours at the hospital; and to Larry Abele, the FSU Provost, and Toni McCoy and Paula Fortunas, the TMH Foundation Directors, who have provided the funds to make the entire program possible.

About the Cover

The cover of this book is a photograph of the public relations brochure designed and funded by the hospital to acquaint patients with the addition of music therapy services to the medical programs. It features Jennifer Batey, music therapy intern.

Contents

Contents

List of Tables

List of Figures

List of Forms

Preface

The Music Therapy Department at The Florida State University began providing practica students to the pediatric and oncology units of Tallahassee Memorial HealthCare (TMH) over 20 years ago. There was no clinical music therapy at the hospital, so students were supervised by university faculty and contacts with patients were convenience encounters without a formal referral system. During these early days, medical research projects were regularly conducted by FSU MT faculty and graduate students. Hospital staff became familiar with, and supportive of, the possibilities of music therapy as a clinical service for their patients. However, hospital budgets were strained and funds could not be obtained to establish a clinical MT position. In 1999, the Florida State University Provost, Larry Abele, provided funds for a position and the development of the program began. Today, it is a comprehensive clinical, educational, and research setting that is one of the most innovative music therapy programs in the world.

The purpose of this book is to provide a model for university/hospital partnerships to further the provision of medical music therapy services. Such partnerships improve the quality of patient care and enhance the educational opportunities for students. It is a situation where everybody wins and the costs are amazingly affordable in comparison to the many benefits derived.

We have included in this book everything that we have developed that contributes to the success of the program. Each piece is integral to the ever expanding array of comprehensive services delivered. Music therapy programs meet the highest clinical standards and are enhanced by an influx of new students every semester. Students in training receive outstanding opportunities while contributing to the innovative expansion of the program. Volunteers are changed forever by their service while improving the quality of life of the many patients at TMH. Faculty have a "real life" platform for the principles professed in the classroom and are forever stimulated by the changing conditions of a vibrant clinical program thereby maintaining coursework on the cutting edge of medical music therapy. Research opportunities at the hospital are rich and varied and contribute new information that is continuously incorporated in the clinical programs to improve services.

Preface

There are many authors associated with this material. Each has contributed greatly to the program as it now exists. No one person could create something so innovative, comprehensive, and well organized. It takes a team and the contents of this book attest to the outstanding qualities of this very special group of people. It is our hope that others will be stimulated by the model that we provide here and embark upon similar endeavors. It is a thoroughly exciting and fulfilling career opportunity.

Section I

The Music Therapy Partnership
Between
The Florida State University and
Tallahassee Memorial HealthCare

Chapter 1

Overview

∽

Jayne M. Standley, Ph.D., MT-BC, and
Darcy Walworth, M.M., MT-BC

OVERVIEW

A rapidly emerging clinical area, medical music therapy services have been established nationwide in children's hospitals, cancer settings, and general medical facilities. The American Music Therapy Association (AMTA) reports that currently 10% of music therapists provide services in medical/surgical settings (AMTA, 2004). Additionally, 16 medical sites are AMTA approved for internship training with another 3 currently being in inactive status.

Research in music and medicine is prolific and reveals a variety of recommendations for clinical application in the practice of medical music therapy. A meta-analysis of music research in medical/dental care examined the primary dependent variable from 92 studies and found an average effect size of 1.17 which increased to 1.40 for those studies using the patients' preferred music (Standley, 2000). This body of research revealed highly positive benefits for the following uses of music: to reduce pain; to reduce anxiety or stress; to reduce nausea in chemotherapy or hemodialysis; to increase motor abilities and joint motility; to shorten labor in childbirth; to increase capacity and strength in respiration ability; to reduce fear or trauma related to serious illness or injury; to assist in acceptance of death or disability; to assist with management of illness or personal affairs; to assist adjustment to organ transplant; to stimulate or elicit responses from those with cognitive dysfunction or those in isolation; to improve short or long-term memory; to increase awareness, self-control, and monitoring of physiological responses; to reduce depression/isolation; and to increase feelings of well-being (Standley, 2000).

A second meta-analysis on music research specific to pediatric patients showed an overall effect size of $d = .64$ for children aged term birth to 21 years with effects being greatest for adolescents and infants/toddlers. These additional objectives for medical music therapy with children were identified: to increase pacification in the newborn nursery, to decrease respiratory distress, to increase enjoyment of physiotherapy, to increase socialization with hospital personnel, to increase listening and auditory processing skills, to increase or maintain developmental milestones and independence of pediatric patients during extended hospitalizations, to eliminate need for sedation during radiology tests, to induce relaxation or sleep, and to facilitate parent training (Standley & Whipple, 2003).

Finally, a meta-analysis of music research with premature infants found an average effect size of $d = .83$ (Standley, 2002) and identified a variety of music therapy clinical objectives for infants in the Neonatal Intensive Care Unit: to improve oxygen saturation levels, to increase weight gain, to shorten hospital stay, to increase tolerance for stimulation, to reinforce non-nutritive sucking and increase feeding rates, and to facilitate parent training for interacting with premature infants.

To date, the music therapy (MT) professional literature contains no description of a comprehensive medial MT clinical program. The purpose of this text is to describe a university/ hospital partnership that has been designed as a model for the integration of the highest level of evidence-based clinical services with opportunities for student and allied health training while promoting further research into the field. Since medical services often cite lack of financial resources to implement music therapy services, a complete cost-benefit is provided to document efficacy. It is hoped that this text will prove helpful to those music therapists and medical administrators seeking to enhance services to patients through the addition of medical music therapy.

The Partnership Between Tallahassee Memorial HealthCare and The Florida State University Music Therapy Department

One of the most innovative medical music therapy clinical programs in the nation is located at Tallahassee Memorial HealthCare (TMH). As a demonstration of evidence based practice in medical music therapy (MT), this clinical program was implemented by the Music Therapy Department of the Florida State University (FSU) more than five years ago. Its purposes are to establish and conduct research-based medical MT services of the highest quality and to provide innovative, cutting edge training for MT students and interns. The clinical services consist of *a priori* MT protocols dictated by specific diagnoses and medical/social problems which use proven music therapy treatment options with predictable outcomes. Medical music therapy services are accessed through a combination of staff, interdisciplinary teams, and patient self referrals.

Description of the Comprehensive Program

The FSU/TMH partnership for a Medical Music Therapy/Arts in Medicine Program was established in March 1999. It is directed by Jayne Standley, Ph.D., MT-BC, Director of the Florida State University Music Therapy Program, and consists of two distinct programs supervised by one non-faculty position entitled, Coordinator of Medical Music Therapy and AIM Programs, that is funded in the School of Music and assigned full-time to TMH. The Coordinator of this program must have a Master's degree in music therapy and must be Board Certified. The founding Coordinator was Jennifer Whipple, Ph.D., MT-BC, who was followed by Darcy Walworth, M.M., MT-BC. The current Coordinator is Judy Nguyen, M.M., MT-BC. All equipment, supplies, internship stipends, expenses, and office space/clerical support are provided by the TMH Foundation. In the last year, the Foundation has funded a second MT-BC position and increased their annual budget contribution from $14,800 initially to $43,000 currently.

Training components of the TMH Medical Music Therapy program are designed in accordance with guidelines of the 4,000 member American Music Therapy Association.

The purposes of the Medical MT program are five-fold:

1. to provide clinical music therapy services to TMH patients in accordance with established medical music therapy practices and approved hospital protocols;
2. to serve as a national training site for music therapy interns who are completing a Bachelor's or Certification/Master's degree in music therapy;
3. to provide training and supervision for FSU music therapy majors in clinical practica at the graduate and undergraduate levels;
4. to conduct research on innovative uses of medical music therapy;
5. to provide a national model for training allied health professionals in the medical uses of music therapy.

Clinical privileges for the Medical Music Therapy staff were established under the auspices of the TMH Medical Director with daily supervision/coordination through the Director of the Neuroscience Department who is a Registered Nurse (her current title is Oncology Service Line Administrator). All medical protocols and bases for referrals to MT clinical services were negotiated separately with each unit of the hospital prior to program implementation. Additionally, it is a standard procedure of the hospital that a social functional assessment is made of each patient upon admission by the unit nurse. Selected items on that assessment trigger an automatic referral to music therapy. Patients or relatives of patients can also request music therapy. All services are provided free of charge to patients of TMH.

Program Description and Staffing

The current program staff consists of:

- 1 M.M., MT-BC Coordinator funded by FSU
- 1 M.M., MT-BC funded by the TMH Foundation, a position added in 2004 as Institute Supervisor
- 2 MT interns (each 40 hrs/wk for 1,000 hours) with stipends funded by TMH Foundation
- ¼-time Graduate Assistant (10 hrs/wk) funded by the School of Music
- 10–22 practica students/semester, FSU MT majors with no funding who receive course credit.

There is also an Art Therapy Intern.

Medical Music Therapy Services

In-hospital clinical music therapy services are provided in response to medical referrals on the following units: Newborn Intensive Care Unit, Pediatrics/Peds ICU, Diabetes floor, Oncology, Heart and Vascular Institute, Pulmonary floor, Geriatric Inpatients, Labor and Delivery, Cardiovascular Lab, Radiology, Intermediate Care Unit, Orthopedic-Neurologic Floor, the Rehabilitation Center, and Neurologic ICU. Clinical MT services are also provided on a regularly scheduled basis in the following outpatient programs: NeuroScience Center Parkinson's Voice Program, Neuro-Rehabilitation, Outpatient Surgery, Pediatric Rehabilitation, Kids Korner Pediatric Services, and Adult Day Services.

All patient contacts are documented in the hospital computerized medical records system. An annual report is drafted from these data to ascertain patient contacts and overall results and distributed to hospital and university administrators involved in funding the program.

Arts in Medicine Services

The Arts in Medicine Program (AIM) is an interdisciplinary group of volunteers composed of artists, musicians, performers, physicians, therapists, clinical practitioners, medical staff, students, and educators. Its purpose is to promote the health and well-being of TMH patients and families through the myriad relationships between the arts and human responses. AIM is designed to bring together the rich resources of the FSU arts and clinical programs with the Tallahassee arts community for the purpose of benefiting TMH patients and their families. The AIM program components include volunteers providing direct patient interactions with the arts, scheduled performances in multiple locations throughout the facility, enhancement of environmental aesthetics, and special projects designed to facilitate use of medical services or improve comfort levels of patients. This program is separate from the volunteer program of the hospital and all training, placement, and ongoing supervision of AIM volunteers are responsibilities of the AIM Coordinator. Additionally, a web-based community service course has been established through the FSU Music Therapy Department for FSU students to participate in AIM (see Chapter 2). Many of these students are arts and pre-medicine majors, but any student at FSU may enroll.

The same person who directs the Medical MT program also coordinates all AIM functions. These duties include:

- Design and implement AIM Programs
- Recruit, orient, train, and coordinate volunteers
- Receive requests, match interests, and facilitate contacts between volunteers and patients
- Ascertain, implement, and monitor hospital guidelines for volunteers, including, dress and grooming standards, use of name tags and sign in procedures, maintenance of confidentiality policies, acceptance of responsibility, etc.
- Budget, maintain, and allocate supplies
- Acquire space for programs and storage of equipment and supplies
- Schedule people and space
- Assist volunteers as needed

In addition to coordinating medical MT and AIM, as a courtesy to other FSU-related degree areas, the Coordinator provides a liaison between FSU degree programs in the arts/child life and TMH clinical programs. She assists with placement of their students and interns, and supervises Art Therapy Interns through an agreement with the Art Therapy degree programs.

AIM volunteers select their service area from a menu of possibilities provided to them at orientation or design a special service through the Coordinator and faculty if they are enrolled in the AIM course. The menu of service opportunities includes items such as the following:

1. Concerts, dance and music performances are regularly scheduled in a variety of locations, including the Atrium, the cafeteria, Extended Care/Long Term Care, patient gathering areas and playrooms, and waiting rooms. Volunteers are sought through the FSU School of Music and Dance Departments, local high school music programs, Florida A&M University music and dance programs, and music and dance groups in the Tallahassee community.
2. Visiting art exhibits are coordinated and placed in the Atrium for varying intervals.
3. Ongoing Projects Menu

    - **"Things Are Looking Up."** Helping pediatric patients paint a ceiling tile while they are patients on the unit that TMH then installs in the ceiling of the Pediatric area for the aesthetic enjoyment of future patients.

- Distributing closed circuit television programs. Adult programming consists of relaxation and leisure tapes.

- Remodeling the Pediatric Playroom and Teen Room.

- Volunteering in Extended Care/Long Term Care facility, including adopting a "foster grandparent," ongoing participation in regularly scheduled art programs, concerts.

- **"Miccosukee Road,"** a Tuesday/Thursday morning children's hour conducted by the MTs and assisted by volunteers. It features "Feed Me a Story" books donated by Publix Grocery, and songs, and puppets.

- **"Computer Pals,"** assisting pediatric patients in fully utilizing the Starbright computer programs created by the Steven Spielberg Foundation.

- Assisting with Labor and Delivery Celebrations: Music, poetry, or art projects with new parents to celebrate the birth of their child.

- Caribbean Festival Mask Making: Helping children make masks to prepare for celebrating the annual Caribbean Festival in Tallahassee.

- Music for Adult Surgery Patients: Distributing tape library and individual tape players to accompany patients through surgery to reduce amount of anesthesia and pain medication needed

- **"Bookmarks,"** conducting literature and Poetry readings throughout the hospital provided by volunteers for patients in all age ranges.

- Bereavement Programs, including memorial and "Celebration of an individual's life" services, memorial artwork, memorial gardens, etc.

- Environmental Aesthetics, including placing visual arts throughout the facility and developing gardens and designs for special areas such as playrooms for children, etc. This program seeks to bring the arts into the TMH environment for enhancing aesthetics and providing stimulation or comfort to its patients.

- Staff Stress Management. Arts programs and volunteer opportunities to reduce staff stress, including concerts, movement and relaxation activities, art projects, gardening, etc.

- Special holiday celebrations and arts performances throughout the hospital.

- Fund Raising. Benefits, sale of art products produced in the program, sorority/fraternity contests to decorate patient room doors, etc.

References

American Music Therapy Association. (2004). *AMTA member sourcebook 2004*. Silver Spring, MD: Author.

Standley, J. (2000). Music research in medical treatment. In American Music Therpay Association (Ed.), *Effectiveness of music therapy procedures: Documentation of research and clinical practice* (3rd ed.; pp. 1–64). Silver Spring, MD: American Music Therapy Association.

Standley, J. (2002). A meta-analysis of the efficacy of music therapy for premature infants. *Journal of Pediatric Nursing, 17*(2), 107–113.

Standley, J., & Whipple, J. (2003). Pediatric music therapy: A meta-analysis. In S. Robb (Ed.), *Music therapy in pediatric healthcare: Research and best practice* (pp.1–18). Silver Spring, MD: American Music Therapy Association.

Chapter 2

Arts in Medicine Service Learning Course: Design and University Student Perceptions

∽

Dianne Gregory, M.M., MT-BC

Quotes from FSU Students

One thing I learned is that I am very fortunate to be where I am today, and that I am lucky to wake up every morning healthy. From working with some extremely sick patients I realized that there are a lot of things that I take for granted, and don't think about, but that it's important to reflect on even the small things in life.

— *A. Cavallaro, Nursing, Junior*

The most valuable part of my experience was learning to work and deal with all types of people. From volunteering in pediatrics to oncology, I saw all kinds of people with all different situations. I really learned to adapt to different people's needs and I was challenged with the different types of situations that arose. I also value the way I look at hospitals now. I have less fear and I am more comfortable with them.

— *M. von Hermann, Communications, Senior*

I learned that I am a much better listener than I thought I was. Most of my time at the Extended Care Unit was spent listening to the patients. I would often find myself thinking about the things they had talked about later in the week. My whole life, my parents have urged me to listen more and talk less, and through the AIMS program, I learned that I can actually do that.

— *K. Trainer, Music Therapy, Freshman*

I learned that it is really simple to hold a conversation with an elderly individual and that it is important to visit the elderly because they really enjoy it and it makes them feel better. I haven't grown up with many elderly people in my life. Not having my grandparents around made it difficult to learn to talk to an elderly person. But this experience made it easy to talk to strangers and the elderly and make them comfortable enough to want to share with me about their lives and their families. There was an elderly patient that one of the nurses said was a little bit rude, and I decided to just try and visit with him to see how he was doing. I ended up talking to him for the rest of my contact hours and he ended up being a nice elderly man. Much of his rudeness I guess was that when you are in a hospital you don't want to be there any longer than you need to be. He had been there almost a week and a half and his emotional state was high. He just wanted to go home.

— *J. Collazos, Exercise Science, Senior*

From this experience I learned that if you don't just throw yourself into a situation, you will never get anything out of it. If I didn't allow myself to talk to the people that I met I would have never known them. I think just talking to people I didn't know in these structured environments helped me in social settings as well, which really makes me happy because I have been struggling with that for a while.

— *S. Fishman, Child Development, Senior*

Many times I have thought of myself as more of an introvert who has a hard time going and talking to strange people. Since I am a business major I am trying to work on this because I have to do presentations and really interact with others. This course really helped me because I had to be outgoing with people I did not know. I think I got a lot more comfortable at it and I learned that I can be an outgoing, friendly and creative person. Once again, with time it got easier and I became more comfortable with it. I never expected this course to help me in that way but it really did.

— *M. Lee, Human Resource Management, Senior*

ARTS IN MEDICINE SERVICE LEARNING COURSE: DESIGN AND UNIVERSITY STUDENT PERCEPTIONS

An elective stand-alone service learning course has been added to the TMH/FSU partnership. It is available for academic credit to all university students at the Florida State University and is entitled "Arts in Medicine Service" (AIMS). Although the title may seem selective toward students either majoring in one of the arts or pursuing medicine-related degrees, the course is open to all students interested in volunteering in the Arts in Medicine program at TMH. The objective of the Arts in Medicine program is to use a variety of arts alternatives, including the more formal venues of music, visual arts, and drama, to humanize the hospital environment for patients, visitors, and staff. Projects depend on student self-selection. The majority of students choose projects that incorporate their particular abilities and their interest in engaging and entertaining individual or small groups of patients. Students practice and monitor their interpersonal skills and creative resourcefulness on a regular basis with each personal contact that ranges from infants and young children recuperating from surgery to adults undergoing tests and treatment for serious illnesses. Some current arts-related AIMS projects include performing music in the hospital atrium at peak visiting times and assisting with individual and small group art projects either in patient rooms or unit rooms designated for group activity. Other entertainment options include less formal experiences such as reading books and magazines for patients or playing board games or computer games in patients' rooms. Students receive academic credit for completing the orientation session requirements, participating in AIMS projects, fulfilling weekly contracts of hourly contacts at the hospital, submitting weekly reports documenting contacts and reflective learning, and completing a final essay. Collaboration between the university and the hospital is critical to the success of the course.

Service learning programs in all levels of education encourage students to become actively involved in community-based agencies serving the general public (Education Commission of the States, 2001; Honnet & Poulsen, 1989). Most higher education faculty view service learning as distinctly different from prerequisite field experiences, course-related community-based practica, and internships that satisfy curricular and professional degree requirements. "Unlike practica and internship, the experiential activity in a service learning course is not necessarily skill-based within the context of professional education" (Bringle & Hatcher, 1996, p. 222). A common goal across formal college service learning experiences in course-related volunteer activities and stand-alone service courses is to provide experiential learning for students to practice sharing with communities within the context of civic responsibility. Most definitions of service learning also include credit-bearing criteria to distinguish it from extracurricular volunteer experiences.

The National Post Secondary Student Aid Survey completed during the 1999–2000 academic year and reported by Lenkowsky (2003) supports the need for higher education service learning. Only 35% of undergraduate students reported volunteering, which is "considerably less than the percentage of all Americans who volunteered" their services during the same year. Although procedures for establishing service learning programs have been formalized to promote volunteerism (Furco, 1999), the assumption that community service experiences actually complement citizenship training for college students is questioned by some administrators.

According to Bok (2001), most surveys regarding college student volunteerism suggest that students perceive community service as an alternative to citizenship and political participation, not an integrated part of civic responsibility. If this is the case, student perceptions related to actual participation in service learning courses provide insight into the function of community service programs in higher education.

This chapter will (1) describe the development and current status of the AIMS service learning course, (2) provide information from an evaluation of the most recent student involvement, and (3) discuss the relevance of service learning in light of AIMS students' perceptions.

Development and Current Status

The AIMS course is listed in the university School of Music offerings at both graduate and undergraduate levels. A music therapy faculty member organizes and supervises AIMS academic components which include creating and maintaining the course web site, directing on-campus orientation and final sessions, assisting students with choices of projects, and evaluating student participation, weekly documentation and final essays. The FSU/TMH Coordinator of Music Therapy administers the on-site orientation session, provides materials and equipment for AIMS projects, and educates the service personnel about the AIMS program expectations from volunteers. Both the FSU faculty and staff member provide assistance to individual students throughout the semester.

Enrollment

Initial enrollment in the AIMS course consisted primarily of relatively small groups of undergraduate music students including music therapy majors (Gregory, 2001). Current enrollment includes undergraduate students from 13 different departments across the university, the result of several recruitment alternatives. The most effective method appears to be "word of mouth" between students. Other methods have included an article appearing in the campus newspaper, flyers posted on departmental bulletin boards, information tables set up at strategic places during days allotted for course advisement and registration, conversations with advisors, class presentation, and letters and flyers sent to academic advisors in several departments. The course is repeatable with the option of receiving from 1 to 3 academic credits for each semester of participation. Each academic credit hour translates into 2 hours per week of hospital contact. A student, for example, taking AIMS for 3 credits, is contracting for 6 hours a week for 15 weeks a semester, a total of 90 hours of hospital contact across the semester. A student enrolling for 1 credit contracts for 30 hours of contact. Except for the group orientation sessions and final session, the course is totally community-based. It is also highly individualized according to students' interests, abilities, project selection, participation contracts, and contact schedules.

Requirements

A course web site provides a common structure and communication avenue between the instructor and students. It includes a home page with staff contact information and email links, a syllabus page explaining course objectives, procedures, and grading policy; a course calendar that is updated weekly with assignments and pertinent announcements; and a course resource page. The resource page provides Internet links to related web sites and includes several course management links. The most practical links include (1) a Weekly Report Online Form that provides a uniform outline for submitting information, (2) a Verification of Receipt of Assignments chart that is updated with the instructor's evaluative feedback within 24 hours of students' submissions, and (3) a Master Schedule depicting AIMS student volunteers' hospital locations by hours of the day in hospital units. Other resource links include several web sites related to Arts in Medicine projects and background information.

Students are required to attend two orientation sessions during the first week of classes. The first orientation session occurs on campus and provides an opportunity for the instructor to meet the students and to introduce the web site and explain course requirements. Students also complete inventories regarding their interests, objectives, and personal qualities. The second orientation session occurs at the hospital and provides an opportunity for students to meet their hospital supervisor and learn protocol including patient confidentiality, medical procedures, dress codes, grooming standards, and hospital clearance procedures. The clearance procedures include completing PPD tests, background checks, and drug screenings, and providing immunization and student liability insurance documentation prior to receiving an AIMS identification badge that allows them entrance into hospital units. The hospital orientation concludes with an escorted trip through various units with stops at AIMS resource rooms where available projects and materials are provided. Attendance at both orientation sessions is mandatory for continuing the AIMS course. An important objective during orientation is to help students discriminate between Arts in Medicine and Medical Music Therapy. They read an online article (Gregory & Whipple, 2000) that describes differences in personnel, objectives, and procedures for the two programs. Music therapists, for example, are specified as clinically trained hospital staff members with at least a Bachelor's degree in music therapy and Board Certification whose primary role is to interact with specific patients referred to music therapy by the medical staff to reach specific clinical objectives. AIMS volunteers, on the other hand, serve a valid purpose as degree-seeking students who use their time and skills to entertain patients and enhance the hospital environment. The article clarifies the role of music for AIMS volunteers, particularly the musically experienced students in addition to music therapy majors and other music majors. It also teaches volunteers how to respond to misconceptions they may encounter. Students role play as volunteers several polite corrective answers to hospital staff members or patients who misidentify them as music therapists or music therapy interns. This discrimination process continues to be a critical step. AIM and MMT are relatively new additions that not only started simultaneously but were relatively unfamiliar services to the majority of staff members. To minimize confusion, the only music project option currently available to AIMS volunteers is performing in the atrium. One person directing both programs facilitates communication with hospital personnel and student volunteers about the differences between AIM and MMT.

Following the orientation sessions, students determine their individual schedules for weekly visits to specific units. No more than two AIMS volunteers are allowed on a unit during the same hour to prevent overcrowding and to spread the availability of AIMS projects throughout different units each period of the day. Students who repeat the AIMS course often volunteer to serve as peer tutors for new students requesting assistance at the beginning of the semester. Individual conferences with instructors are offered to assist students. The only other scheduled group meeting occurs during the last week of the semester. Students meet on campus to submit final essays and accountability logs, complete inventories and web site evaluations, and share personally enlightening AIMS anecdotes. At various times during the semester some students elect to work in small groups to provide additional projects around specific holidays or particular interests. The majority of students, however, complete regularly scheduled hours during the week interacting with patients in their selected units.

Evaluation of Student Participation

As the AIMS course evolved during the first two years, several policies, procedures, and forms were selected and adapted based on student feedback and practicality. As a result, students during the early semesters did not complete all of the documents subsequently standardized during the last two years. Complete data sets of first time AIMS volunteers during the last two academic years ($N = 120$) provide ample data for describing and evaluating the most recent participants' AIMS experience. It is important to note that 17 students, or 14.2% of the evaluation sample of 120, repeated the course at least once during this period. Their "second enrollment" data are not included in this sample of 120. In other words, this evaluation is based on responses from "first-time" AIMS volunteers and does not include additional responses of repeating students.

Descriptive Information

The majority of students in the evaluation sample, 70%, completed the course in a regular 15-week semester. The remaining 30% completed the course during a 6-week summer session. Most of the students, 91%, were female. Several different majors were represented with the two largest categories being medical (including nursing and pre-med) and music therapy (Table 1). The "other" category included students majoring in business, political science, finance, public relations, English, communications, and undecided. The arts majors group included a theatre major and music students majoring in performance, music education, and the Bachelor of Arts degree programs. A slight majority of AIMS volunteers, 63%, were upperclassmen or graduate students (Table 2). The youngest student was 17 years old, and the oldest was 30; the mean age was 20.6 years. Approximately half, 48%, enrolled in the AIMS course for 1 academic credit, while the same percentages, 26%, enrolled for 2 and 3 credits. Only 24.2% reported previous experience working or volunteering in a hospital setting, while 51.7% reported previous experience performing in the arts. A third of the group reported no experience in either hospital settings or arts performance. A tenth of the group reported experience in both hospital settings and arts performance.

The unit in the hospital selected by the largest proportion of AIMS volunteers was the pediatric unit. Approximately 41.7% volunteered in the pediatric unit of the hospital exclusively. Another 24.2% volunteered exclusively in the long-term care unit with older frail adults. Many students, 26.7%, particularly students completing the course for 3 credits, volunteered in several units during a single week, including the pediatric and long-term care units, diabetes, oncology, and cardiac units. A very small group, primarily music majors and 7.5% of the total sample, performed exclusively in the atrium as their sole means of AIMS contact.

Table 1. Percentage of Students in Majors by Academic Levels

Major	Academic Levels					All Levels
	Fr	So	Jr	Sr	Grad	
Medicine-Related (Nursing and Pre-Nursing $N = 39$) (Pre-Med $N = 2$)	4.9	51.2	34.1	7.3	2.4	34.2
Music Therapy ($N = 28$)	17.9	7.1	32.1	25.0	17.9	23.3
Other* ($N = 20$)	0.0	23.8	9.5	66.7	0.0	16.7
Arts-Related (Music $N = 19$) (Theatre $N = 1$)	0.0	31.6	21.1	36.8	10.5	16.7
Behavioral Science** ($N = 11$)	0.0	9.1	36.4	54.5	0.0	9.2

* Undecided, Business, Finance, Political Science, Religion, Public Relations, Communications
** Child Psychology, Child Life Specialist, Psychology

The majority of the students, 68.3%, met or exceeded all academic requirements such as completing assignments on time, fulfilling their contracts in a timely manner, and submitting thorough reflective weekly reports and final essays. They received an "A" letter grade for the course. Another group, 21.7%, had occasional lapses in contract fulfillment or failed to submit thorough weekly reports or essays and received "B" grades. A very small group, 10%, either did not complete assignments in a timely manner, did not complete all assignments, or fulfilled only a portion of their AIMS contract within the semester. They received grades of "C" or below, depending on the percentages of assignments and hours completed. The semester was divided into two grading periods—one at midterm and another from midterm to the final week. The mean of the two grades provides the final grade.

Table 2. Percentage of AIM Students Enrolled for Credit Hours

Academic Level	Credit Hours			All
	1	2	3	
Freshman	3.3	2.5	0.0	5.8
Sophomore	16.7	6.7	5.8	29.2
Junior	15.8	5.8	5.8	27.5
Senior	7.5	10.0	13.3	30.8
Graduate	5.0	.8	.8	6.7
Total	48.3	25.8	25.8	

Personal Inventories

Students completed two personal paper-pencil inventories at the first orientation session on campus and again at the final class meeting. One inventory consisted of three subsets of questions from the Quality of Life Questionnaire (QOLQ) (Evans & Cope, 1989) pertaining to "creative/aesthetic behavior," "personal growth," and "altruistic behavior." There were 12 statements related to each subset. Example statements include "I rarely buy art work for my home (e.g., pictures, pottery)" and "I seldom lose my temper." The 36 statements were randomly presented, half with reverse coding, and a "true–false" response was requested for each item. A single score (maximum = 12) for each subset was derived from each student's pre- and post-course QOLQ responses. High scorers in creative/aesthetic behavior indicate people who "involve themselves in cultural activities (plays, movies, museums, etc.), purchase art works, and engage in hobbies." High scorers in personal growth indicate people who are secure, and level-tempered, have a sense of humor, and have attainable goals that are modifiable if the need arises." High scorers in altruistic behavior indicate individuals "oriented toward helping others by making donations, canvassing and participating in charitable or volunteer organizations" (Evans & Cope, 1989, p. 3).

The second inventory, the Interpersonal Skills Self-Evaluation (ISSE), is an adaptation of a 32-item semantic differential checklist developed by medical school faculty to assess interpersonal qualities of maturity, compassion, morality, calm disposition, and sociability of medical school applicants during initial interviews (Carothers, Gregory, & Gallagher; 2000). The adaptation for the AIMS course incorporated self-evaluation instead of instructor evaluation and included only 29 paired word items. The items were randomly listed with seven blanks between the words in each pair. Respondents marked an "X" in a blank to indicate which one of the words in the paired item was more descriptive or applied to them. A "maturity" item, for example, was the word pair "Insecure–Secure." A "compassion" item was the word pair "Empathetic–Self-centered." Reverse coding was used for half of the items to promote discriminative responding. Values between 1 and

7 were assigned to the placement of the "X" in a blank between each word pair. Totals were calculated resulting in 5 raw scores, one for each subset.

Maximum possible scores, group mean pre- and post-course scores, and difference scores for each subset in both personal inventories are provided in Table 3. Differences between pre- and post-scores were negligible. The only positive difference score occurred in the QOLQ altruistic behavior subset. The greatest negative difference score occurred in the ISSE compassion subset. A repeated measures analysis of variance of each inventory subset pre–post scores for two groups of students—those reporting previous performance experience in the arts ($N = 58$) and those reporting no previous experience in the arts ($N = 62$)—revealed no significant differences. The analysis for one subset, however, was interesting. Pre–post ISSE compassion scores for the group reporting no previous arts experience were 44.57 and 44.14, respectively. Pre–post scores for the group reporting previous arts experience were 43.26 and 41.73, respectively. The difference within subjects in the two groups approached significance ($F(1,118) = 3.85$, $p = .052$).

Table 3. Mean Inventory Responses Before and After AIMS Course Completion

		Quality of Life Questionnaire				
		Pre		Post		
Difference	*N*	*M*	*SD*	*M*	*SD*	Ceiling
Creative/Aesthetic Behavior	12	8.33	1.97	7.96	2.48	−.37
Personal Growth	12	9.75	1.75	9.48	1.75	−.27
Altruistic Behavior	12	8.02	2.09	8.57	1.99	+.55

		Interpersonal Skills Self-Evaluation				
		Pre		Post		Difference
	N	*M*	*SD*	*M*	*SD*	Ceiling
Maturity	70	60.78	5.26	60.23	5.08	−.55
Compassion	49	43.89	3.93	42.89	4.18	−1.00
Morality	42	37.65	2.81	36.98	2.76	−.67
Sociability	21	18.63	1.87	18.13	1.99	−.50
Calm Disposition	21	11.75	2.52	11.45	2.82	−.29

Pearson correlation statistics between all post-course subset scores revealed no significant correlations between QOLQ subset scores or between QOLQ subset scores and ISSE subset scores. Significant positive correlations ($p < .000$) were found, however, between 4 ISSE subset scores (Table 4). Correlations of self-perception compassion scores with morality, maturity, and sociability scores were .61, .53, and .41, respectively.

The maturity and calm disposition ISSE subsets in the AIMS inventory were identical to the subsets used by evaluators scoring interview behavior of medical school applicants ($N = 147$) in the Carothers et al. (2000) study. The mean maturity score of medical school applicants was 65.59 ($SD = 10.32$). The calm disposition mean score was 13.98 ($SD = 2.84$). Although the procedures were totally different, it is interesting to compare these scores with the slightly lower self-perception scores of the predominantly undergraduate group of AIMS volunteers.

Table 4. Pearson Correlations* Between Interpersonal Skills Self-Evaluation Subset Scores

	Morality	Compassion	Sociability
Maturity	.71	.52	.48
Morality		.61	.42
Compassion			.44

* $p < .000$ (all correlations are significant).

Final Essays

Portions of students' final essays documented their perception of the AIMS experience. Students were requested to fully answer 12 open-ended questions with examples from their experiences and, when applicable, refer back to their weekly reports. Two questions related to general service-learning objectives are "What did you learn about yourself personally?" and "What, if any, impact did your experience have on your future plans?" The majority of responses to the first question, 60.8%, indicated that students experienced an unsuspected ability to quickly or through time become comfortable interacting with unfamiliar people in new situations and/or in an environment initially perceived as stressful or sad. Other responses to this question pertained to a variety of topics such as enjoyment of working with a particular age group, learning how to be patient, recognizing false preconceptions and stereotypical thinking, and learning the value of communication. Regarding the impact on future plans, responses were related to careers (64.2%), volunteerism (17.5%), or both careers and volunteerism (6.7%). The career responses indicated the AIMS experience validated or reinforced current degree/career choices or provided assistance in deciding on a service profession career. Greater proportions of students in music, music therapy, nursing, and behavioral sciences reported impacts on career choice. Three students in the "career impact only" grouping acknowledged that their AIMS experience provided an impetus for considering a change from a less people-oriented major or to a non-medical service profession.

The relatively small proportion of volunteerism responses indicated a new enthusiasm for volunteering in hospitals specifically or community service in general, and continuing to volunteer in college or after graduation. It is interesting to note that a third of the music therapy majors included volunteering as a future impact. Half of the students in the "other" category and a third of the students in the music majors group (non-service profession majors) mentioned future volunteering. Responses from the remaining 9.7% of the sample did not mention career issues or volunteerism but indicated impacts that were more individualized in nature such as "taking care of my health," "being sensitive to my co-workers," and "spending more time with elderly members of my family." Two students indicated "no impact" in their responses to this question.

Evaluation of Course Components

Three interrelated components are equally important in maintaining the effectiveness of a community-based, individualized, non-traditional course like AIMS. The course web site, which is updated weekly, provides the structure and avenue for communication between instructor and students and basically replaces a traditional weekly group class meeting. Cumulative time cards maintained by students at the hospital provide the primary means of documenting student commitment in lieu of class attendance. And finally, it is assumed that the hospital staff members' attitude toward the AIM program and college student volunteers affect the quality of their on-site assistance and encouragement to students. Evaluations of these components provide an insight into the course mechanisms probably affecting students' perceptions of their experience.

During the final group meeting at the end of the semester, students completed a questionnaire requesting information about their use of the web site. In addition, they were asked to rate the overall course web site quality on a 7-point Likert scale anchored with 1 indicating "poor" quality and 7 indicating "excellent" quality. They were also asked to rate their level of enthusiasm about course web sites in general with 1 indicating "low" and 7 indicating "high." The mean quality rating for the course web site ($N = 120$) was 6.42 for a group whose mean rating of enthusiasm for course web sites in general was 5.74. When requested to suggest needed changes/additions to the course web site, only a very small portion, 4.1%, wrote comments, which varied from "include chat room," "add more pictures," to "include a discussion board." The large majority indicated the web site content did not need additions or changes.

The primary means of documenting students' participation was a systematic use of time cards at the hospital. Students were instructed to find their time card in the AIMS file box at the desk in the hospital's main entrance and write the time in, time out, the unit(s) visited, and the cumulative number of hours for each visit to the hospital. They also reported in their weekly online communiques to the instructor the number of hours completed in a week and the cumulative number of hours, before describing their AIMS contacts and reflections for the week. In addition, each student was given a paper–pencil personal accountability form at the campus orientation meeting at the beginning of the semester and instructed to record weekly the dates, times, units, and activities for each hospital visit and the date they submitted each online weekly report. The personal accountability form was turned in with the final essay at the end of the semester. The time cards remained at the hospital. Two reliability checks provided helpful information. A midterm reliability check between the data written on time cards maintained weekly at the hospital desk with the time commitment data submitted in the students' weekly online reports was completed for a sample of 20 students during one semester. Minimal inconsequential discrepancies were found at the midterm check. A second reliability check ($N = 33$) between time card data and the accountability form data submitted with the final essay at the end of the semester revealed useful information. The data on both records for 27 students, 82% of the sample, were in total agreement. Data from 5 records revealed discrepancies ranging from 30 minutes to 3 hours for 5 student records. The mean time discrepancy was over-reporting 40 minutes on the final accountability log. The sixth record ($N = 1$) varied greatly; data from the final 3 weeks on the accountability log were missing from the time card maintained at the hospital. It was interesting to note that the students with the largest time card discrepancies were also less than responsible in meeting other course requirements.

During the spring and summer semesters of 2003, 32 hospital staff members, primarily nurses and unit technicians, completed a very brief paper–pencil attitude survey. Data collected suggest that 22 respondents had at least 2 years of experience with AIMS volunteers. The remaining 10 reported contact only within the last 12 months. The majority, 30 out of 32, reported seeing AIMS students on a weekly basis. All respondents reported that AIMS students followed hospital protocol. A request to rate their level of support for the Arts in Medicine program on a 7-point scale from 0 indicating "low" and "7" indicating "high" resulted in a mean rating of 5.78. Eleven of the 32 respondents added comments that were highly positive and often included specific volunteer's names.

Discussion

The underlying structure and operational components of the AIMS course—the orientation sessions, the web site, the time-card system, weekly reports and final essay reflections, and hospital staff attitudes—are basically intact and sufficient for continuing the course without major change. The structure allows for early identification of students with problems and immediate assistance for individuals. It also promotes self-confidence, self-monitoring, and commitment reliability— important prerequisites for students' independent efforts in subsequent course-based, extracurricular, or post-graduation volunteer experiences. Learning to feel comfortable in an unfamiliar setting with unfamiliar people on a weekly basis, as reported in most students' essays, is an important skill related to most community service opportunities.

The accountability system resulting in academic grades obviously differentiates service learning experiences in courses like AIMS from extracurricular community service. Some may argue that it is counterproductive to teaching the value of volunteering. In fact, it may contribute to students' perception of volunteerism as an alternative to civic responsibility referred to earlier by Bok (2001). The accountability system reinforces, however, continuous unstructured personal reflection on a weekly basis. It seems probable that students who increase their enjoyment of reflection in experiential learning courses like AIMS may not only transfer this practice to professional and personal situations but search for new volunteer experiences as opportunities for unique life-long learning. The "future impact" responses in the essays suggest that elective service learning courses may function as supplements to degree programs that offer few, if any, community service-related practica or internships.

The personal inventories, QOLQ and ISSE, provided descriptive information unavailable through other course assignments. The moderately positive self-perceptions at the beginning and end of the course could be interpreted as a desired outcome for a group of inexperienced hospital volunteers. The absence of significant positive change, however, raises relevant questions. Are the inventories insensitive to changes that can be anticipated in the AIMS experience? The time-spent variable presents a related question. Do self-perceptions of students completing 90 hours of contact differ from those of students completing 30 hours? As the course continues and the sample size increases, additional statistical analyses will provide useful information about these and other self-selection factors. Although some advisors encourage students to enroll, students who select AIMS as an elective course may perceive themselves differently compared to other undergraduates. Analyses of QOLQ and ISSE scores of non-volunteer and extra-curricular volunteer comparison groups across a semester or longer would provide helpful information. In addition, initial inventories of students who repeat the course may differ from initial inventories of students who enroll only once. Multiple inventory scores from a larger number of repeating students will help determine the relationships between self-selection, time-spent, and self-perception. It is also important to note that post-course inventory scores were obtained during the last week of the semester when student self-perceptions are probably influenced by extraneous factors not present during the first week. The absence of a comparison control group prevents generalization but predictable end-of-semester time constraints and pressures may negatively affect responses to personal questions, particularly the ISSE items. Administering the "post" inventory during the 13th week would decrease the duration of hospital contact before responding, but extraneous factors during an earlier time of the semester may more closely resemble the first week.

The decrease in compassion scores of students reporting previous experience in the arts, although not significant, suggests further study particularly for a service learning course using the arts. Factors related to project selection probably contribute. Musically experienced volunteers who selected atrium performances as their *sole* AIMS project and students who chose to spend a large portion of their contact time in atrium performances may differ in pre- and post-compassion measures. Anecdotes from performers regarding their conversations with hospital visitors and staff members about the pleasant effects of live performances prevent assumptions about a non-interactive less interpersonal perspective of performing. Yet such interactions may offer less experiential learning in compassion than efforts to engage lonely adults or children with serious medical complications. It is possible that arts-experienced students who selected direct contacts with patients as their predominant AIMS contact were confronted weekly with unfamiliar situations requiring compassion and became more realistic in their self-perceptions resulting in lower estimates of compassion on questionnaires. Future studies with larger samples will allow for extensive correlational data across many factors.

An important issue from an educational perspective is the relationship between AIMS participants' self-perceptions, project selections, and quality of course assignments. New documentation forms have been implemented, and we are currently collecting these data. Following are the three forms currently in use.

ATRIUM PERFORMANCE
Arts in Medicine Service – Tallahassee Memorial HealthCare

Directions: Complete the form immediately after you perform. Sign the form. Get a staff member to sign the form. Put the completed form in the AIMS Documentation Notebook at the Atrium Desk BEFORE leaving the hospital.

Day of Contact (Circle one):   *Mon   Tues   Wed   Thurs   Fri   Sat   Sun*   *Write Date:* ___/___/05

Time: What time did you start performing?   *Time In* ____:____ *am or pm* (circle one)
What time did you stop performing?   *Time Out* ____:____ *am or pm* (circle one)
What was the total amount of time performing?   *Total Time* _____ *hours* _____ *minutes*

Describe Performance (circle)**:** *Solo* or *Group* | *Music – Dance – Drama – Art* |
If group included people not currently enrolled in AIMS, *how many people?* _____
If group included other currently enrolled AIMS students, *please write their names:*

_____

Content of Performance: List selections or describe activity (Use back if necessary)

Observations: Estimate the number (#) of people who:

Sat near the performance area but engaged in reading, talking with others, etc.	#
Came close to the performance area and listened	#
Verbally complimented your performance	#
Engaged you in conversation	#
Stopped to listen briefly (gestured with smiles, pointing) and left the atrium area	#
Other: (specify)	#

Additional Relevant Information:

_____

_____

Your Signature _____ Print Your Last Name _____

Get signature from a TMH Staff person:
TMH Staff Member's Signature

_____

MAIN HOSPITAL UNIT
Arts in Medicine Service – Tallahassee Memorial HealthCare

Directions: Complete the form immediately after volunteering in a TMH unit. Sign the form. Get a staff member in the unit to sign the form. *__Complete a different form for each unit__*. Put all completed forms in the AIMS Documentation Notebook at the Atrium Desk BEFORE leaving the hospital.

Day of Contact (Circle one):   *Mon   Tues   Wed   Thurs   Fri   Sat   Sun   Date: ___/___/05*

Unit (Circle one):   *Peds | Cardio | Oncology | Ortho-Neuro | Pulmonary-Med | Diabetes*

Other (specify) _____

Time: What time did you start in the unit? *Time In ____: ____ am or pm* (circle one)
What time did you leave the unit? *Time Out ____: ____ am or pm* (circle one)
What was the total amount of time on the unit? *Total Time ____ hours ____ minutes*

Contacts: How many people in the hospital unit did you contact? _____
How many of the contacts in this unit did you spend AIMS time with? _____
How did you spend time in the unit? (Circle all listed below that apply):

Card games	Cleaning play room	Coloring, drawing	Computer games	Conversation
Crafts	Crossword puzzles	Feeding	Imaginary play	Jigsaw puzzles
Making greeting cards	Organizing supplies	Origami	Painting	Playing with toys
Playing board games, dominoes	Performing music	Performing dance	Performing skit/play	Puppet play
Reading books, magazines	Rocking, holding infant	Sewing, knitting	*STARBRIGHT*	Tea cart
Transporting	Watching TV	Watching video	Writing poetry	Writing letters

Other (specify) _____

Who did you interact with while on the unit: (Circle all that apply)
Patients | Parents | Siblings | Other family members | Nurse | Doctor | Therapist | Tech staff

Were you working with another AIMS volunteer during these interactions? *Yes or No*
If Yes, *who?*
_____

Description of Activities and Observations
_____
_____
_____
_____
_____

Volunteer Signature _____ Print Last Name _____
Get signature from a TMH Staff person in Rehab:
TMH Staff Member Signature_____

REHAB – EXTENDED CARE
Arts in Medicine Service – Tallahassee Memorial HealthCare

Directions: Complete the form immediately after volunteering. Sign the form and get a staff member to sign the completed form. Put the form in the AIMS Documentation Notebook in the Rehab Unit BEFORE leaving.

Day of Contact (Circle one):   *Mon   Tues   Wed   Thurs   Fri   Sat   Sun*   Date: ___/___/05

Time: What time did you start in the unit?   *Time In* ____: ____ *am or pm* (circle one)
What time did you leave the unit?   *Time Out* ____: ____ *am or pm* (circle one)
What was the total amount of time on the unit?   *Total Time* _____ *hours* _____ *minutes*

Contacts: How many people in the hospital unit did you contact? _____
How many of the contacts in this unit did you spend AIMS time with? _____
How did you spend time in the unit? (Circle all listed below that apply):

Card games	Cleaning areas	Eating/Feeding	Computer games	Conversation
Crafts	Crossword puzzles	Jigsaw puzzles	Making greeting cards	Organizing supplies
Playing board ames, dominoes	Reading books, magazines	Origami	Painting	Sewing, knitting
Distributing refreshments	Performing music in lobby I dining area	Transporting to therapies	Watching TV	Watching video
Writing letters	Writing – recording reminiscences	Writing poetry, short stories	Decorating unit for holidays	Composing songs

Other (specify) _____

Who did you interact with while on the unit: (Circle all that apply)
Patients | Patient's family members | Patient's visitors | Nurse | Doctor | Therapist | Tech staff

Were you working with another AIMS volunteer during these interactions?   *Yes* or *No*
If Yes, *who?*
_____

Description of Activities and Observations
_____
_____
_____
_____
_____

Volunteer Signature _____ Print Last Name _____

Get signature from a TMH Staff person in Rehab:
TMH Staff Member Signature _____

One obvious and potentially consequential point of information relevant to the AIMS experience but inadvertently left out of the present study is frequency, recency, and recollection and current perspective of previous personal experiences in hospitals as patients or family members. References to personal experience in hospitals were often included in weekly reflections, particularly from students working with older adults and very young children. A systematic request for the information from all students can be easily added to the orientation session questionnaire. The item in the current questionnaire regarding previous hospital experience only referred to volunteer or course-based experiences.

In conclusion, the AIMS experience as perceived by undergraduate students in several disciplines and at different stages of their college career provides a productive opportunity for experiential learning and personal reflection. It is not surprising that students majoring in service profession degrees such as nursing and music therapy used the course for reality checks from classroom to clinical settings as indicated in their "future impact" responses. The fact that these students used an elective course with relatively unstructured context and non-specific content to explore, practice, and transfer skills, personal qualities, and concepts related to professional interests satisfies one objective of service learning in higher education. The fact that a smaller group of students including some service profession majors, but predominantly volunteers in non-service related degree programs, expressed enjoyment of volunteering with a desire to continue indicates that the course possibly functions as a civic responsibility training experience. The individualized approach to the course apparently provides an opportunity for students to reach personal objectives and practice requisite volunteering skills while humanizing the hospital environment for patients, visitors, and medical staff.

"What, if any, impact did your experience have on your future plans?"

I plan on being a third grade teacher. I guess I could say that if one of my students has to be in the hospital I would go visit them and bring them games and play with them and try to help them have fun while they are staying in the hospital. I also plan on being a mother. If one of my children has to be in the hospital I would most definitely be there for them the entire time and want to play games or color and draw with them.

—A. Yiakotola, Child Development, Senior

After being at the hospital, my heart and mind have seen a lot. I know that my place in this world belongs with those who are sick. Any apprehension of being a nurse has vanished. I learned that in order for my patients to feel at peace I must always show compassion. I must look deeply into their worried eyes and allow my heart to smile. I must allow them to be comforted by the warmth of my heart.

—C. Budris, Nursing, Sophomore

When I witnessed the children being in pain, this was the most challenging part of my volunteer service. I then had to realize and accept that this would be a part of my professional medical career. The impact this experience had on my future was that I should be compassionate towards patients' needs and keep a respectful distance for my own emotional well-being.

—D. Roberts, Exercise Science, Senior

Working in the hospital and helping these people in need however I could reassured me of my goals as a professional Speech Language Pathologist. The nature of this profession is centered on offering help to those in need. This experience made me realize that helping people will make me happy.

—D. Cicchitto, Communications Disorders, Senior

References

Bok, D. (2001). Universities and the decline of civic responsibility. *Journal of College and Character*. Retrieved July 6, 2003, from *the Internet Journal of the Center for the Study of Values in College Student Development Featured Journal Articles, Volume 2* http://www.collegevalues.org/articles.cfm?a=1&id=570

Bringle, R. G., & Hatcher, J. A. (1996). Implementing service learning in higher education [Electronic version]. *Journal of Higher Education, 67*(2), 221–239.

Carothers, R. W., Gregory, S. W., & Gallagher, T. J. (2000). Measuring emotional intelligence of medical school applicants. *Academic Medicine, 75*(5), 456–463.

Education Commission of the States (ECS) Notes. (2001). *Institutionalized service learning in the 50 states*. Retrieved July 6, 2003, from http://www.ecs.org/clearinghouse/ 23/77/2377.pdf

Evans, D. R., & Cope, W. E. (1989). *Quality of Life Questionnaire*. North Tonawanda, NY: Multi-Health Systems.

Furco, A. (1999). *Self-assessment rubric for the institutionalization of service learning in higher education*. Retrieved July 6, 2003, from http://www.richmond.edu/vacc/Forms/rubric.pdf

Gregory, D. (2001). *Arts in Medicine service: An elective course for university students*. Presentation at the 2001 Society for Arts in Healthcare. Retrieved July 6, 2003, from http://otto.cmr.fsu.edu/memt/sah/

Gregory, D., & Whipple, J. (2000*). Music in arts in medicine and medical music therapy: Same or different?* Retrieved July 6, 2003, from http://otto.cmr.fsu.edu/memt/tmhaim/article.htm

Honnet, E. P. & Poulsen, S. J. (1989). *Principles of good practice for combining service and learning: A Wingspread special report*. Retrieved July 6, 2003, from http://www. servicelearning.org/article/archive/87

Lenkowsky, L. (2003). *Higher education and the making of citizens*. Retrieved July 6, 2003, from http://www.nationalservice.org/news/ll032103.html

Chapter 3

Cost/Benefit Analysis
of the Total Program

∽

Jayne M. Standley, Ph.D., MT-BC, and
Darcy Walworth, M.M., MT-BC

COST/BENEFIT ANALYSIS OF THE TOTAL PROGRAM

A cost/benefit analysis of the FSU/TMH partnership programs was conducted for the fiscal year July 1, 2002–June 30, 2003. The cost analysis isolated budget/staffing figures for each of the clinical, training, and volunteer functions. The benefit analysis used MT clinical data from the hospital's computerized patient charting system with records compiled for: total medical referrals for MT, and total individual MT patient visits. Data maintained within the music therapy program were used to compute number of community in-service participants, number of students trained, number of AIM volunteers and hours served, total group MT patient visits, and number of research studies conducted.

Results of Cost Benefit Analysis

The top priority for this program is to provide research-based quality medical MT clinical programs. Table 5 is a line item budget that compares cost data with scheduling data by position. It shows total work hours funded, the proportion of these hours allotted to direct medical MT patient services, and expenditures contributed by Florida State University vs. those contributed by Tallahassee Memorial HealthCare vs. those contributed by the MT staff-acquired National Brain Tumor Foundation Grant for research in MT with brain surgery. This table reveals the total funds expended for the year to have been $63,730. During this period, staff were scheduled and assigned duties to maximize direct patient services. The % load column demonstrates an average workload allocation for this purpose being 73%. This table shows a maximum potential for 4,820 patient contact hours per year by the medical MT staff.

Table 6 shows actual patient contacts across a variety of categories for both the medical MT and AIM components for the year under study, including: actual patient visits in response to a medical referral for MT, volunteer hours interacting with patients donated through the Arts in Medicine course component, contact hours with community participants in Neuroscience Center support groups and participants receiving in-service presentations. Total actual patient contacts were 9214. Table 6 does not reflect patient contacts generated through supervision of art therapy interns, art therapy practica students or contacts involved in research studies. It is noteworthy that several research studies completed this year by FSU MT graduate students had widespread implications throughout the hospital:

- Jarred (2003) found highly beneficial effects of live music therapy for families in the surgical waiting rooms, $N = 192$;
- Roberts (2003) found significantly improved gait for children aged 2-6 years when MT was added to Physical Therapy training to improve toe-walking, $N = 9$;
- Scheve (2002) found significantly less preoperative anxiety in pediatric patients receiving MT, $N = 60$;

- Kendelhardt (2003) found that live contingent music significantly decreased pain and anxiety perception while increasing exercise duration in physical therapy for adult physical rehabilitation patients, $N = 30$;
- Nguyen (2003) found significantly lower anxiety in end-of-life patients who participated in two music therapy life celebration sessions and a 97% family satisfaction level for use of MT in the medical setting, $N = 20$.

Table 5. Cost of Medical Music Therapy and Allotted Patient Contact Hours

Personnel	FSU Expenditures	TMH Expenditures	NIH Grant Expenditures	% Load[1]/ Annual Hours	Allotted Patient Contact Hours
Dir., MT-BC	$35,800			35% / 2000	700
¼-time Graduate Assistant	$3,000		$2,500	70% / 500	350
Part-time MT-BC			$3,630	100% / 220	220
4 Interns/yr.		$4,000		80% / 4000	3,200
OPS/Equip/ Supplies		$14,800			
Totals[2]	$38,800	$18,800	$6,130	Mean % Load = 73	4470

[1] indicates estimated % of total hours devoted to medical MT patient services and number of hours worked annually

[2] Total expenditures across categories: $63, 730

Table 6. Actual Medical MT and Arts in Medicine Patient Contacts

Total Medical MT Individual Patient Visits	2451
Total Medical MT Group Patient Visits	1912
Total Medical MT Patient Contacts	**4363**
Total Arts in Medicine Volunteer Hours	**4620**
NeuroScience Support Group Contacts	103
Community Attendees – In-service Presentations	128
Total Other Contacts	**231**
Total Patient/Other Contacts Combined	**9214**

Ongoing MT research being currently conducted by staff and students includes the following:

- MT to reduce pain and anxiety of craniotomy and stereotactic radiosurgery patients, to shorten length of hospitalization, and to reduce amount of pain medication needed;
- MT as procedural support for pediatric patients undergoing echocardiogram and CAT scans that eliminates the need for sedation and RN supervision;
- descriptive analysis of the medical referrals given for MT with premature infants;
- music to reinforce sucking skill of premature infants;
- training in multimodal stimulation for parents of premature infants in the NICU.

A second major priority of the FSU/TMH partnership is to provide well-supervised, innovative training of MT majors and interns. Table 7 shows hours of music therapy student training supervised by the TMH MT staff. Training is provided for MT interns (each working 40 hours/week for 6 months), for MT practica students (each spending 2 hours/week for a semester), and for FSU students enrolled for a semester in the Arts in Medicine course (each volunteering 2 hours per week per hour of registered credit). This table shows that total hours of student training were 9740 for the year under study.

Table 7. Actual Hours of Supervised Student Training[1]

Type of Training	Number Trained	Hours Completed for Each	Total Hours of Training
MT Intern	4	1040	4160
MT Practica/Sem			
Fall	20	28	560
Spring	10	28	280
Summer	10	12	120
AIM Students	25	84	2100
	26	56	1456
	38	28	1064
Total	**133**		**9740**

[1]Additionally, five research studies were completed by students.

The AIM course is highly popular. In addition to exposing pre-medical and other students interested in health-related careers to the benefits of the arts, the registration hours generate funds for the School of Music (Table 8). The Florida Legislature appropriates funds according to FTE (full-time equivalent) enrollment at each academic level, upper/lower division undergraduate and upper/lower division graduate. Some of these legislative funds are reserved by FSU to student support services. Others are transmitted to the academic unit generating the enrollment. The allocations in this table are solely the funds distributed by FSU for academic purposes (Alvarez, 2003). The AIM course is variable credit (1-3 hours) at both the upper division undergraduate and lower division graduate levels. Table 8 shows the enrollment and computed FTE at each level and subsequent funds generated by this computer-assisted course that is taught 3 semesters per year. It was added to the MT department 3 years ago with no additional expenditure of funds or change in faculty course load. This table shows the course generated $27, 039 for the School of Music in 2002–03.

Table 8. AIM Course FTE (Full-time Equivalent): Academic Appropriation

Level	N	Hours Registered	Total Hours	Computed FTE	Academic Appropriation per FTE	Total
Upper Division	25	3	75			
	25	2	50			
	36	1	36			
			$161 \div 40^1$	4.025	$6,356	$25,583
Graduate Division	1	2	2			
	2	1	2			
			$4 \div 32^2$	.125	$11,644	$1,456
Total	**89**					**$27,039**

[1] One upper division FTE = 40 annual hours
[2] One level 1 graduate FTE = 32 annual hours

Hospital savings were calculated for echocardiograms in a prior study by Walworth (2002) and are shown in Table 9. She reported that Procedural Support MT is provided to pediatric patients undergoing Computerized Topography (CT) scans and echocardiograms. Data demonstrated that MT alone is sufficient for these tests and precludes the need for sedation and its subsequent need for RN supervision. Savings for CT scans have not been calculated.

Table 10 combines data from the previous tables and shows the cost benefit analysis for the comprehensive program. Overall cost is computed by subtracting course enrollment funds generated and hospital funds saved from total funds expended and reveals a total outlay for the two partners of $17,247.

Table 10 shows that for each of the partners, FSU and TMH, costs exceeded financial benefits by approximately $11,700 and $5,400, respectively, for the comprehensive program. For this amount of money, each received over 9,000 hours in direct service provision, either student training or patient contacts. Additionally, the field of music therapy benefited this past year through the completion of eight medically related research studies.

Table 9. Cost Analysis for Echocardiograms (Walworth, 2002)

Without Music Therapy	Staff Time per Procedure	Cost per Procedure	Total Cost per Patient
RN	2 hours	$55.00	
Sonograper	1 hour	$23.00	
Medication		$9.45	
			$87.45
With Music Therapy			
RN	0	0	
Sonographer	1/3 hour	$7.66	
Music Therapist	1/3 hour	$5.55	
Medication		0	
			$13.21

Note. Savings per patient = $74.24; Total savings for 92 patients = $6,830; Total RN hours saved for other duties = 184 hours @ $27.50/hr. = $5060 saved in staff costs. Total Sonographer hours saved = 62 hours @ $23/hr. = $1426.

Discussion of Cost Benefit Analysis

The purpose of this descriptive study and chapter was to document benefits for hospital/university partnerships for medical MT. Results show huge benefits for both partners at minimal cost to each. This descriptive study provides a rationale and model for others wishing to establish university/hospital partnerships. This programmatic model also has implications for AMTA future plans to achieve reimbursement for medical MT services.

Reimbursement of Medical Music Therapy Services

Although medical services in the FSU/TMH partnership program are being provided free of charge at the current time by preference of all parties involved, medical patients could be charged for services with reimbursement through third party payers. MT has been a reimbursable service under the Federal Medicare Partial Hospitalization Programs since 1994 (AMTA, 1998). AMTA is currently moving toward acquisition of third party reimbursement of medical MT through private insurers.

Table 10. Cost/Benefit Analysis of Comprehensive Program

Florida State University		Tallahassee Memorial HealthCare		Totals	
Expenditure	$38,800	Expenditure	$18,800		
AIM FTE Reimbursement	–$27,038	Echocardiagram Savings	–6,158		
		RN Hours Freed (184)	–5,060		
		Sonographer Hours Freed (62)	–1,426		
Total Outlay	$11,762	Total Outlay	$5,485	$17,247	Outlay
Total Hours Student Training	9,740	Total Hours Patient Contact	9,086	18,826	Contacts
Student/Staff Research Studies Completed	8			8	Research Studies

The reimbursement primer by Simpson and Burns (2003), a recent AMTA publication, provides complete information about acquiring reimbursement for music therapy services which have the following characteristics:

- are physician prescribed;
- are necessary for the treatment of the individual's illness or injury based on diagnosis, symptoms, and documented treatment procedures;
- are goal directed and based on a documented treatment plan implemented by a qualified provider; and
- exhibit improvement in the individual's condition (AMTA, 1998).

Reimbursement is provided only for services with pre-approved intent and billing codes. The Physician's Current Procedural Terminology (CPT) codes are a list of services performed by doctors and other health care professionals, including therapists, which are outcome- rather than discipline-specific (AMTA, 1998). Each code is attached to a specific amount of funds agreed by the payer to be reimbursed per 15-minute procedure.

AMTA is meeting with private insurers to establish MT as a pre-approved process for specific CPT codes. Such codes might be established for the following intended functions of MT which already have a strong research base and are an integral part of the TMH medical MT clinical services:

- to reduce pain (patients being treated post-operatively for physical rehabilitation, for burns, or for chemotherapy);
- to reduce anxiety (patients being treated preoperatively, those receiving radiology procedures, those sustaining traumatic injury, those confused about the medical process due to aging or dementia, and those women trying to forestall premature birth);
- to induce sleep (patients in acute pain, pediatric patients, confused patients);
- to reduce nausea (those receiving chemotherapy or hemodialysis treatment).

Other services provided in the comprehensive TMH program described in this paper include those designed to impact quality of life issues for patients in extended hospitalization, stimulus deprivation, or end-of-life situations. It is expected that these objectives will be harder to meet reimbursement guidelines since little research actually connects improved quality of life issues with increased medical benefits. It is recommended that the profession focus on this type of research in the near future so that data exist to document benefits for specific procedures when third party payers begin establishing pre-approved MT CPT codes.

References

Alvarez, R. (2003). *Florida Legislative FTE Appropriation for 2002–2003*. Personal interview with FSU Associate Vice President Administrative Affairs, Budget Analysis. June 30, 2003.

American Music Therapy Association. (1998). *Reimbursement primer: The ABC's of healthcare reimbursement for music therapy services*. Silver Spring, MD: Author.

American Music Therapy Association. (2002). *AMTA member sourcebook 2002*. Silver Spring, MD: Author.

Jarred, J. (2003). *The effect of live music on anxiety levels of persons waiting in a surgical waiting room as measured by self-report*. Unpublished master's thesis, Florida State University, Tallahassee.

Kendelhardt, A. (2003). *The effect of live music on exercise duration, negative verbalizations, and self-perception of pain, anxiety and rehabilitation levels of physical therapy patients*. Unpublished master's thesis, Florida State University, Tallahassee.

Nguyen, J. (2003). *The effect of music therapy on end-of-life patients' quality of life, emotional state, and family satisfaction as measured by self-report*. Unpublished master's thesis, Florida State University, Tallahassee.

Roberts, P. (2002). *The effect of contingent music with physical therapy in children who toe-walk*. Unpublished master's thesis, Florida State University, Tallahassee.

Scheve, A. (2002*). The effect of music therapy intervention on preoperative anxiety of pediatric patients as measured by self-report*. Unpublished master's thesis, Florida State University, Tallahassee.

Simpson, J., & Burns, D. (2003). *Music therapy reimbursement: Best practices and procedures*. Silver Spring, MD: American Music Therapy Association.

Standley, J. M. (2000). Music research in medical treatment. In American Music Therapy Association (Ed.), *Effectiveness of music therapy procedures: Documentation of research and clinical practice* (3rd ed., pp. 1–64). Silver Spring, MD: American Music Therapy Association.

Standley, J. M. (2002). A meta-analysis of the efficacy of music therapy for premature infants. *Journal of Pediatric Nursing, 17*(2), 107–113.

Standley, J. M., & Whipple, J. (2002, November). *Music therapy with pediatric patients: A meta-analysis*. Research paper presented at the American Music Therapy Association National Conference, Atlanta, GA.

Walworth, D. (2002, November). *Music therapy as procedural support: Benefits for patients and staff*. Research paper presented at the American Music Therapy Association National Conference, Atlanta, GA.

Section II

Training Opportunities for Music Therapy Majors

Chapter 4

The Music Therapy Internship

∽

Jennifer Whipple, Ph.D., MT-BC

THE MUSIC THERAPY INTERNSHIP

The information contained in this chapter ranges from general advice for prospective internship training sites to specific experiences of developing and implementing a medical MT internship at TMH that integrates training with the highest clinical standards. The goal is that transfers may be made to other medical or non-medical facilities with their own unique needs and organizational structures.

It is important to note that the first tangible expression of gratitude for the medical MT program at TMH, beyond the intrinsic reward of a job well done, praise from staff or families and caregivers, or patient progress toward a specific goal, was the result of an intern's work. One afternoon a surprise delivery of flowers arrived at the MT department sent by the mother of a pediatric surgical patient who had been the beneficiary of an early morning pre-surgical session conducted by an MT intern. This story is shared to illustrate that integrated medical MT internship programs, while requiring much careful planning and monitoring, can simultaneously advance the MT program as a whole, serve the hospital's patients and their families, and meet intern training needs.

The first step in designing a music therapy internship program is to determine its appropriateness within the facility and department structure. Certain needs should be assessed and arrangements made prior to proposing an internship program. Interns will need a work space, including a desk, chair, and access to office equipment, such as a computer, copy machine, phone, etc. In addition, the site should determine if funding is available for at least minimal intern needs (i.e., administrative supplies) and possibly for more involved provisions (e.g., meals, housing, and stipend).

A facility should ensure an adequate MT client base before incorporating interns. While competent interns can be valuable additions to patient care staff due to their fresh ideas and energy, as well as an additional pair of hands to complete necessary work, they are not additional employees. Consequently, a separate full case load is not necessary in the same way that it would be in order to justify adding a new music therapist position. In fact, since interns must have opportunities for observation and then be supervised while providing services, an additional full case load could be detrimental to their training. However, because some music therapists work as case managers and administrators in addition to providing clinical MT services, music therapists in those situations should assess their client base to ensure enough opportunity for clinical services in which the prospective intern can be involved. Similarly, a MT program should offer a broad spectrum of MT services for the intern to observe and implement, whether through varied medical populations due to patient diagnoses and ages, individual and group sessions, or co-treatment opportunities with other disciplines.

The MT program at the facility should be well established prior to involving interns, which is not necessarily dependent on length of program existence. A solid program in this sense requires a clear referral and documentation system and MT services integrated into patient care services and accepted by hospital staff. The program will continue to change with time, which can provide valuable experience for interns; however, a firm foundation will aid continuity of MT services throughout these changes. Also, a facility that is nurturing and accepting of students and willing to participate in intern training, accepting interns as clinicians for their patients will go a long way toward the success of the MT internship program.

The supervising music therapist must have competent clinical and professional skills. In addition, this person needs positive relationships with hospital staff. The former National Association for Music Therapy (NAMT) guidelines for clinical training stated that the supervising music therapist "must be a practicing clinician in music therapy who will be a viable role model for interns" (NAMT, 1997, p. 14). This person needs to have time, teaching skills, and a desire to shape future music therapists.

The Internship Proposal

Once appropriateness is determined, the next step is the proposal, which can take multiple forms. Some facilities may require a proposal, which could be in the form of casual conversation with immediate department and/or facility administrators or an actual written proposal outlining time schedules, and time and financial costs.

At Tallahassee Memorial HealthCare (TMH), for example, The Arts in Medicine and Medical Music Therapy programs were established as a partnership between TMH and Florida State University (FSU), with the university providing the coordinator's salary and benefits and the Foundation providing office space and a program budget. The resulting job description dictated that the music therapist hired would:

- design and implement MT clinical services throughout the inpatient and outpatient areas of TMH, excluding only the already served Behavioral Health Center (BHC);
- establish an approved MT internship;
- supervise practicum students and interns;
- collaborate with FSU Art Therapy department programs and students;
- establish, coordinate, and support AIM volunteer programs with the purposes of enhancing the hospital environment for patients, visitors, and staff and providing an outlet for community volunteers for service through the arts.

Due to those overall program constructs, one of the first tasks in establishing the medical MT clinical services program at TMH was to establish an internship. Of utmost importance was the integrity of the internship as a valid and nurturing educational field experience, a priority clearly established with the staff of the Foundation prior to selection of the first intern and reiterated as needed throughout the coming years. Interns were not to be viewed as laborers for unlimited Foundation tasks. They could, however, be given opportunities to learn about and assist in coordinating some AIM and Foundation projects since they would likely be involved in similar programs in the future. Regardless, MT services, including session observation, planning, and implementation; research; and integration of their own projects, were to be their primary focus.

In addition, the internship must be approved as a valid clinical training experience. Formerly, this required a written proposal to be submitted to the American Music Therapy Association (AMTA), a format initially established by NAMT, but then continued once that organization joined with the American Association for Music Therapy (AAMT) to form AMTA. The official proposal format included the following elements:

- location and description of the geographic and cultural area and the facility, including type and number of population served, treatment services provided, treatment philosophy, accreditation/licensure of the facility, other clinical training programs provided, library services, and inservice training;
- description of MT services to include current job descriptions and academic and professional experience of staff, available space and equipment including music instruments, types of sessions (i.e., large and small groups and individual), units where services are provided, frequency of sessions, and philosophy of the MT program;
- description of orientation procedures, the overall MT internship experience, skills expectations, records and progress notes, and staff meetings;
- plan for number of interns per training period, internship termination procedure, and availability and provision for living arrangements, meals, stipend, liability coverage, and transportation;
- provisions for intern self-awareness and professional growth;
- outline of supervision and evaluation procedures, including informal and formal observations.

The music therapist planning to serve as the Clinical Training Director (CTD) who could also, but not necessarily, serve as the supervising music therapist, must complete a 5-hour Continuing Music Therapy Education (CMTE) course for prospective CTDs. This person must have three years of clinical experience beyond internship with at least one year of that in the current facility, be working at the facility for at least 20 hours per week, be a member of AMTA, and be certified by the Certification Board for Music Therapists (CBMT). The supervising music therapist must also be board certified and have two years of clinical experience with at least one year spent in the current facility. Placement is limited to two interns per supervising music therapist at one time (NAMT, 1997).

Beginning in the spring of 2001, provision was made for an alternative form of approval called a University Affiliated Internship (UAI). This change followed the establishment of new Standards for Education and Clinical Training adopted by AMTA in the previous year. The UAI entails that an internship be approved by an AMTA-approved academic degree program, established at the local level between a music therapist and university faculty to train interns from that school. Internship sites can have training agreements with multiple universities simultaneously. One advantage of the UAI format is that it allows for greater flexibility in internship planning based on a student's educational needs and life circumstances, with opportunities for part- or full-time training, experience in multiple settings, and training during varying time periods. Upon the addition of this option, formally NAMT- and AMTA-approved internship programs are now referred to as National Roster Internships (NRI). The role formerly referred to as CTD is now called Internship Director. The new AMTA Standards for Education and Clinical Training reflect that clinical training occurs in both pre-internship and internship periods. Music therapists can choose to establish internships as either NRI or UAI or both (AMTA, 2000; AMTA Clinical Training Committee, 2001).

At the time the internship at TMH was established, the formal AMTA approval process was the only option. This process for the medical MT program at TMH was relatively simple because the existing internship at the BHC was used as the foundation with a request for expansion into the medical areas (see Appendix A at the end of this chapter). Tallahassee Memorial HealthCare is a 770-bed facility, with only 60 of those beds in the BHC. In addition, the BHC has outpatient and partial hospitalization programs. The other areas of TMH, within the scope of the medical MT program, in addition to the remaining 710 beds, offer multiple outpatient rehabilitation, surgical, diagnostic, treatment, and support group services. Within the proposal, intern opportunities were not limited to specific units and programs because the internship was established within the first few months of MT program development. This provision seems advisable for most facilities, since programs, regardless of organizational structure or maturity, tend to continue to grow and evolve throughout their existence. Exceptions are conceivable in situations where internship directors are concerned that interns and the MT program as a whole could be expected by administrators to stretch beyond their capabilities and begin offering services in other departments without adequate staffing or training. In such cases, it might be wise to take precautions in expressly limiting intern responsibilities within the internship proposal itself.

The AMTA Clinical Training Committee granted an exception to allow the MT coordinator to be the on-site supervisor, though this person had not yet completed the minimum of two years of MT clinical experience set forth in AMTA guidelines in use at that time. At first, the CTD at the BHC remained the CTD for the medical internship track, as well. In fact, interns were initially offered the option of a split psychiatric/medical internship, which was chosen by two interns. Staff reorganization within the BHC necessitated changing the CTD of record to be the academic director of MT at FSU who served in a supervisory role due to the hospital and university partnership, until the time when the program coordinator serving as Internship Supervisor had obtained sufficient clinical experience to meet the AMTA requirements to be named as the CTD. By this point, the TMH MT programs had developed such that a split medical and psychiatric internship was no longer feasible. At that time and upon the BHC internship program requesting inactive status, additional information and internship format modifications were sent to AMTA and the medical MT internship at TMH was approved as a separate entity with the Internship Supervisor designated as the Internship Director (see addendum to Appendix A at the end of this chapter).

Hospital Coordination

Not only does an internship need to be approved by AMTA or by one or more universities, but also it must meet the approval of, and be integrated within, the facility. Already discussed was the emphasis at the TMH Foundation on ensuring the education and therapeutic focus of the internship to protect interns from additional expectations and to preserve the integrity of the MT experience itself. Beyond that are other tasks that must be completed prior to the arrival of the first intern.

The Risk Management department of the facility should be contacted to develop an agreement between the hospital and, depending on facility guidelines and organizational structure, the MT department, the intern, and the university at which the intern is or was a student. At TMH the agreement used by FSU for practicum student involvement was used as the basis for an intern agreement between universities and the hospital.

Employee Health screening and services at TMH were extended to MT interns free of charge due to the Florida state law health requirements for those persons working in clinical areas of hospitals. These benefits included basic care should an intern become sick or injured while working. During orientation, interns were screened with a basic health history, including verification of varicella (chicken pox) immunity, rubeola/mumps/rubella immunity, polio vaccination, and tetanus vaccination. In addition, a PPD tuberculin skin test was administered if the intern's last test had not been administered within the past year, and the intern was fitted for a tuberculosis mask due to interaction with patients in isolation. Because of interns' close interaction with patients and their assistance with pain management during IV starts and other painful procedures involving an increased risk of contact with bodily fluids, Employee Health also agreed to offer interns the hepatitis B vaccination series and titer as well as the flu shot free of charge, should they desire to receive them.

Ideally, a clinical training program will support the intern financially through complimentary meals, housing, and a stipend. At TMH, the Foundation agreed to provide equipment and materials for sessions and projects, office space and equipment including a phone and computer, and acceptance as a staff member with the access that provides to periodic meals and events. However, no funding was available for a stipend. At some facilities, a stipend may be able to be arranged through the foundation, fund-raising events, donations, specific departments receiving services, or grant funding initiatives. Neither was housing provided to interns by TMH, though efforts were made to assist interns in obtaining housing information and guidance prior to their arrival in Tallahassee. Fortunately, meals were provided free of charge in the hospital cafeteria. Initially, one meal, not to exceed $5.00, was provided daily through the support of the Foundation. The intern was given meal tickets to be used in either the main hospital or BHC cafeteria and the Foundation's account was subsequently charged. A simpler option was later arranged through the Volunteer Services department. Because of the connection between the AIM volunteer and MT clinical services programs at TMH, the program coordinator/Internship Supervisor was aware that hospital volunteers received a free meal whenever they worked four hours straight. When approached, the hospital's volunteer coordinator gladly agreed for this benefit to be extended to MT interns. Meal coupons were obtained daily from the main hospital information desk and could also be used in either cafeteria. While this process was still somewhat inconvenient, the benefit of a free meal made it worth the effort. In later years, the Foundation agreed to a $1,000 stipend for each intern.

The Management Information Systems (MIS) department must also be contacted in order to arrange for interns to have email accounts within the hospital system. The MIS department usually handles training in and access to computerized patient medical charts for the purposes of documentation, as well. Once trained in the system and documentation format and dependent on facility policies, interns may have access to on-line documentation and the internship supervisor can review and co-sign the note entered into the patient's chart. Pagers can also be a valuable resource for interns and supervising music therapists since the geographic area of a medical center can often be very broad. Also, session length and beginning and ending times are quite variable and often unpredictable. An example is a pre-surgical session that could last from a few minutes to a few hours and is wholly dependent on the progression of the day's surgical schedule. Certain types of sessions, such as those for pain management for pediatric patients receiving intravenous line starts or lumbar punctures or for women in labor, occur at a moment's notice. Pagers, not only for MT staff to assist other patient care staff in making referrals, but also for interns can increase communication and training opportunities for interns. This equipment may also be available from MIS, but could be obtained from a different department, depending on facility organization. Regardless, this may incur a charge, since it involves specific equipment and not simply a service, in contrast to the provision of email and electronic medical record documentation accounts.

Creating a conducive work space can be a challenge. The Foundation at TMH was very gracious in eventually providing space to the AIM and MT programs, including adequate furniture, storage, kitchen, bathrooms, and fresh paint and carpet. This transformation did not occur overnight and required awareness of opportunities for change as well as tenacity and some manual labor on the part of the program staff and interns to ensure that change. Often hospitals will have surplus furniture, computer equipment, and office supplies. The Foundation at TMH held an annual surplus sale, similar to a yard sale, to allow employees to purchase these items at very low cost, while still raising money for the hospital. Because of the close relationship with the Foundation, the AIM and MT programs staff and interns were given the opportunity to claim items for program use free of charge prior to the sale. They also gladly assisted with the surplus sale.

Last, but certainly not least, all patient care unit and program contacts must be made aware that highly competent interns will be providing clinical services under supervision for their patients. Ideally, there should be a provision made for intern and practicum student involvement at the time protocols are established when adding MT services to a particular unit or within a particular program, even if an internship program has not yet been proposed.

Intern Selection and Necessary Qualities

Since few medical MT internships existed when the program at TMH began, a large number of prospective interns applied for most internship cycles. When selecting interns at TMH, the application (see Appendix B at the end of this chapter) and letters of recommendation served to narrow the pool of applicants. The subsequent interview, whether in person or via a phone conversation, provided a stronger sense of the appropriateness of the fit of a prospective intern to the TMH site and vice versa. The same basic interview questions were used for each intern (Appendix B). One question, in particular, nestled within the others, most often provided an opportunity for the greatest insight:

At TMH, we receive patient referrals for music therapy services from nursing, rehab (i.e., physical therapy, occupational therapy, speech-language pathology), social work, psychology, dieticians, and physicians. What would be your response if a staff member were to give you a referral, stating, "Why don't you go see Ms. Smith? She might really enjoy music today?"

This is of utmost importance at TMH due to the coexistence of the AIM program and likely is at most medical facilities as it addresses how to determine the appropriateness of referrals and a course of action. Interestingly, some prospective interns did not look beyond the concept of interacting effectively with hospital staff, yet another important element of this question, to realize that some referrals might not be appropriate. Answers also provided insight into a student's understanding of the scope of and potential goals in medical MT programming.

Not every intern is right for every internship, nor is every internship site right for every intern. The following, created in consultation with former TMH intern Heather Hodorowski, MT-BC, is a list of specific qualities necessary for an intern working in a medical MT program to possess in order for the intern to be successful and make the internship the best possible experience.

1. The intern should be very comfortable with and have a working knowledge of medical terminology (i.e., diagnoses, procedures, treatments, symptomatology) with a variety of medical populations. Team meetings and rounds can be extremely overwhelming if this piece is not in place. The intern will spend a great deal of time trying to decipher the verbiage as opposed to spending time determining how MT can best meet patient needs. If an intern seems interested in the medical field, but does not yet have the concrete knowledge required, this can be aided by provision of a list of terms to be learned either prior to internship commencement or within the orientation period.
2. The intern should be aware that MT in a medical setting often requires the ability to be effective in a very short-term setting. At times the intern may be called to a situation (e.g., pediatric venipuncture, pre-surgery, etc.) where he or she is required to assess, treat, and discharge in the course of even one brief meeting with the patient. The ability to adapt to this model and be an effective clinician by assessing the situation quickly and developing a therapeutic rapport and relationship with that patient in a very short period of time is crucial.
3. Professionalism in speech, dress, and overall attitude is of utmost importance.
4. An overall attitude of willingness to try new things is optimal in a medical internship. An intern who has creative, innovative ideas can be a definite asset to a medical program that is constantly evolving. Regardless of population, interns can provide fresh ideas, time, and energy, manifested in day-to-day sessions as well as independent projects.
5. Interns must possess the ability to effectively articulate what MT is and is not and its efficacy with varied medical populations. This is particularly true as AIM initiatives become more common.
6. A level of independence and maturity often not necessitated by other internship placements is highly important in a medical setting since treatment areas may be geographically spread out and the case load and patient needs are constantly changing.

Intern Orientation

On the first day of internship, interns may be given packets of information to which they will refer throughout the remainder of their clinical training experience (see Appendix C at the end of this chapter for intern's acknowledgment list). Among those papers at TMH were:

- an overall description of the MT internship experience (included in the official proposal, Appendix A);
- a list of competencies to be met (included in the official proposal; see addendum to Appendix A);
- specific instructions regarding Employee Health provisions, appointment time, location, and documentation to take to the appointment;
- instructions for obtaining meal coupons;
- phone, fax, pager, voice mail, long distance instructions and contact lists for FSU departments, BHC departments and therapists, specific patient care areas, and therapists, social workers, and nurses from whom the majority of patient referrals were obtained and with whom music therapists and interns frequently co-treat patients;
- descriptions of opportunities for field trips to local MT programs, including the BHC, a state psychiatric hospital, a school system, assisted living and memory care facilities, hospice, and private practice;
- a liability coverage statement to clarify that the intern is responsible for providing his or her own liability coverage through independent insurance, unless the intern's university provides this service or the medical facility in which the internship program is being established provides liability coverage for its students or the MT department has funding to provide this option; a brochure from a company that provides student health care worker insurance, if needed; and an explanation that liability coverage protects the intern, supervisors, and facility from financial responsibility should accidental harm befall a patient during therapy;
- specific documentation guidelines for each unit;
- an index of commonly used medical terms, medical abbreviations, and commonly prescribed drugs (see Glossaries and Indexes at the end of the book);
- dress code and grooming standards to meet with hospital and department standards (see Appendix C at the end of this chapter.);
- evaluation and observation forms that will be used for formal observation of intern clinical skills at periodic intervals, mid and final intern evaluations by the supervisor and by the intern his/herself, and training site evaluation by the intern upon internship completion (see Appendix D at the end of this chapter).

During the orientation period, interns will likely participate in a facility-wide new employee orientation and will need to obtain a hospital badge. Interns may also be entrusted with keys to their work space as well as to patient care areas as needed. Accountability can be encouraged by requiring that the intern and supervisor sign a form upon receipt of keys and then at the completion of internship once keys are returned, whether this is established through the MT department or a broader facility policy or department.

Expectations and assignments should also be discussed at this time. Interns may be required to complete any or all of the following:

- Independent Projects. With approval of the university academic advisor, these could be the same as projects that may be required by some universities or even be related to a thesis for master's students. Suggestions may be provided to interns, but they may be given autonomy to select their projects with supervisor approval.

- Case Studies of patients seen over a period of time, documenting treatment and related patient progress.

- Weekly definitions of medical terms and descriptions of medications. Interns may be given a list of terms and medications as suggestions, though options need not be limited to that list, as interns should investigate terms and medications relevant to their patients or of particular interest.

- Regular Case Reviews. These could be required weekly, bi-weekly, or monthly and would be an overview of patients to provide greater opportunity to focus on application of medical terminology, diagnoses, medications, and therapeutic options. A format can be provided to interns for this purpose. It could be that weekly definitions and descriptions are required from interns during the first half of the internship experience and then case reviews are required during the second half.

- Assistance with practicum student supervision, though not to the point that practicum students are limited in their access to supervision by board-certified music therapists or when the intern feels incapable or actually lacks the clinical and teaching skills to guide students.

All assignments should be based on intern knowledge and future plans assessed at the beginning of the orientation period when establishing assignments, re-evaluated at the halfway point of the internship experience, and monitored throughout so that deficiencies can be rectified as well as strengths recognized and busy work eliminated. Independent projects based on interns' own interests, skills, experiences, and resources can provide some of the most valuable experience gained by interns during clinical training. Interns can add programs and projects that the program director may have identified already as beneficial to the overall program or patient base, but not yet had the manpower to implement, or they may develop ideas that the program director had not before considered. Options include adding clinical services to patient care areas not yet served by MT; conducting research studies with data that lend support to MT programming or add to the MT literature base; creating a proposal and buying equipment, thereby providing the intern experience in budgeting and purchasing; and writing grants for funding of specific program initiatives or to increase services in a particular area, either with the assistance of a hospital grant writer or based on previous experience of the intern through a grant writing class or hands-on experience. To give an idea of the breadth of possibilities, descriptions of a few projects completed by interns at TMH follow.

- Development of a protocol signed by the head nurse of Labor and Delivery to provide MT services to patients in that unit and completion of in-services for unit staff to educate them to the benefits of MT during childbirth and make them aware of referral procedures (Heather Johnson, MT-BC);

- Development of protocols for individual and group MT sessions in the Long Term Care (LTC) Unit and Extended Care Unit (ECU) signed by both head nurses and establishment of a sensory stimulation group for low-functioning LTC patients, complete with equipment, original songs, and clear documentation forms for each patient. (Corey Domec, MM, MT-BC);
- Establishment of a reality orientation group for appropriate patients in the ECU, complete with clear documentation forms for each patient (Rachel Pulver Thompson, MM, MT-BC);
- Purchasing of music instruments through a personal contact at a local music store (Corey Domec, MM, MT-BC);
- Development of a signed protocol for Adult Day Services, complete with a clear documentation system (Darcy Walworth, MM, MT-BC);
- Development of a signed protocol for NeuroScience programming, including scheduling procedures for involvement in support groups (Darcy Walworth, MM, MT-BC);
- Establishment of Music To Live By classes through the childbirth education department of the hospital to be taught by MT staff and interns to prepare parents to use music during the labor and delivery process, including advertisement of classes and curriculum to be used (Jennifer Batey, MT-BC);
- Visitation of other medical MT programs throughout the region to obtain ideas and resources for funding sources, documentation methods, and unique programming (Heather Hodorowski, MT-BC).

In addition, interns should be made aware of scholarship opportunities throughout their training. For example, application could be made for the AMTA E. Thayer Gaston Award should the intern conduct a research project. Other options include regional internship scholarships, regional and national conference attendance scholarships, and facility and community scholarships.

The orientation period should incorporate an overview of services throughout the medical facility across disciplines and specific to MT programming. In that way, interns can have a feel for the whole treatment process, how the areas in which they will be working initially fit into the whole, services MT staff and other interns are providing simultaneously, what to expect later when working in other areas, and ideas for independent projects. However, caution should be taken not to overwhelm the intern for whom everything is new. Therefore, early focus on the units and programs in which the intern will be working for the first half of the internship is advisable.

During orientation to specific schedule responsibilities, the intern should be oriented to the referral and documentation system utilized on each unit. In addition, decisions must be made regarding the quantity of sessions and assessments the intern should observe and co-lead, treatment meeting to attend with the supervisor, individual and group sessions to plan and present to the supervising music therapist with appropriate goals and objectives, and sessions to document prior to leading sessions and assuming full responsibility for treatment. This number should be re-evaluated and adjusted depending on intern level of independence and understanding and speed of acquisition of skills. As the MT experience progresses, interns may be required to maintain a notebook or file of all session plans implemented to assist in the development of his or her own planning materials and to provide a reference to note any areas for change or improvement in planning.

Intern Scheduling and Transitions

Each time one intern completes his or her clinical training and a new intern begins, coordination is required. As one intern finishes his or her training and a new intern begins, or in the case of internship where one intern begins as another moves to the second half of his or her training, all of the items discussed in the section about hospital coordination must be addressed. Appointments for badges, orientation, and health screening must be made. Whichever department may be handling meal provision should be made aware of name changes that will be appearing on the meal coupon sign-in list or whatever tracking system used by the facility. If funding is available for a stipend, then those factors must be tended to as well. This is also the time to ensure that new interns complete the necessary paperwork and pay for student health care worker insurance (unless it is already provided by their university) prior to contact with patients. Also to be completed is paperwork for opening and closing email and electronic medical record documentation accounts, including having completing interns forward any personal emails to their own personal non-hospital accounts prior to closing the account.

As with any internship, multiple scheduling models are possible. Interns could be given the option to work with patients in all programs and units throughout the internship experience, regardless of the number of interns training in a program at one time. However, in full-service medical facilities where sessions and meetings may necessarily occur simultaneously or in immediate succession, but with much geographic distance between them, this may not be the most viable option. Instead, it could be more advisable to group units and programs into two separate internship rotations to facilitate ease of scheduling based on geographic location of units and programs, optimal session times and regular treatment team meetings, similarity (or diversity) of patient goals and age groups, and the possibility that more advanced skills could be necessary for some patient populations than others. Supervisor experience may assist in creating a fairly standard format for the rotation of clinical training experiences within internship programs, though this will likely be reassessed with each new intern to make it accessible, yet also ensure that the intern gains the broad experience unique to a full-service medical facility. An advantage of beginning interns on an overlapping schedule so that one is finishing the first rotation and moving to the second while another is arriving at the internship and beginning the first rotation is that the established intern can mentor the other, though this support should not replace input from staff music therapists. Units must be notified of intern transition and long-term patients, whether receiving group or individual therapy, need to be prepared for one intern's departure and introduced to the next. At least a week of transition should be incorporated into intern schedules. The supervising music therapist and the established intern can jointly orient a new intern to the nuances of units, as each will have different perspectives and experiences. New interns must be introduced to contacts, which could include program or unit directors, receptionists or unit clerks, and physicians, nurses, and therapists involved with particular patients.

Intern schedules at TMH were determined based on established feasibility of unit and program groupings with additional responsibilities contingent upon intern interests, provided interns had the opportunity to at least observe all aspects of the program. Since all unit and program MT service protocols incorporated a provision for practicum student and intern involvement, interns were not limited in areas in which they could provide patient care. Consequently, intern needs took precedence and the MT department coordinator and other MT staff members adapted their schedules to meet patient needs not already covered by interns. When assigning ad hoc sessions like pain management for pediatric venipunctures primarily referred with only a few minutes of preparation, current geographic location of MT staff and interns as well as level of intern competence to conduct such a session should a supervisor not be available were the primary determining factors. For pre-surgical sessions generally announced only one day in advance, an assignment factor was again an intern's level of competence and comfort in addition to whether an intern or MT staff member desired extra early morning hours and if they had scheduling conflicts, such as early morning treatment team meetings. Interns may be treated as employees from the standpoint of empowering their independence and validating their initiative, teaching them to make decisions on their own as well as when to defer to supervisors. This model can facilitate hospital staff viewing the intern as a competent member of the treatment team, while at the same time teaching the intern problem solving skills. However, throughout the internship experience, the intern and his or her time and focus should be protected. Should new MT services be established, management changes (e.g., new head nurse) occur within a program with established MT services, or interpersonal relations be less than positive in a particular area, it may be necessary for the intern's schedule to be adapted to allow for the supervisor to step in with greater supervision than was previously provided in order to protect the intern from unnecessary strife, preserve the integrity of the MT program, and expose the intern to problem-solving opportunities and methods.

Former NAMT and AMTA guidelines required 1,040 hours of internship, which approximated a six-month time commitment (NAMT, 1997). At TMH, interns were given six days (one per month based on the original 1,040 hours or six-month format) when they could choose to be absent, yet still credit toward their internship hours (48 hours total), modeled after the structure of a long standing and well established internship in the same region. When AMTA reduced the requirement to 900 post-academic clinical training hours (AMTA, 2000), some internship programs chose to reduce their time requirement, while others chose to observe the original lengthier requirement. Regardless, many internship programs offered and still offer variable hours. This can be particularly valuable within the ever-changing time schedule of patient service delivery.

Flexibility in schedule coordination between the intern and supervisor can assist in continuity of care, since it is often impossible to predict how long a patient will be receiving services. If an intern has worked with a patient for an extended period of time, that intern could be given the opportunity to continue treating that patient when rotating to new areas at the halfway point of training, or that patient's care could be transferred to a music therapist or a new intern. Once discharged, should the patient be readmitted to the facility for further medical treatment, the supervisor might assign the same intern to the patient, regardless of the units and program with which the intern is currently working, purely to provide the opportunity for long-term treatment for the patient and intern, seldom available in medical populations.

In addition, such scheduling freedom allows interns to finish their training ahead of schedule if they desire and to assist with a challenging schedule as hospital services often begin before dawn (e.g., surgical services) and continue into the evening (e.g., support groups) or even night (e.g., labor and delivery) and weekend (e.g., education programs). It also allows interns to work extra time prior to holidays and other desired vacations or to "bank" extra hours in case of illness or family emergency, and still finish at the predicted completion date if they desire. At TMH, interns were given the option to work more or less than the standard 40-hour work week based on their own health and family needs and a perceived need or desire to complete the internship by a certain date. They were offered the opportunity to be as involved as they liked in pre-surgical services, support groups, weekend and evening education seminars, and labor and delivery classes, none of which were part of their established schedules. Interns were highly encouraged to explore and take on any extra responsibilities, but any involvement was based on their own interests and desire to participate in programming beyond a regular 40-hour weekday work schedule.

Interns may be asked to keep track of their own hours, perhaps on a specific form to be turned in weekly or monthly, including a running total of hours completed, so supervisor and intern can know how many hours remain. However, it is the responsibility of the supervising music therapist to ensure that the intern is receiving adequate supervision, completing a balance of administrative and clinical tasks, and not working so hard to lead to exhaustion, to protect the quality of patient care; intern physical, mental, and emotional health; and integrity of the clinical training experience. Also, depending on independent projects selected, it may be necessary for the supervisor to adjust the intern's schedule to provide time for project completion.

Intern Supervision and Evaluation

Interns should be told during orientation about the skills on which they will be evaluated, to include a list of competencies that must be met. In addition, they may be made aware of methods of evaluation that will be used, including being given a copy of blank formal observation, mid and final supervisor and self-evaluation, and site evaluation forms (see Appendix C at the end of this chapter). At TMH, at least one formal observation for which the supervisor completed a written observation form for an entire individual and group session, followed by a conference with the intern to discuss the observed treatment was completed for each of the two rotations. However, more frequent informal observation of intern professional and clinical skills was completed at times when the supervisor would visit portions of or entire sessions led by interns, co-lead sessions with interns, and even while interns were observing the supervisor, yet still interacting with patients. These observation periods may or may not have resulted in discussion of the experience, depending on intern needs. While weekly meetings were scheduled for each intern to meet with the supervisor, these casual observation periods also offered an opportunity to discuss any concerns or successes, and the supervisor had an open door policy so interns could broach any subject at any time.

Beyond the formal observation and evaluation forms and informal observation, other methods of evaluating intern progress can occur through the following:

- writing skill development evident in weekly assignments;
- changing patterns of interest in topics selected for weekly assignments and project choices;
- growing independence in decision making about individual patient session scheduling, staff interactions, and session planning;
- creativity and clarity in session planning evidenced in the possibility already mentioned of a session plan archive;
- case studies documenting patient progress as well as intern ability to select appropriate interventions and document progress;
- improved clarity of writing in patient documentation reviewed and co-signed by the supervisor.

The above methods of formal and informal evaluation will assist in the process of constant re-evaluation of intern assignments. Most importantly, interns come with differing skill levels in various areas and will progress at varying speeds. The goal is to move toward independence and clinical competence as quickly as possible while not sacrificing the integrity of the training experience or quality of patient care, yet to not limit an intern's autonomy when he or she is ready to accept broader responsibility.

University Affiliation Status

The FSU/TMH internship is maintained at all times as a university affiliated internship site and sometimes as an AMTA National Registry site. Appendix E at the end of this chapter provides a copy of the affiliation agreement completed with other universities to allow their students to intern at TMH. Appendix F provides the AMTA application for National Roster Affiliation.

References

American Music Therapy Association. (2000). *Standards for education and clinical training.* Silver Spring, MD: Author.

American Music Therapy Association Clinical Training Committee. (2001). *Frequently asked questions II.* Silver Spring, MD: Author.

National Association for Music Therapy. (1997, November). *Clinical training guidelines.* Silver Spring, MD: Author.

Appendix A:

Original Proposal to AMTA
to Extend the TMH MT Internship
from the Behavioral Health Center
into the Medical Areas

and

Addendum:

Proposal to Establish a Separate
Medical MT Internship Program

Original Internship Proposal to AMTA

TALLAHASSEE MEMORIAL HEALTHCARE
MUSIC THERAPY INTERNSHIP OVERVIEW

Location

Tallahassee Memorial HealthCare (TMH) is located to the east of downtown Tallahassee, the capital of Florida. This city, known for its canopy roads and family-oriented atmosphere, is found in the northwest region of Florida, only 20 minutes away from Georgia. It is only 2 to 6 hours from such Florida cities as Orlando, Gainesville, Jacksonville, St. Augustine, Panama City, and Pensacola, as well as Atlanta, Georgia, New Orleans, Louisiana, and Birmingham, Alabama.

Tallahassee was recently voted by the National Civic League to be one of the nation's 10 All-American cities for 1999. The city is continually growing as families look for a slower-paced rural community with access to such city amenities as a local bus system, and long distance ground and air travel (Greyhound Bus lines, Amtrak train service, and a regional airport).

Not far from the beaches, this university town, home of the FSU Seminoles and the FAMU Rattlers, provides a variety of cultural, educational, and social activities. Health and fitness, and sports and recreation are well promoted throughout the town via the very active parks and recreation department.

Downtown Tallahassee combines both historical and modern state buildings, around which centers a variety of annual events. The unique combination of Southern hospitality and rural atmosphere make Tallahassee a city of growing interest in Florida.

Type and Number of Population Served

TMH is a 770-bed regional medical center serving Northwest Florida, South Georgia, and Southeast Alabama, within a 200-mile radius of Tallahassee. Services include a full-service hospital, a psychiatric center, a long-term care/extended care facility, a diabetes center, the Women's Pavilion, the Heart and Vascular Institute, the Surgery Center, the Neuroscience Center, home health care, pediatric rehabilitation, a memory disorders clinic, and a family practice residency program, as well as numerous other specialized clinics both on-site and throughout the surrounding communities.

Tallahassee Memorial Behavioral Health Center (TMBHC) is a free standing 60-bed psychiatric facility of TMH. It is comprised of four inpatient units and two day treatment programs, with a total average daily census of 34–42 persons. The facility's program is designed to provide short-term inpatient psychiatric treatment for children, adolescents, adults, and senior adults with mental disorders, as well as day treatment for adults and senior adults with mental

Note: This proposal was adapted from a model provided by Ann Berlin, Director of Music Therapy at Florida State Hospital at Chattahoochee, FL and was prepared by Colleen Cox, Nora Corasco, and Jennifer Whipple.

disorders. These mental disorders may include, but are not limited to, depression, behavior disorders, dementia with psychotic features, and schizophrenia, and may involve such symptoms as threats of suicide, withdrawal, hallucinations, extremely abnormal moods or mood swings, or difficulty concentrating on or completing simple tasks.

Tallahassee Memorial HealthCare (TMH) is a 597-bed inpatient and acute care facility, housing the Heart and Vascular Institute and the Women's Pavilion in addition to the emergency room, medical/surgical intensive care, pediatric/pediatric intensive care, family care including gynecology/urology/antenatal care, labor and delivery, newborn intensive care/newborn intermediate care/newborn nursery, cardiac intensive care/cardiovascular progressive care/ cardiovascular surgical care, inpatient and outpatient surgery, orthopedic, neurology/neurology intensive care, intermediate care, and oncology units. Extended Care/Long Term Care is a 113-bed free standing facility offering both a nursing home environment in Long Term Care and a rehabilitation program in Extended Care.

Treatment Services Provided

Inpatients and outpatients at TMH receive interdisciplinary treatment and care from a combination of the following:

- Physicians (psychiatric and physical/medical evaluation and care)
- Nursing Staff
- Psychology (testing and support services)
- Nutrition
- Social Work
- Physical Therapy
- Occupational Therapy
- Speech/Language Pathology
- Music Therapy
- Recreation Therapy
- School-Age Education
- Adult Education
- Family Education and Support groups
- After Care Planning
- Food Services/Cafeteria
- Volunteer Services

Treatment Philosophy

The mission of TMH is to provide cost-effective age and disability appropriate care in a humane, patient and family-centered environment. The programs are designed to afford patients an array of multimodal treatments including medicine, psychiatry and psychology, social work, psychology, physical/occupational and speech therapies, and music and recreational therapies. Patients and families are the focus of our efforts, the reason for our existence.

Accreditation/Licensure of the Facility

TMH is accredited through JCAHO and licensed by the State of Florida.

Other Clinical Training Programs Provided

- Family Practice Residency Program
- Student Nurses from FAMU, FSU, Tallahassee Community College (TCC), and Lively Technical Center
- Medical Students
- Social Work Interns
- Psychology Interns
- Speech/Language Pathology Interns
- Recreational Therapy Interns
- Pharmacy Students
- Histology Students

Library Services

- TMH Medical Research Library
- Florida State University Libraries (located within 15 minutes)
- Florida A & M University Libraries (located within 15 minutes)
- Leon County Public Libraries (located within 15 minutes)
- TCC Library (located within 20 minutes)
- TMBHC Psychology Department Resources
- TMBHC and TMH Unit Library Resources
- TMBHC, TMH, and FSU Music Therapy Department Library Resources

Note: Our music therapy departments purchase source books, literature, and journals pertinent to music therapy, psychology, and medicine on a regular basis.

Philosophy of the Music Therapy Program

The value of music in therapy at TMBHC reaches beyond the actual activities in which the patients are involved and focuses on the music and the patients' responses to the music. A smile in recognition of a song, a toe that taps to the beat when other clinicians are unable to achieve a verbal or nonverbal response, a patient's ability to focus on a music activity or task, or the acknowledgment of meaning found within the lyrics of the music or within the music activity itself. All these are examples of responses on which we focus in music therapy at TMBHC. Music is not just an activity. It is the facilitation of emotional, cognitive, physical, and social responses. Music stimulates memories and emotions, increases social interactions and sensory awareness, provides a pleasurable, non-threatening environment, and motivates patients to focus or refocus their attention and remain on task. Music provides the environment to elicit responses other therapeutic mediums have been unable to achieve. Music therapy is an integral part of the programming on each Unit at TMBHC and maintains an important role in providing assistance to the patients in achieving goals in such areas as communication, self-expression, cognition, socialization, self-awareness, physical functioning and movement, self-esteem, and goal setting. In order to address their individual treatment goals defined in their master treatment plan, patients are assessed to determine their strengths and weaknesses, music preferences, physical, mental and social needs, and their responses to the music. Our music therapy program at TMBHC provides patients with an opportunity for self-expression through the use of music. Patients may participate in a drumming session, lyric analysis and discussion, song writing and analysis, or movement with music. The music also establishes a non-threatening environment in which patients can engage in positive social interaction, both verbal and nonverbal, in a spontaneous manner. Individuals in a group cooperate with one another in song writing, playing tone chimes to accompany songs, and singing or rhythmically improvising utilizing various rhythmic instruments, simultaneously addressing their problem solving skills, group social interaction, affective response, and self expression. The opportunity to recall recent and remote memories often occurs during a music therapy session when a particular song triggers a memory, pleasant or unpleasant, and the individual discloses this experience. Activities involving music and selections specific to group need (for example, addiction, loss, or anger) may be implemented to utilize this technique. Patients with dementia are able to recall long-term memories through the use of familiar songs and musical, verbal, or visual prompts. Familiar songs have been noted to elicit spontaneous vocalizations from withdrawn patients with dementia or depression. Music then becomes the therapy and a pleasurable experience. Music therapy at TMBHC utilizes a variety of psychotherapy procedures within a cognitive and behavioral framework. The following psychotherapies may be used: rational-emotive therapy, psychotherapy, validation therapy, and social learning theory/behavior therapy.

Medical music therapy at TMH in the main hospital and the outlying buildings utilizes music and counseling techniques to meet non-music, therapeutic goals with patients of all ages from premature infants to seniors. Whenever possible and appropriate, families are involved in treatment. Except for the semi-weekly music therapy group in Pediatrics, all music therapy services require referral from medical or nursing staff, social work, or related therapy staff. While needs are similar for patients across the different units (pain and anxiety reduction, development or rehabilitation, coping skills for illness, disfigurement, or disability, mood elevation, cognitive stimulation, socialization, and parent training or family education), certain objectives are most prevalent in certain units. The music therapist participates in the patient care conferences on all units to receive referrals and chart patient progress, assesses patients and evaluates treatment, documents in patient charts, and conferences and works closely with other related disciplines (physical therapy, occupational therapy, respiratory therapy, speech and language pathology, social work, nursing, and medical staff) to provide the best possible care for each patient. In the Newborn Intensive Care Unit, infants are referred for music therapy based on clinical stability and readiness for developmental stimulation. They receive multimodal stimulation, which is a combination of audio, visual, vestibular, and tactile stimulation based on the progression of neurological development, which can result in increased weight gain, decreased length of hospitalization, increased efficiency of development, and fewer infant stress behaviors. These techniques are taught to parents when appropriate, resulting in improved parent-neonate interactions with fewer infant stress behaviors and more appropriate parent behaviors. In addition, infants needing assistance in learning to feed by mouth are exposed to Pacifier Activated Lullabies (patent owned by the Florida State University) where music is played contingent on the infant's sucking. In addition to addressing needs of specific patients in individual sessions based on referral, much of the focus in Pediatrics/Pediatric Intensive Care Unit is on normalization of environment and increasing the patient's perception of hospitalization, achieved through individual and group sessions. Heart transplant inpatients of the Heart and Vascular Institute receive individual sessions with the purpose of reducing pain and anxiety, increasing coping skills, and providing cognitive stimulation and mood elevation necessary during prolonged hospitalization. Outpatents of the institute receive training in relaxation techniques for use during monthly procedures following transplant and, when necessary, coping skills are addressed with the purpose of increasing compliance with diet, medications, and exercise regimen. For geriatric inpatients throughout the main hospital, encompassing the Medical/Surgical Intensive Care, Intermediate Care, Neurology/Neurology Intensive Care, and Family Care Units, individual music therapy sessions are provided with the purpose of reducing pain, anxiety, and restlessness, increasing coping skills, providing cognitive stimulation and mood elevation, and increasing reality orientation, necessary due to chronic and terminal conditions, long-term hospitalization, depression, dementia, and surgical and other painful procedures. In Oncology, patients receive individual music therapy sessions to address any and all of the previously mentioned inpatient needs, as well as music listening and relaxation training for outpatients receiving chemotherapy and radiation treatment. In addition, music therapy is a part of the established Oncology and Neuroscience Center outpatient and family support groups and exercise groups. There are possibilities for music therapy involvement in Labor and Delivery, Pediatric outpatient audiology testing in the Professional Office Building, Extended Care/Long Term Care, and other outlying TMHc buildings and programs. Music therapy programs are augmented by the TMH Arts In Medicine program in which volunteers from the Tallahassee community provide patients with experiences in computer discovery, dance, literature, music, and visual art to improve the hospital environment.

Various creative approaches such as Orff Schulwerk, dance, art, drama, sign language, improvisation, and music with aerobic and strengthening exercise are used within music therapy sessions at TMH to address the patient's individual treatment goals. Because of a generally short length of stay, a crisis intervention model is often implemented. This provides the patients with the opportunity to make choices and gain control through the verbalization of their feelings. Flexibility plays a key role; however, the patient's needs/treatment goals and how they can most effectively be addressed is the first priority. Finally, music therapy inservice sessions are regularly provided for hospital clinicians to allow the programs continued growth.

Music Therapy Internship Experience

According to AMTA guidelines, the internship at TMH is 1,000 hours which amounts to 25 weeks at 40 hours each week and 8 hours each day, not including lunch. Interns will have the opportunity to observe, co-lead, and lead both individual and group sessions, participate in treatment team meetings, document patient progress both daily and weekly, and implement patient assessment and evaluation. Weekly individual supervision, formal and informal observation, and performance evaluations will be provided in addition to the completion of special projects and case studies.

Availability and Provision for:

- *Living Arrangements*—Assistance in locating housing will be provided once the intern has been accepted and a start date assigned. A detailed listing of apartments and housing available in the area will be mailed to the MTI.

- *Meals*—One meal provided daily free of charge.

- *Health Care*—Employee Health screening and services are extended to interns free of charge, including the administration of the hepatitis B vaccine series, if desired, (for the period of time when the MTI is actively interning at TMH and can be completed after internship for a fee) and the administration of the tetanus and varicella vaccines, if necessary. These services do not replace the need for health insurance and may not be used as a primary health care provider.

- *Stipend*—There is no stipend or other financial assistance available for interns.

- *Liability Coverage*—The MTI will be responsible for providing his or her own liability coverage through their university or their independent insurance. Our facility does not provide liability coverage for interns.
- *Transportation*—public transportation is available—a local bus system and various taxi services. However, it is recommended that the MTI have a car for his or her own safety and convenience.

Skills Expectations

The entering MTI will be expected to demonstrate:

- Ability to play I, IV, V basic chord progressions on the guitar to accompany a song.

- Ability to play I, IV, V chord progressions on the keyboard/piano to accompany a song.

- Ability to accompany a song using guitar and piano/keyboard and lead a group while singing.

- Ability to play a melody on the piano and accompany it with simple chord progressions.

- Ability to read music.

- Ability to assess, observe, and document a patient's mood, affect, behavior, and responses to music interventions.

- Ability to document a patient's progress during Music Therapy sessions.

- Functional vocal proficiency (i.e., ability to sing in time and in tempo).

- Respect toward other persons in response to a variety of situations or circumstances.

- Knowledge of individual and group session plan development.

- Ability to recognize all five axis of the DSM-IV.

- Ability to locate necessary psychiatric information within the DSM -IV.

- A general knowledge of psychiatric illnesses, terms, and treatments.

- Ability to locate necessary medical information within medical dictionaries, *Physician's Desk Reference*, and other related sources.

- A general knowledge of medical illnesses, disabilities, terms, and treatments.

- Ability to adequately express themselves in a professional manner.

- Punctuality, professionalism, and organization, and ability to interact effectively with related disciplines.

- Ability to follow hospital policies and procedures.

- Ability to transpose songs to meet patients' vocal range.

- Ability to compose songs or simple arrangements using I, IV, V chords.

- Ability to improvise, utilizing rhythmic instruments, guitar, piano or keyboard.

- Ability to sight read easy to intermediate musical pieces on piano in order to accompany a song.

- General working knowledge of music theory (i.e., recognize various clefs, time signatures, tempos, etc.).

- General knowledge of music history.

The above entering skills will be required of each entering MTI. Prospective interns will submit a detailed application, a resume, a copy of their best written work, two letters of recommendation, and a current college transcript to help determine the intern's qualification for the internship (see Internship Application). An interview with each prospective intern will be conducted, either in person or by telephone. If necessary, either a video tape or audio tape of a music therapy session led by the prospective intern may be requested.

Number of Interns Per Training Period

With three supervising MTs (the CTD and two other MT-BCs), the clinical training site at TMH will be able to accept no more than six interns per training period—two interns per supervising MT. The CTD may accept overlapping interns, provided the number of interns to be supervised does not exceed AMTA's requirements. Based on availability and preferred start time, three internship track options are possible: Medical, Psychiatric, and Medical/Psychiatric.

Application Deadlines

Applications should be received six months prior to preferred internship start time: July 1 for January/February, September 1 for March/April, December 1 for June/July and March 1 for September/October. Notification of internship acceptance or denial will be sent at least three months prior to the preferred internship start time.

Addendum 1 to Appendix A. Proposal to AMTA to Establish a Separate Medical MT Internship Program

TALLAHASSEE MEMORIAL HEALTHCARE MEDICAL MUSIC THERAPY INTERNSHIP EXPERIENCE

During orientation, the Music Therapy Intern (MTI) will be oriented to the referral and documentation system utilized on each unit. The MTI will be assigned to at least three units on a rotating schedule and will be expected to implement MT groups and individual one-to-one (1:1) sessions on the assigned units. The MTI will observe the groups/sessions, conduct assessments, co-lead and lead groups/sessions, develop appropriate MT group plans and 1:1 interventions, attend weekly/monthly treatment team meetings on assigned units, and document patient progress on the appropriate medical chart form.

Prior to co-leading or leading groups, the MTI will be expected to complete four initial group session plans—two for co-leading groups and two for leading groups. The MTI must also complete session plans with appropriate goals and objectives prior to their 1:1 interventions. These will be reviewed by the supervising MT. As the MT experience progresses, the MTI will be required to maintain a notebook or file of all session plans implemented to assist in the development of his/her own planning materials and to provide a reference to note any areas for change or improvement in planning.

The MTI will document in patient charts after each 1:1 session and will evaluate whether or not the session objectives were met. The supervising MT will provide verbal and written feedback on the evaluation of sessions and patient responses. The supervising MT will be present during at least the first two sessions the MTI leads and co-leads. The MTI will then be supervised on a weekly basis.

Observing MT Groups/Individual Sessions

The MTI will be required to observe MT group/sessions on the assigned units. This observation time will occur during the first week of each of the unit rotations in addition to observation during orientation. During the observation portion of the MT experience the MTI will be asked to write observations after each session on a sample of the appropriate medical chart and begin formulating session plans to be implemented during the leading and co-leading portions of their MT experience.

Co-leading

Throughout the MT experience, the MTI will be given the opportunity to co-lead groups/sessions and will be required to co-lead sessions with the supervising MT prior to leading groups. The remainder of sessions to be co-led will be spread throughout the unit rotation and may be co-led with another MTI, MT, or related therapist (SLP, PT, OT, RT, etc.). Two initial session plans for a co-led group/session will be required prior to co-leading any groups.

Leading

After co-leading sessions, the MTI will begin leading MT groups. Once again two session plans will be required prior to leading.

One-to-One Interventions

The majority of patient contact at TMH is in the form of 1:1 interventions. The supervising MT will assign specific patients from the assigned units to be followed by the MTI. It will be the intern's responsibility to review the patient's record, assess the patient, and meet with the members of the treatment team to determine and design an appropriate program for the individual. The MTI will be encouraged to use 1:1 programs for case study requirements. The MTI may request to do a 1:1 with a patient from any unit and such feedback and treatment ideas will be considered when determining 1:1 patient assignments.

Records and Progress Notes

Materials and information regarding terminology pertinent to the medical setting and documentation will be provided to the MTI to assist them in this process. All patient chart documentation must be signed by the supervising MT. Documentation demands at TMH include:

- Recording verbal referrals on appropriate unit MT referral forms and filing written and verbal referrals in the MT notebook for each unit

- Recording patient demographics and session summary in the MT notebook for each unit for each group implemented

- Documenting patient behavior, response to music, ability to meet goals and objectives of session, and MT plans for further treatment on appropriate form (different for each unit) in each patient's medical chart after each 1:1 session and, when deemed necessary, after MT group sessions

Staff and Inservice Meetings

The MTI will be required to attend weekly/monthly treatment team meetings for assigned units and other planning meetings for program and project development as needed.

The multi-disciplinary treatment teams meet for approximately one hour every week or month (depending on each unit's schedule). The MTI will attend the treatment team meetings for assigned units in order to chart patient progress, receive referrals, and share observations of patients during MT treatment.

Intern Self-Awareness and Professional Growth

In addition to hospital and related inservice training, the MTI will be given the opportunity to attend either the National or Regional Conference for AMTA, and any and all state MT workshops. The MTI will be credited for time spent in these activities and, in the case of conferences, will earn 8 hours for each day spent at the conference plus two 8-hour days for travel. The MTI will also be encouraged to keep a journal regarding feelings and/or experiences in the internship.

Formal and Informal Observations

CTD or supervising MT observation of each MTI will occur both formally and informally while the MTI is observing, co-leading, and leading sessions. The Formal Observation Form will be used to document the MTI's ability to lead, co-lead, or observe MT groups in a therapeutic and professional manner. The MTI will have an opportunity to see the CTD's observations, comments, and suggestions, and discuss areas and plans for improvement. The MTI will be given a copy of the completed Formal Observation Form. Constructive verbal feedback will be given regarding the MTI's improvement or need for improvement in areas noted on the Formal Observation Form. Informal observation will occur during groups, documentation time, and treatment team meetings. Constructive feedback will be given and suggestions will be made during the MTI's supervision meetings.

Supervision

Each intern will receive a minimum of one hour consultation each week with the supervising MT. During supervision, formal and informal observations will be discussed in more detail. The Formal Observation Form will be reviewed and a more detailed improvement plan will be developed. This will be a time for the MTI to ask questions or express concerns about their MT experience, documentation, or other areas. The following is a list of potential topics to be covered during supervision:

- Conflict Resolution
- Professional Staff Interaction
- Music Therapy Marketing Techniques
- Documentation
- Music Therapy Group/Individual Session Planning
- Evaluations
- Plans for Special Requirements or Administrative Skills Projects

Projects and Assignments

Throughout the six-month internship, the MTI will be expected to complete at least two case studies and one project (administrative skills or special requirements). Projects may be selected from the lists below or the MTI may propose a project not listed. Prior to the intern beginning a project, the CTD will review the project for its appropriateness and applications.

Administrative Skills

Each MTI will be given at least an hour each week to develop administrative skills. He or she will be given the time to attend meetings, do research, and develop projects relating to the following:

- Formulating a Resume
- Creating a Sample Budget
- Developing a MT Supply Inventory Procedure and Forms
- Constructing Visual Aids
- Ordering / Purchasing Supplies
- Writing Program Proposals
- Developing and Implementing New MT Assessment and Documentation Forms
- Meeting with Other Hospital Departments for Special Programming
- Developing an Inservice to Be Presented at TMH

Special Requirements

- Research Project(s)
- Creation of a Special Event for Patients at TMH
- Creation of a Field Trip or Special Event for Patients at ECU/LTC
- Development of a Detailed Song List for Various Counseling Topics
- Development of a Detailed Song List for Meeting Speech/Language, Respiratory, or Physical/Occupational Therapy Objectives
- Researching Payment/Reimbursement Options for MT Services within the Main Hospital
- Development of a MT Program for One of the Main Hospital Medical Units, ECU/LTC, or Other Inpatient or Outpatient Service

Clinical Training Director's Job Description

The proposed clinical training director, employed as Coordinator of Medical Music Therapy, spends 20 hours per week leading group sessions and participating in patient care and treatment team meetings. In addition, time is spent leading sessions with individual patients as referred by patient care staff and then assigned to either the program coordinator/proposed clinical training director or the additional staff music therapist.

Intern Evaluation and Site Evaluation

The Music Therapy Internship Rating Scale Forms will be used for both the mid-term and the final evaluations. The MTI will be given a packet of information during orientation which will include a copy of the Music Therapy Internship Self Evaluation, as well as the Music Therapy Internship Rating Scale and the Music Therapy Clinical Training Site Evaluation in order to provide the intern with a deeper understanding of internship expectations. The intern will be expected to complete the Music Therapy Internship Self Evaluation and return it to the CTD prior to their mid-term appointment. The CTD will be responsible for completing a mid-term Music Therapy Internship Rating Scale for each intern supervised prior to their review date. The MTI will be given the CTD's evaluation prior to the meeting, allowing the MTI time to read and review the evaluation. Each intern will then meet with the CTD for the scheduled review, at which time both evaluations will be reviewed and areas for improvement will be discussed. If necessary, a plan will be implemented to address those areas with follow up dates for review. The intern will be given a final Music Therapy Internship Self Evaluation and a Music Therapy Clinical Training Site Evaluation to be completed prior to the scheduled final review date. The CTD will complete a final evaluation using the Music Therapy Internship Rating Scale for each intern. The final review date will be prior to the end of the internship and the same procedure will be followed for the final review. The evaluations will be discussed and previous concerns will be reviewed. The Clinical Training Site Evaluation will be discussed to clarify any problem areas. The supervising MT, if different from the CTD, will be notified regarding areas needing improvement.

Following review of the three-month evaluation, a copy of the completed and signed Music Therapy Internship Rating Scale will be given to the MTI to keep and a copy will be sent along with a progress letter to the MTI's academic program. Following review of the final evaluation and internship completion, a copy of the completed and signed Music Therapy Internship Rating Scale will be given to the MTI to keep and a copy will be sent along with a letter of completion to the MTI's academic program. In addition, a copy of the Music Therapy Clinical Training Site Evaluation will be given to the MTI to keep and a copy will be sent to the regional Clinical Training Committee Coordinator.

Orientation to AMTA Standards of Clinical Practice and Internship Expectations

Interns receive the attached forms on their first day of internship. They are also given copies for the AMTA "Standards of Practice," "Clinical Training Guidelines," and "Code of Ethics." After the intern reads the materials, each document is discussed, following which the attached "Acknowledgment Form" is signed by both the intern and CTD, a copy is made for the intern to keep, and the CTD keeps the original. All forms and reading materials are kept by the intern.

Appendix B:
Music Therapy Internship Application and Interview Forms

TALLAHASSEE MEMORIAL HEALTHCARE
MUSIC THERAPY INTERNSHIP APPLICATION

Mr.
Mrs.
(1) Name: Ms. _____
                 (Last)   (First)   (MI)

Address:_____

Telephone: (Home) _____ (Work) _____

(2) Medical History: Indicate general health status, plus any chronic or permanent disabilities that would require special accommodations.

(3) Instrument Proficiency: List instruments (including voice) on which you are proficient, with years of study and proficiency level rating (poor, average, excellent) for each.

(4) Strengths and Areas for Improvement: Describe your personal strengths as well as areas that may need improvement.

Please include in your application packet:

    X   Resume (include practica and related volunteer experience)

    X   Two letters of recommendation (one must be from the Director of Music Therapy at your college or university indicating your eligibility to begin internship)

    X   Current college transcript

    X   Copy of a music therapy project, treatment plan, or case study which you consider to be an example of your best work

Please indicate:

    X   Your preferred internship start time:

Winter _____   Spring _____   Summer _____   Fall _____

THE MUSIC THERAPY INTERNSHIP AT TALLAHASSEE MEMORIAL HEALTHCARE REQUIRES THAT INTERNS BE PROFESSIONAL IN MANNER AND APPEARANCE. IF SELECTED AS AN INTERN, I AGREE TO ABIDE BY THIS REQUIREMENT.

_____

(Applicant's Signature)

Please mail application packet to:

Clinical Training Director
TMH Foundation
1331 East 6th Avenue
Tallahassee, FL 32303

(850) 431-7468

Note: This application was adapted from models provided by Colleen Cox, Director of Music Therapy at the TMH Behavioral Health Center, and Ann Berlin, Director of Music Therapy at Florida State Hospital in Chattahoochee, FL.

TALLAHASSEE MEMORIAL HEALTHCARE
MUSIC THERAPY INTERNSHIP INTERVIEW

1) Clarification of application information:
   Date
   Track Preference
   Contact Information

2) The music therapy program in the medical areas of TMH is fairly new. What are possible challenges that could be involved in developing and implementing a new music therapy program in a hospital setting?

3) I currently have a patient who is a 55-year-old quadriplegic African-American man. He is depressed, confused at times, confined to a ventilator with the possibility of weaning to alternative respiratory assistance, able to speak and eat solid foods with monitoring when the ventilator cuff is deflated, and may be regaining some arm movement. List 3 possible goals for him and describe a music therapy intervention for each.

   goal: intervention:
   goal: intervention:
   goal: intervention:

4) What is an activity you could do with a group of six- to eight-year-old children in Pediatrics? (Goal/Objective?)

5) At TMH, we receive patient referrals for music therapy services from nursing, rehab (PT, OT, SLP), social work, psychology, dieticians, and physicians. What would be your response if a staff member were to give you a referral, stating, "Why don't you go see Ms. Smith? She might really enjoy music today."

6) At TMH, we have an Arts In Medicine (AIM) volunteer program as well as a music therapy program. The purpose of the AIM program is to enhance the environment for hospital patients, visitors, and staff by providing experiences in dance, computer discovery, literature, music, theatre, and visual art.
   Does involvement in this program interest you?
   Why/in what way?
   What challenges could the presence of the AIM program present for the music therapy programs?

7) What steps would you take to begin a Sensory Stimulation group in a Long Term Care facility (research, contact, documentation, etc.)?

8) Describe three methods of pain management and an appropriate situation, including age of patient and type of session (group or individual), in which each could be used.

method: situation:
method: situation:
method: situation:

9) How independent could you be and feel comfortable?

10) Do you have any questions about our internship (hospital services, programs, music therapy model, equipment, provisions for interns—office, health, meals, etc.)?

Appendix C:
TMH Grooming Standards

TMH Grooming Standards

Dress Code

Visitors must wear their identification badge whenever on hospital grounds. Attire should be professional in appearance. No sleeveless shirts, open-toed shoes, denim, corduroy, or shorts are permitted. Skirt length should fall below the knee.

Hair

All hair styles should be clean, neat, and conservatively styled and in good taste. The length and/or bulk of the hair will not be excessive or present a ragged, unkempt, or extreme appearance. It should be neatly cut. No rattails or spike hairdos are permitted. Men's hair styles should be conservative and businesslike and not excessively long. Sideburns should not extend downward beyond the upper part of the exterior ear opening. Sideburns should also be straight and not flared. Women's hair falling below the shoulder should be contained and back. Hairpieces can be worn if they are conservative and in good taste. No hair glitter or sparkling jewelry is to be worn either in the hair or on the hairpiece. Beards and mustaches are permitted if they are short and neatly groomed.

Hands and Nails

Hands should be clean and neatly manicured. Nail polish should be in keeping with the hospital's conservative image. When working in the Newborn Intensive/Intermediate Care Units, acrylic and other artificial fingernails are prohibited and natural fingernails should not extend beyond the fingertip, in order to prevent the spread of bacteria.

Jewelry and Accessories

Jewelry should be in good taste, not lavish or overly ornate. Only moderate amounts should be worn. Multi-colored garnish beads or heavy chunky style beads are not permitted. Single strands of one color are allowed. Dangling earrings of one inch or less are permitted, with one earring in each ear. Males are not allowed to wear earrings. Pins are limited to wear on scarves, collars, or lapels. Rings are limited to the third and fourth fingers of each hand, with no more than one ring per finger (wedding rings and engagement rings are considered one), and with no more than three total rings. Neck chains and necklaces should be tasteful and not too thick. Students may not wear a hat, cap, visor, scarf, or headband unless used as part of a costume. However, it is acceptable to wear those items to and from the hospital.

Cosmetics

Makeup should be subdued, without heavy or dramatic effects. Perfumes, colognes, and scents should be minimal and should not be a heavy fragrance that dominates a room.

Identification Badges

Interns will need badges to identify them as appropriate members of the hospital team to interact with patients and their families and caregivers and have access to confidential information. For practicum students at TMH, student badges are obtained through the Medical Staff Office; however, badges for interns are obtained from the Human Resources department either prior to or during new employee orientation. These badges display Music Therapy Intern as the job title and, unlike the practicum student badges, resemble employee badges, which can be beneficial to interactions with hospital staff.

Appendix D:

Internship Orientation Acknowledgment Form, Intern Evaluation Forms, and Site Evaluation Form

TALLAHASSEE MEMORIAL HEALTHCARE
MUSIC THERAPY INTERNSHIP ACKNOWLEDGMENT FORM

The following information was provided to me by the Clinical Training Director (CTD) regarding expectations of the internship. (Please check all items that apply)

_____ Preliminary Instructions

_____ Competency Requirements

_____ Orientation Schedule

_____ Internship Schedule

_____ Written Assignments and Project Requirements

_____ Placement and Supervision Provisions

_____ Grooming Standards and Dress Code

_____ Liability Coverage Requirements

_____ Health Care Provisions and Requirements

_____ Meal Provisions and Procedure

_____ Copies of AMTA Standards of Practice, Clinical Training Guidelines, and
Code of Ethics

_____ Copies of Evaluation Forms

_____ Inservice, Conference, and Field Trip Opportunities

_____ Termination Policy and Procedure

_____   _____
Intern Signature/Date   CTD Signature/Date

Note: This acknowledgment form was adapted from models provided by Colleen Cox, Director of Music Therapy at the TMH Behavioral Health Center, and Ann Berlin, Director of Music Therapy at Florida State Hospital in Chattahoochee, FL.

TALLAHASSEE MEMORIAL HEALTHCARE
MUSIC THERAPY INTERN
FORMAL OBSERVATION FORM

MTI: DATE:
SUPERVISING MT: UNIT:

Rating Scale:
4 = Above Satisfactory – Exceeds Requirements
3 = Satisfactory – Meets Requirements
2 = Conditional – Needs Improvement
1 = Unsatisfactory – Demonstrates Few Skills in this Area

_____ Appropriately groomed/dressed.
_____ Adequately prepared for session(s).
_____ Appropriate therapeutic interaction with patients.
_____ Able to set and meet realistic goals and objectives that address the patient's
           rehabilitative needs.
_____ Demonstrates ability to instruct and lead a MT group.
_____ Demonstrates ability to modify plans when necessary.
_____ Able to assess the patient's needs and progress and clearly document such.

Comments/Suggestions: _____
_____
_____
_____
_____
_____
_____
_____

Date Discussed: _____

_____   _____
Supervising MT-BC Signature   MTI Signature

Note: This evaluation form was adapted from models provided by Colleen Cox, Director of
Music Therapy at the TMH Behavioral Health Center.

TALLAHASSEE MEMORIAL HEALTHCARE
MUSIC THERAPY INTERNSHIP RATING SCALE
(also used for intern self-evaluation)

KEY: 5 = Outstanding - Excels in this area
        4 = Above Satisfactory - Exceeds requirements
        3 = Satisfactory - Meets all requirements
        2 = Conditional - Needs improvement
        1 = Unsatisfactory - Demonstrates very few skills in this area

Intern:
Evaluation Period: _____3 month _____6 month   Date:
Supervisor:
Clinical Training Director:

A. APPEARANCE
1. ____ Dresses appropriately for work situations.
2. ____ Is neat and tidy in grooming.

B. DEPENDABILITY
1. ____ Is consistently at work on time.
2. ____ Gives reasonable excuses for absence and lateness.
3. ____ Completes assignments promptly and correctly.
4. ____ Meets deadlines consistently.
5. ____ Follows through on suggestions, decisions, and projects.
6. ____ Holds assigned activities consistently.
7. ____ Responds appropriately in tense or difficult situations with patients.
8. ____ Responds appropriately in tense or difficult situations with other staff members.
9. ____ Does assigned work with few reminders.
10. ____ Keeps written work up to date.
11. ____ Demonstrates dependability in inter-departmental situations.
12. ____ Takes proper care of all equipment for which he or she is responsible and returns on time to appropriate place.
13. ____ Is prompt to meetings and appointments.
14. ____ Secures appropriate levels of approval before initiating projects.

Note: This form was adapted from a model provided by Ann Berlin, Director of Music Therapy at Florida State Hospital at Chattahoochee, FL.

C. QUALITY OF WORK

1. _____ Applies to daily programmatic situations knowledge of medical terminology, diagnoses, and treatments.
2. _____ Applies educational knowledge to training situation in such a way that the possibility of patient progress is maximized.
3. _____ Applies knowledge of various psychotherapies and counseling techniques in programming.
4. _____ Applies knowledge of individualized programming and objectives for patients.
5. _____ Demonstrates ability to make rational decisions.
6. _____ Demonstrates ability to utilize resources (materials, equipment, space, and services) appropriately.
7. _____ Seeks other sources of information through readings, workshops, seminars, etc., to expand knowledge and skills.
8. _____ Displays an acceptable quality of required written work.
9. _____ Collects data on patients and patient programs in a clear, concise manner.
10. _____ Selects and utilizes appropriate treatment materials.
11. _____ Communicates useful information in staff, treatment team, and patient care conference meetings.
12. _____ Gives easily understood directions in sessions.
13. _____ Follows the logical sequence or order of a task.
14. _____ Prepares adequately for sessions.
15. _____ Poinpoints and tries to improve areas of weakness.
16. _____ Demonstrates ability to modify plans when necessary.
17. _____ Sets realistic goals for patients.
18. _____ Demonstrates ability to document patients' progress clearly.
19. _____ Selects and utilizes music appropriate to the clients' needs, age, and preference.

D. QUANTITY OF WORK

1. _____ Strives to maintain consistency in programming.
2. _____ Budgets time efficiently.
3. _____ Demonstrates ability to stay on task.
   <u>Initiates and follows through on time:</u>
4. _____ Concerning own scheduled activities.
5. _____ Concerning team/departmental projects.
6. _____ Demonstrates ability to work efficiently under stressful conditions.
7. _____ Demonstrates willingness to accept new responsibilities.
8. _____ Volunteers to assist others with major projects as schedule permits.
9. _____ Participates in treatment team/patient care process as needed.

E. RELATIONSHIPS WITH PEOPLE

Demonstrates a sensitivity to the feelings and goals of:

1. ____ Patients.
2. ____ Peers.
3. ____ Supervisors.
4. ____ Seeks supervisory aid in making difficult decisions.
5. ____ Recognizes other opinions, possibilities, and consequences in decision making.
6. ____ Treats all persons with courtesy and tact even in difficult situations.
7. ____ Seeks information through correct channels.
8. ____ Demonstrates respect and concern for clients' welfare, needs and goals.
9. ____ Maintains control of own emotions and does not let personal problems interfere with his or her work.
10. ____ Demonstrates ability to give and receive constructive criticism.
11. ____ Respects and supports decisions made by supervisors.

Demonstrates patience in new or difficult situations with:

12. ____ Patients.
13. ____ Staff.
14. ____ Demonstrates willingness to adapt to new ideas, procedures and assignments.
15. ____ Demonstrates willingness to alter schedule when necessary.
16. ____ Deals appropriately with visitors, volunteers, students as well as employees of the facility.
17. ____ Works cooperatively in a team situation.

Communicates effectively with:

18. ____ Peers.
19. ____ Supervisors.
20. ____ Demonstrates a positive attitude toward job.
21. ____ Demonstrates discretion in dealing with other staff.
22. ____ Demonstrates ability to protect the confidentiality of patients.
23. ____ Accepts responsibility for own actions.
24. ____ Does not demonstrate discriminating biases regarding race, religion, sex, etc.

F. KNOWLEDGE OF JOB

1. ____ Demonstrates knowledge of music therapy processes and techniques.
2. ____ Demonstrates adequate proficiency in music performance on major as well as functional instruments.
3. ____ Demonstrates knowledge of a variety of treatment modalities: behavior modification, psychodynamic processes, developmental and rehabilitative models, etc.
4. ____ Demonstrates knowledge of music literature and resources pertinent to music therapy processes.

5. ____   Demonstrates knowledge of the interdisciplinary team concept.
6. ____   Demonstrates basic knowledge of pertinent laws, rules, and regulations.
7. ____   Demonstrates ability to assess patients' needs, progress.
8. ____   Demonstrates ability to develop programs based on assessments.
9. ____   Demonstrates ability to collect data on patient programs.
10. ____   Seeks advice when needed from supervisor.
11. ____   Demonstrates knowledge of the AMTA Code of Ethics and Standards of Clinical Practice.
12. ____   Demonstrates awareness of necessary safety and security precautions for self, patient, other staff, and other patients.
13. ____   Demonstrates ability to discover and use appropriate reinforcers for patients.
14. ____   Demonstrates ability to play simple chord progression (i.e., I, IV, V, IV, I) on piano.
15. ____   Demonstrates ability to play simple chord progression (i.e., I, IV, V, IV, I) on guitar.
16. ____   Demonstrates ability to lead a group and individual in singing.
17. ____   Demonstrates ability to teach a group and individual a new song.
18. ____   Demonstrates knowledge of various styles of music.
19. ____   Demonstrates sensitivity to the patient's musical preferences (i.e., style, culture, era, etc.).

SCORE:

A   ____ ÷ ____ = ____

B   ____ ÷ ____ = ____

C   ____ ÷ ____ = ____

D   ____ ÷ ____ = ____

E   ____ ÷ ____ = ____

F   ____ ÷ ____ = ____

Score: ____ ÷ ____ = ____

MTI Signature/Date _____

CTD Signature/Date _____

Supervisor Signature/Date_____

TALLAHASSEE MEMORIAL HEALTHCARE
MUSIC THERAPY CLINICAL TRAINING SITE EVALUATION

NAME: _____

SCHOOL: _____

DATES OF INTERNSHIP: _____

      Ranking Scale: 1 = Strongly Agree
                       2 = Mildly Agree
                       3 = Neither Agree or Disagree
                       4 = Mildly Disagree
                       5 = Strongly Disagree
             NA = Not Applicable

Directions: Read each statement and determine the degree with which you agree or disagree with each statement. Note that evaluation of each item involves determining whether the experiences were provided as stated in the Clinical Training Proposal and the quality of such experience.

I. Provisions for Orientation.

_____ 1. My orientation to the agency/ facility was provided to me as specified in the Clinical Training Plan.

_____ 2. My orientation to the facility was adequate for my needs.

_____ 3. My orientation to facility personnel and department standards, policies, and procedure was provided to me as specified in the Clinical Training Plan.

_____ 4. My orientation to the standards in Question #3 was adequate for my needs.

_____ 5. My orientation to AMTA Standards of Practice, organizational structure, Code of Ethics, and Clinical Training Guidelines was provided to me as specified in the Clinical training Plan.

_____ 6. My orientation to AMTA standards listed in Question #5 was adequate for my needs.

_____ 7. My orientation included verification procedure specifying acknowledgment of expectations and competencies, where interns do not fall under facility policies and procedures.

_____ 8. My orientation verification process was adequate for my needs.

Comments about the orientation phase of the internship:

Note: Site evaluation form was adapted from a model provided by Ann Berlin, Director of Music Therapy at Florida State Hospital at Chattahoochee, FL.

II. Provisions for the Music Therapy Experience.

_____ 9. My internship provided me with the observation experiences as described in the Clinical Training Plan.

_____ 10. My opportunities for observation of Music Therapy sessions were adequate for my needs.

_____ 11. My internship provided me with the co-leading experiences as described in the Clinical Training Plan.

_____ 12. My opportunities for co-leading of the Music Therapy sessions were adequate for my needs.

_____ 13. My internship provided me with the session leading experience as described in the Clinical Training Plan.

_____ 14. My opportunities for leading sessions were adequate for my needs.

Comments on the music therapy experiences:

III. Provisions for Records and Progress Notes.

_____ 15. My internship provided me with the record and progress notes experiences a described in the Clinical Training Plan.

_____ 16. My opportunities for learning the process of completing documentation requirements such as records and progress notes were adequate for my needs.

_____ 17. My schedule allowed adequate hours to complete records, progress notes, and other documentation.

_____ 18. My schedule allowed adequate hours to complete lesson and/or session plans.

Comments on records, progress notes, assessments, treatment plans, attendance records, discharge summaries, annual/monthly reviews, transfer evaluations:

IV. Provisions for Staff and Inservice Meetings.

_____ 19. My internship provided me with staff and inservice meeting opportunities a described in the Clinical Training Plan.

_____ 20. My opportunities to attend staff and inservice meetings were adequate for my needs.

_____ 21. My attendance at staff and inservice meetings was helpful.

_____ 22. My participation at staff meetings was respected, well received, and considered active and professional by the treatment team members.

Comments on staff and inservice meetings:

V. Provisions for intern self-awareness and professional growth.

_____ 23. My internship provided me with the self-awareness and professional growth opportunities as described in the Clinical Training Plan.

_____ 24. My opportunities for intern self-awareness and professional growth were adequate for my needs.

_____ 25. My self-awareness and professional growth assignments were helpful.

_____ 26. My opportunities for self-awareness and professional growth included establishing my own goals and plans.

_____ 27. My goals for self-awareness and professional growth were met.

_____ 28. My internship allowed me the opportunities to develop my own personal style.

Comments on intern self-awareness and professional growth:

VI. Provisions for Observation of Intern Sessions and Providing Feedback.

_____ 29. My internship provided me with the formal and informal observation opportunities as described in the Clinical Training Plan.

_____ 30. My opportunities for informal observation were adequate for my needs.

_____ 31. My opportunities for formal observation were adequate for my needs.

_____ 32. My formal and informal observations averaged at least four hours per week.

Comments on formal and informal observation:

VII. Provisions for Supervision.

_____ 33. My internship provided me with the supervision experiences described in the Clinical Training Plan.

_____ 34. My supervision opportunities were adequate for my needs.

_____ 35. My supervision time per week was at least one hour.

_____ 36. My supervisor was available outside the one hour supervision time if I needed extra assistance.

_____ 37. My supervision meetings included discussion of items/input which I prepared in advance for feedback, clarification and assistance.

Comments on supervision:

VIII. Provisions for Administrative Skills.

_____ 38. My internship provided me with the administrative skills experiences described in the Clinical Training Plan.

_____ 39. My opportunities for developing administrative skills were adequate for my needs.

Comments on administrative skills:

IX. Provisions for Special Requirements.

_____ 40. My internship provided me with the special requirements described in the Clinical Training Plan.

_____ 41. My opportunities for special requirements were adequate for my needs.

Comments on special requirements:

X. Provisions for Academic Training.

_____ 42. My academic training prepared me to meet the entrance requirements/entry level skills for this internship placement.

_____ 43. My academic training prepared me to use music in a therapeutic manner.

_____ 44. My academic training prepared me to play accompaniment instruments.

_____ 45. My academic training prepared me to adapt and create activities.

_____ 46. My academic training prepared me to plan activities and sessions.

_____ 47. My academic training prepared me to act professionally and responsibly.

_____ 48. My academic training prepared me to act in an ethical manner with clients.

_____ 49. My academic training prepared me to express my professional opinions verbally.

_____ 50. My academic training prepared me to write using standard grammar.

_____ 51. My academic training prepared me to express my professional opinions in writing.

_____ 52. My academic training prepared me to meet the documentation requirements in my internship.

_____ 53. My academic training prepared me to deliver Music Therapy services according to the AMTA Standards of Practice.

_____ 54. My academic training prepared me to effectively structure and lead sessions.

_____ 55. My academic training prepared me to deliver Music Therapy services to three or more clinical populations.

_____ 56. My academic training prepared me to develop a personal Music Therapy philosophy and theory of practice.

_____ 57. My academic training prepared me in time management skills and the ability to prioritize tasks.

Comments on academic training:

PROBLEM AREA IDENTIFIED:

SUGGESTED
PROCEDURE TO
RECTIFY PROBLEM AREAS:

PROCEDURES TO RECTIFY PROBLEM AREAS:
(To be filled out by Clinical Training Director)

ADDITIONAL COMMENTS:

_____

Clinical Training Director   Date

_____

Music Therapy Intern   Date

Appendix E:
Agreement Form for University Affiliated Internship

THE FLORIDA STATE UNIVERSITY MUSIC THERAPY PROGRAM AND CLINICAL AGENCY

COOPERATIVE AGREEMENT FOR UNIVERSITY AFFILIATED INTERNSHIP

THIS AGREEMENT, made and entered into this 18th day of February, 2003, by and between the ACADEMIC MUSIC THERAPY PROGRAM, _____, herein called MTP and the CLINICAL TRAINING PROGRAM, _____ herein called_____.

WITNESSETH:

WHEREAS, the MTP educates students in the profession of music therapy and utilizes community facilities to provide clinical experience for such students; and

WHEREAS, ___ provides services to clients who may benefit from music therapy services, has available facilities necessary for providing clinical training and experience for students of music therapy, and employs an individual, _____, deemed by MTP to be a Qualified Music Therapy Clinical Training Supervisor, herein called CTS.

NOW, THEREFORE, the MTP and the _____, in consideration of the mutual benefits to be attained by both, do hereby agree each with the other to participate in a cooperative program of instruction whereby the CH will accept internship students from the MTP for supervised learning experiences in the treatment of CH's clients as follows:

1. The MTP will provide, and the _____ will accept, music therapy majors, provided such students are available. The eligibility of individual music therapy students will be determined by MTP according to their curriculum plan for students. The selection of individual students and the dates they are to be received shall be mutually agreed upon by MTP and ____.

2. The MTP shall provide students placed at _____ with an individual contract specifying academic requirements, total hours, internship roles and responsibilities. All ____ clinical training hours will be accrued in full-time clinical service.

3. The ____ will provide orientation and training in professional guidelines, ethics, confidentiality issues, and client treatment issues for 900-1200 hours according to the intern's individual contract; and will provide supervision of the students to the extent mutually agreed upon with the MTP, including: direct observation at least weekly in the first 2 months of internship and written evaluation provided by the CTS to the intern at the midpoint and conclusion of the internship with copies provided to MTP.

4. The ____ has the right to withdraw a student from its services whose conduct or work with clients or personnel is not in accordance with acceptable standards of safe, effective, legal or ethical performance. This termination can be immediate. In such circumstances, the MTP will be notified within 24 hours. The MTP may at any time withdraw a student whose progress, conduct, or work does not meet the standards of its program. Final academic action regarding the student is the responsibility of the faculty of MTP.

5. This AGREEMENT shall be a continuing agreement until terminated by either party hereto upon six (6) months notice to the other in writing; and shall be reviewed by the parties at any point deemed necessary by either party.

6.

IN WITNESS WHEREOF, the parties hereto have caused this AGREEMENT to be executed in their behalf on the day and year first above written.

Acting for and on behalf of the
Music Therapy Program of
The School of Music of
The Florida State University

By:_____
Jayne M. Standley
Dir. of the MT Program

Acting for and on behalf of the
Music Therapy Program

By:_____

By:_____
Clinical Training Supervisor

Adapted from a model developed by Russell Hilliard, 1999.

Appendix F:
AMTA Application for
National Roster Internship Status

AMERICAN MUSIC THERAPY ASSOCIATION
NATIONAL ROSTER INTERNSHIP APPLICATION

Facility Name: _____

Address: _____

_____

Telephone/Fax/Email: _____/_____/_____

Proposed InternshipDirector: _____

Supervising MT's: _____

_____

Licensure/Certification of Site: _____

Population served: _____

Internship Director Information:
How many years have you practiced music therapy? (indicate full or part time)

_____

How long have you worked at your present facility? (indicate full or part time)

_____

How many hours of direct **music therapy** contact do you provide each week?

_____

List your credentials _____

Have you ever been reprimanded or sanctioned for misconduct
or found negligent in your professional practice?

_____(Yes/No)

(If yes, please provide more information)

Supervising music therapist information: (complete for all supervising music therapists)

How many years have you practiced music therapy? (indicate full or part time)

_____

How long have you worked at your present facility? (indicate full or part time)

_____

How many hours of direct client **music therapy** contact do you provide each week?

_____

List your credentials _____

Have you ever been reprimanded or sanctioned for misconduct

> or found negligent in your professional practice?

> _____(Yes/No)

> (If yes, please provide more information)

Attachments
Please attach the following:

A. A copy of a **"fact sheet"** for your specific internship site, suitable for distribution to prospective interns, academic sites, and professional colleagues, including at least the following information:

- Name and address of internship site
- Description of population served
- Description of the internship experience—what should the intern expect?
- Description of entry level requirements/competencies and how they will be evaluated
- Description of professional staff working with the intern (list music therapy staff and describe other professional disciplines with whom the student would have contact)
- List other on-site training programs
- Name and contact information for the Internship Director
- Information on housing, meals, stipend, transportation, and liability insurance

B. Written response to two **essay questions**:

1. What is the philosophy of your music therapy program? (In your own words, discuss your views about how and why music is effective in therapy/as therapy). You may include your beliefs regarding the value of music in therapy, the role of music in therapy, the role of music as therapy, clinical techniques, uses of music, and/or theoretical models. When mentioning specific, theoretical frameworks, describe how and why those models are used in your clinical practice.

2. What is your philosophy regarding training interns? (In your own words, describe your beliefs about how interns effectively learn skills in clinical practice). You may include

statements regarding your style and approach, the methods of training you intend to employ, what you consider to be the most important aspects of a successful internship experience.

C. A series of at least three (3) **sample internship schedules** (indicating the number of hours of music therapy treatment groups, documentation, team meetings, in-services, supervision and observation time in an average week) reflecting the developmental sequence of the training process.

D. A written example of three (3) measurable **sample treatment goals**, related to your program/philosophy.

E. Copies of **internship forms** developed for your site, including:

- **Application for internship**
- **Orientation Checklist**
- **Competency-Specific Intern Evaluation Form/Intern Self-Evaluation Form (Midterm and Final)** This form must include reference to expected level of performance in the areas of Music Foundations, Clinical Foundations, and Music Therapy.
- **Site evaluation form**.
- **Intern Dismissal Policy and Procedure Document** Include a form that documents intern's acknowledgment of the policy

F. A **vita** for the Internship Director and each supervising music therapist, indicating education, internship experience, and work history.

G. **Letters of support/recommendation**, including:
- A letter of support for the internship program from the facility administrator
- Two (2) letters of recommendation for the Internship Director which reflect professional clinical skills, supervisory skills, professional qualities and characteristics, and verbal and written communication skills.

H. **Documentation of supervision training** (i.e., certificate from the Clinical Training Supervision workshop offered at national and regional AMTA conferences)

Responsibilities of the Internship Director

- Structure and implement an internship program in accordance with the AMTA National Roster Internship Guidelines.
- Respond to student requests for information and applications.
- Review applications, select music therapy interns and communicate with students.
- Develop an individualized contract based on the needs and abilities of each intern, including types of/numbers of music therapy groups, documentation, special projects, etc., in partnership with the academic faculty.
- Provide the intern with a thorough orientation, including facility tour, review of AMTA documents (i.e., Standards of Practice, Organizational Structure, Code of Ethics, National Roster Internship Guidelines, and the AMTA Professional Competencies), the CBMT Code of Professional Practice, applicable Policies and Procedures of the Site, and Intern Dismissal Policies.
- Provide viable music therapy role model(s) for interns.
- Provide at least one (1) hour of supervision per week for the intern. (adjust accordingly for part time schedules)
- Provide for at least four (4) hours of observation (formal and informal) per week for the intern. (adjust accordingly for part time schedules)
- Establish and coordinate a network of supportive professional contacts.
- Communicate information to the intern regarding ongoing seminars, conferences, workshops, and community resources.
- Complete and review midterm and final evaluations with the music therapy intern; Provide copies of the evaluation to the intern's academic site.
- Provide the intern with a site evaluation to be completed at the end of the internship.
- Review the site evaluation with the intern. (This review should occur after the intern's final evaluation has been discussed and should be used to help identify areas for improvement in the site.)
- Maintain continuous communication with the intern and his/her academic faculty.
- Initiate performance improvement plans with the intern and academic faculty, when necessary.
- Accept no more than two interns per full time supervising music therapy staff at any given time.
- Accept interns no more than a year in advance of the internship start date.
- Upon request of the intern, provide a letter of verification documenting successful completion of internship.
- Notify the national office and regional clinical training representative of any significant changes within the established clinical training program.
- Adhere to National Internship Roster Guidelines and initiate exception requests as needed.
- Monitor and act on any non-compliance issues that may arise.

- Follow established policy and procedure regarding dismissal of interns.
- Submit an annual report to the national office, as requested by the Executive Director.
- Maintain communication with the clinical training regional representative.

I understand and accept the above-stated responsibilities of the role of the internship director. I verify that the content of this application is my original work, unless credit has been given to the original author.

_____   _____

Signature   *Date*

Note: Application developed by AMTA Staff.

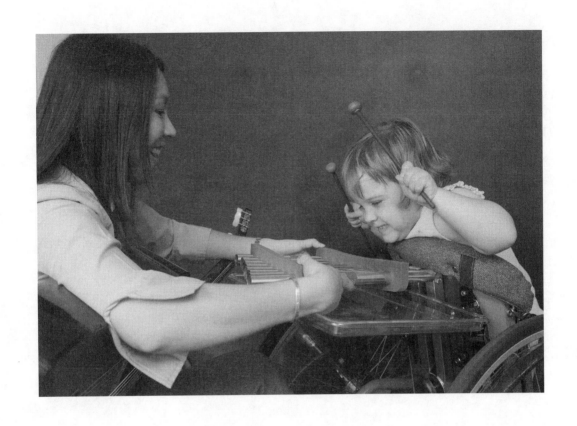

Chapter 5

The Medical Music Therapy Practicum

☞

Judy Nguyen, M.M., MT-BC, and
Jennifer Jarred, M.M., MT-BC

THE MEDICAL MUSIC THERAPY PRACTICUM

The practicum experience in the music therapy major at Florida State University is carefully structured to ensure adequate services to clients though students' therapeutic skills are at the beginning level. Therefore, the practica are nested within the overall curriculum in the final two years. Throughout the program of study, students are screened and accepted as music therapy majors according to the educational philosophy of the department.

Departmental Philosophy

Selection and preparation in Music Therapy at Florida State University is based upon an important yet extremely simple premise—it is that every client receiving music therapy services should have the best clinical assistance possible. This implies that every therapist should be committed to the subject of music and its therapeutic use with people. The strength of this commitment is evidenced by the academic and social behaviors of the prospective therapist in life, both in and out of the university environment. The FSU Music Therapy student is characterized by diligence in the pursuit of musical and academic excellence and active dedication to the improvement of the quality of life of their fellow human beings.

Personal Qualities

For those who value knowledge, the learning process is perpetual throughout life's time. To be an effective music therapist, one must develop:

1. the ability to think, and therefore, value and discriminate;
2. the ability to feel, and therefore, become sensitive to aesthetic qualities in music and life; and
3. the courage to act, and therefore, translate those abilities to think and feel into overt behaviors.

Successful music therapists evidence personal qualities of leadership, intellectual curiosity, social commitment, and emotional stability. They approach life, music, and the therapeutic profession in a positive, imaginative, and enthusiastic way. The music therapist attempts to create a respect and desire for quality life experiences, teaching others to learn and mature, react positively, listen responsively, and relate sensitively. Toward this goal, music therapists provide a variety of learning and therapeutic experiences for their clients and are stimulated by current research to seek, evaluate, and appropriately implement current ideas and developments in the therapeutic applications of music.

- Music therapists promote positive relationships with clients, colleagues, and others.
- They are empathetic with people of differing social and ethnic backgrounds, and demonstrate mature attitudes and values.

- They consistently maximize client opportunities and accomplishments, and minimize self-aggrandizement.
- Their public performances are part of therapeutic programs geared to helping people become sensitive to aesthetic, educational, vocational, and social opportunities in life.

Comprehensive Competencies

Music therapists must be prepared and eager to assist those in need: the young, the poor, the underprivileged, the handicapped, the aged, those unable to cope, and the medically or mentally ill. In addition to personal competencies in music performance, improvisation, conducting, applied music, composing, arranging, analysis, history, repertoire, and other musical skills, they must have competencies in the teaching of music on all levels, nursery school through adulthood, and in the methods of music therapy in the full array of habilitative and rehabilitative settings. They must be exposed to techniques of teaching in the humanities, related arts, and general music areas, as well as become proficient in the areas of psychology, anatomy, and other health/behavioral sciences. Concurrently, the music therapist must be able to express knowledge through verbal communication (oral and written) and through overt, demonstrable music and teaching/therapy behaviors.

Liberal Studies Curriculum Component

A general knowledge and understanding of history, science, art, philosophy, and communication serves to enhance one's ability to function effectively in contemporary society and facilitates greater understanding of the human condition. The Liberal Studies requirements of the Florida State University are designed to:

1. help the student understand him/herself as a person,
2. assist in the development of positive attitudes and penetrating insights toward others and the world,
3. encourage acceptance of change and approach new ideas with an open mind,
4. provide the ability to apply appropriate evaluative techniques and establish an attitude of curiosity, and
5. promote the relating of one's own art to other disciplines.

Internalization

The task of structuring and managing life's environment in which individuals, regardless of ability, may positively experience, successfully achieve, and hence, come to control and value the quality of their own life, demands a breadth of knowledge and skills, as well as high levels of perception and sensitivity on the part of the music therapist. The acquisition and development of these abilities require an intellectual commitment that is realized in daily living and is maintained and strengthened during the years of training and throughout the professional career. Music therapists are empathetic with people of differing social and ethnic backgrounds, and demonstrate mature attitudes and values.

The Practicum

Students are assigned to several practica as a part of the music therapy methods course that is of two semesters duration. Prerequisite to the methods course is the development of musical and group leadership skills through the orientation class where MT majors doing practica are shadowed, class guitar where basic accompaniment skills are learned, and recreational music where basic group leadership skills are learned.

For the students in the Music Therapy Methods and Procedures Course, practica sites are selected from a menu of possibilities in the Tallahassee area including special education, geriatric, mental health, medical, hospice, speech and language, and counseling programs. Each practicum requires a minimum of 2 hours/week of client interaction across a 13-week semester.

Students are supervised by local music therapists within guidelines from the university program. Clinical competencies are delineated for each site and include musical, group leading, therapeutic, teaching, counseling, clinical protocol, professional , and/or documentation skills. During the semester in which the practicum is being completed, the student is also enrolled with the faculty member in a weekly group lab. Clinical skills are practiced with classmates in simulation with each student individually evaluated, counseled, and assigned skill development tasks using the text, *Music Techniques in Therapy, Counseling, and Special Education* by Jayne Standley. Any problems with competency development for the practicum site is taught and practiced through group lab. Additionally, the students attend class with the faculty and learn about music therapy methods organized according to client type. It is the student's task during the semester to assimilate classroom knowledge, classroom practice, and clinical demonstration of skills. Student grades for the semester-long course are an average of achievements in the three areas of lecture/test, group lab demonstration, and practicum demonstration.

Following are minimal competencies for basic components of the MT methods and procedures course. Entrance into the second semester course is contingent upon satisfactory completion of the first semester. Satisfactory completion of the course requires that all the competencies above be met at least as stated resulting in a grade of B–, the lowest acceptable grade for continuation in a major course in music therapy.

Group Lab

Entry level criteria for undergraduates following courses in class guitar and recreational music: Adept at leading group singing with musical accompaniment and memorized repertoire of at least 10 songs.

Entry level for new graduate/equivalency students without above courses: Adept at leading group singing with beginning guitar skills and repertoire. Demonstration of progress toward further development of these skills in all future group labs.

Midterm criteria for all students: Repertoire of 20–25 songs with ability to plan and implement assigned lab tasks using music to teach information for variety of special education, medical, and geriatric populations at skill level 2.0. Demonstrated ability to personally use techniques learned in lab in practicum and to transfer techniques demonstrated by others. Demonstrated ability to use feedback from instructor.

End of term criteria: Demonstrated excellence in song leading, use of accompaniment, and giving directions for musical activities using movement, dance, and music performance for a variety of clinical populations. Demonstrated ability to plan and implement assignment at skill level 2.0 with little or no guidance even though technique has not been previously taught or demonstrated in class. Demonstrated ability to lead a focused group discussion on assigned topic and deal with prescribed "roles" of unusual, inappropriate, or bizarre behavior.

Academics

- Minimal criteria include satisfactory scores on quizzes, or, if deficient, timely make-up of assignments demonstrating mastery of deficient material.
- Demonstrated ability to successfully balance personal life and complete assigned tasks, such as Client Treatment Objectives, assigned labs, and practica. Absenteeism and tardiness should not exceed professional guidelines.

Practicum

- Demonstration of basic ability to plan, write, implement, and document a music therapy treatment plan for assigned situation, including assessing client needs and abilities, development of identified objectives, development of MT procedures to meet objectives, implementation of same, and evaluation of results as indicated by videotapes, written work, and personal 1:1 consultation with instructor.
- Evidence of feedback being used to improve practica skills.
- Demonstration of appropriate transfer and application of treatment techniques taught in class and group lab.
- Evidence of decision making which is oriented to therapeutic change for clients, i.e., students' priorities, use of time, judgment, etc.

Internship Placement

- Each student consults individually with Dr. Standley for advising and guidance in securing an internship placement prior to the end of this course. The following hierarchical tasks are critical.
- Finalize a plan with advisor to complete required courses in order to identify eligible date for internship.
- Discuss possible internship sites with Dr. Standley.
- Select 3 internship sites and submit applications.

- Plan practica and group lab experiences with faculty to qualify you for each of the types of sites selected.
- Maintain 3 active applications until accepted by an internship of your choice.

TMH Practicum

Students first shadow MTs doing clinical music therapy at the hospital and are then assigned a musical repertoire to prepare in the style preference and age group most likely to be encountered in future visits. Practica students first begin providing musical selections during sessions at the direction of the therapists. Then, therapeutic responses to patients are cued and integrated with music provision. Finally, students are expected to achieve independence in providing clinical music therapy for at least a portion of the session. Individual feedback is given after each session. The form on the following page is the one used by the TMH music therapy program for supervision and training of practicum students.

Tallahassee Memorial HealthCare and Florida State University
Practicum Competencies

All of the minimum competencies listed below should be met by the end of your practicum experience in order to receive a satisfactory grade.

Minimum Requirements

1. The student is able to follow all hospital policies and procedures.
    ____ YES   ____NO
2. The student is professional when interacting with hospital staff.
    ____ YES   ____NO
3. The student is punctual to all sessions.
    ____ YES   ____NO
4. The student is able to play basic I, IV, and V chord progressions on the guitar.
    ____YES   ____NO
5. The student is vocally proficient (sings in tune and matches pitch).
    ____ YES   ____NO
6. The student can sing and play guitar at the same time.
    ____ YES   ____NO
7. The student can provide varied strumming patterns and basic fingerpicking skills.
    ____YES   ____NO
8. The student displays an appropriate amount of learned and memorized musical repertoire.   ____ YES   ____NO
9. The student is able to appropriately document a Music Therapy session.
    ____ YES   ____NO
10. The student has the ability to therapeutically respond to a patient's mood, affect, and behavior.   ____ YES   ____NO
11. The student has shown positive results from the supervisor's feedback.
    ____ YES   ____NO

Comments:

I, _____ have read, discussed, and understand the above competency requirements for a satisfactory grade.

Student: _____ Date: _____

Supervisor: _____ Date: _____

Chapter 6

Training in Research

∽

Jayne M. Standley, Ph.D., MT-BC

TRAINING IN RESEARCH

Research methods are taught at Florida State University by Dr. Clifford Madsen. The course teaches basic research methodology for both actualization and discrimination of research issues and requires demonstration of research skills through the development of three mini-experiments (Madsen & Madsen, 1997). By course completion, all students, graduate and undergraduate, are accomplished enough to conduct independent research and have a lifelong appreciation of investigative endeavor.

Completion of the Master's degree at FSU requires a final, synthesizing individual project, either a demonstration of clinical competence or a demonstration of research competence. Approximately 90% of FSU Master's students select the thesis or research option. A number of these students have completed medical research projects, many of which have been published in refereed journals thereby making a contribution to the music therapy literature.

All FSU MT faculty are productive researchers and medical research is a primary area of emphasis. The development of evidence-based practice in medical music therapy has been profoundly impacted by the FSU integration of research into the education and training of music therapists. Many of these studies have also resulted in staff and patient benefits and understanding of the possibilities of medical music therapy. Following are abstracts of medical research projects completed by both faculty and students of the Florida State University Music Therapy Department.

Medical Research Abstracts Completed by
FSU Faculty, Staff, and Students

∽

The Effects of Music Therapy and Deep Breathing on Pain in
Patients Recovering From Gynecologic Surgery in the PACU

Kristen S. Adams

This study examined the effects of music therapy paired with deep breathing in the PACU. Dependent variables were amount of pain medication administered (measured in morphine equivalents), hospital length of stay, and perceptual data. Subjects were 50 women undergoing gynecologic surgery requiring a hospital stay of at least one night. Subjects were randomly assigned to an experimental music group ($n = 25$) or control group ($n = 25$). Results showed no significant differences for pain medication between groups. The length of hospital stay was significantly shorter for the music group. Subjects in the music group also reported their post-

PACU pain levels to be significantly lower than the control group. Further results and implications are discussed.

Music Therapy Master's Thesis
The Florida State University
Spring 2005

ᔕ

The Effects of Amplitude and Rhythmic Strength on Heart Rate Entrainment and Perceived Relaxation

Alpha Mu Alpha, The FSU MT Student Organization

The main objective of this study was to determine the effect amplitude (measured in decibels) and rhythmic strength had on heart rate entrainment and perceived relaxation. Subjects were rotated between four experimental groups (Groups A, $n = 18$; B, $n = 18$; C, $n = 17$; and D, $n = 19$) and one control group (Group E, $n = 17$). Subjects in each experimental group listened to 8 minutes of music that was preselected by the researchers to have either a weak or strong rhythmic beat and a constant or fluctuating amplitude. The control group sat in silence for the 8-minute duration. The experimenter monitored the heart rate of the subject every 15 seconds throughout the test period via an earlobe pulse monitor. Prior to the music, as well as immediately following the 8-minute testing period, subjects filled out a self-evaluation to determine their perceived relaxation at that moment in time. Additionally after the music, subjects filled out a questionnaire to record age, familiarity with the musical selection, and whether or not the piece was enjoyed. All groups, except Group C, resulted in a significant difference between pre- and posttests for perceived relaxation. The degree of enjoyment appeared to be a factor in Group C's perceived relaxation. Correlational tests were run within each group. Group C was the only group with a significant correlation between heart rate fluctuations and amplitude changes. Other musical components not anticipated may also have influenced the physiological response. By graphing the means, a definite pattern between the heart rate and amplitude was indicated; however, the heart rate changes were much more subtle. Additionally, there appeared to be a 2- to 4-minute window at the beginning of each experimental group in which the heart rate adjusted to the music; after this period the association between the heart rate and decibel level was more stable. This study suggests that enjoyment of music plays a role in perceived relaxation. It may also be extrapolated that amplitude is more influential in parallel heart rate movement than rhythmic strength, although additional musical variables may influence the physiological response.

Study presented at National Conference Poster Session, AMTA, Atlanta, GA, November 2002.

ᔕ

The Effects of Music on Relaxation as Measured by Heart Rate and Self-Evaluation

Alpha Mu Alpha, The FSU MT Student Organization

This study measured the effects of music on perceived relaxation and heart rate. Subjects consisted of collegiate music students ($n = 35$). During the selected piece (Samuel Barber's *Adagio for Strings*), the heart rate was measured in 10-second intervals. The subjects completed a pre-and posttest that measured their level of perceived relaxation using a 10-point Likert scale. Subjects also completed a background questionnaire with information such as familiarity with the piece. A paired-samples t test showed no significant difference ($\alpha = .05$) between the heart rate and perceived relaxation. The mean heart rate was graphed at each time interval and compared to a graph of the amplitude. A strong correlation was noted between the direction of the heart rate and the level of volume.

Study presented at Regional Conference Poster Session, SER-AMTA, Chattanooga, TN, March 2003.

ဢ

The Effect of Preferred Music on the Amount of Pain Medication Administered by Patient Controlled Analgesia Pump in Patients Recovering from Abdominal Hysterectomies

S. Eulalia Ayers

This study investigated the physiological and psychological effects of preferred music on patients recovering from abdominal hysterectomies. Twenty females ages 29 to 77 recovering from abdominal hysterectomies were randomly assigned to either the music or control group, with 10 per group. Statistical analysis, using a Mann–Whitney U test, of age, race, marital status, height, weight, surgical experience, and preoperative physiological data of women in the two groups revealed no significant differences on all variables except pulse and temperature, which were significantly lower preoperatively for the music group. Dependent variables in the study included postoperative blood pressure, pulse, temperature, respiration rate, length of stay, self-report pain, PCA use, other pain medications, and medicines for surgical or analgesic complications. The only significant difference in postoperative vital signs was the control group's lower systolic blood pressure. Women in the music group were discharged sooner and had lower self-report pain scores than women in the control group, but these differences were not statistically significant. The doses of PCA morphine plus the doses of schedule 2 analgesics were significantly less for the music group. The music group used less combined doses of all prescription pain medications as well as total doses of pain medication including over-the-counter analgesics, though the difference was not statistically significant. There was not a significant difference in the amount of nausea or anti-infective medication received by the two groups. Although the music group used less total medication (pain and non-pain), the difference was not statistically significant. Ninety percent of the music group stated that they would recommend music to other postoperative patients.

Music Therapy Master's Thesis
The Florida State University
Summer 2000

ᔕ

The Effects of Live Music on the Distress of Pediatric Patients Receiving Intravenous Starts, Venipunctures, Injections, and Heel Sticks

April Lee Batson

Currently there is a growing interest about non-invasive methods of pain management with pediatric patients. Needle insertions are a major source of distress for children. The term *needle insertions* includes intravenous starts, venipunctures, injections, and infant heel sticks. The way a child copes during an invasive procedure is influenced by his or her age, developmental level, locus of control, whether the child is an active or avoidant seeker of information, how the child perceives his or her parent's anxiety level, and the parent's interaction with the child during the invasive procedure. Distraction has proven effective in helping children to cope and adding music as a non-invasive method of pain management is a unique way to achieve this technique of distraction. To assess the benefits of live music on the behavioral distress levels of pediatric patients, an experimental group of 20 patients age 7 and under received live music. These children were experiencing a variety of needle insertions in a treatment room and emergency room setting in a local hospital. The music intervention consisted of age-appropriate children's songs led by the researcher with guitar accompaniment. This group was compared to a control group of 20 pediatric patients who did not receive music. Groups were matched on the basis of age, site of procedure (floor or ER), and type of needle insertion. Two-way analysis of variance (ANOVA) revealed a statistically significant difference between groups for the pre-needle and post-needle stages ($F = 9.6$, $p < .05$) with the music group exhibiting less behavioral distress. A Mann–Whitney U test revealed statistically significant differences between age groups with less behavioral distress exhibited in the music group for children 1 years old and younger ($U = 14$, critical value = 15).

Music Therapy Master's Thesis
The Florida State University
Summer 1994

Published: Malone, A. B. (1996). *Journal of Music Therapy, 33*(1), 19–33.

ᔕ

Is Music Therapeutic or Distracting When Life Hangs in the Balance: Surgeons' Perception

Rochelle J. Blackstone

The purpose of this study was to find out if background music in the operating room is perceived as distracting when full concentration is required in unusual or complicated situations. Also part of the study was to see if there was a difference between the surgeon specialties, the age and years of experience compared to the type of music played in the OR, personal preferences, and objectionable music. One hundred surgeons from all over the United States were surveyed through personal and telephone interviews. The response rate of the telephone survey was 61% while the personal interview response rate was 100%. The results showed that music in the operating room was not perceived as distracting by surgeons. There were some differences between age, specialty, and years of experience compared to the personal preferences and objectionable music, and the type of music played in the operating room (OR). The more experienced surgeons preferred classical music both in the OR and personally. The younger surgeons preferred pop/rock. The results of musical tastes showed that most surgeons play lassical music in the OR with pop/rock being the second choice. Classical music is personally preferred, while pop/rock and country music are personally disliked.

Music Therapy Master's Thesis
The Florida State University
Summer 1998

ш

The Effects of Music Therapy on Motivation, Psychological Well-Being, Physical Comfort, and Exercise Endurance of Bone Marrow Transplant Patients

Susan Boldt

This study assessed the effects of music with bone marrow transplant patients on exercise endurance, motivation, psychological well-being, and physical comfort. Exercise, although difficult due to treatment effects, is necessary to reduce or prevent muscle atrophy. The subjects were 3 females and 3 males ranging in age from 14 to 53 years. Two subjects received 10 sessions, while 4 others were seen between 2 to 3 sessions each. A music/non-music reversal design ABABAB (etc.) was used. Independent variables included live and recorded music for participation, interaction with the therapist, relaxation and imagery; progressive relaxation exercises; range of motion exercises; and aerobic exercise. The dependent variables included an observational behavior scale, subject self-report of relaxation, comfort, pain and nausea levels, exercise endurance, and an end-of-study effectiveness questionnaire. Due to variations in the music therapy protocol, and to changing physiological conditions, the results were compiled in the form of individual case studies. Long-term results (10 sessions) indicated that music sessions were most effective in increasing subjects' self-report relaxation and comfort levels and less effective in reducing perceptions of pain and nausea. Endurance for both subjects increased during sessions with music. More cooperative behavior and higher levels of participation were also observed during music sessions. Short-term results (2–3 sessions) indicated that music sessions were more effective in increasing relaxation and comfort levels and less effective in decreasing pain and nausea levels. No short-term subjects showed an increase in endurance during music versus non-music sessions.

Music Therapy Master's Thesis
The Florida State University
Fall 1995

Published: *Journal of Music Therapy* (1996), *33*(3), 164–188.

ᔕ

The Effects of Music on the Selected Stress Behaviors, Weight, Caloric and Formula Intake, and Length of Stay of Premature and Low Birth Weight Neonates on a Newborn Intensive Care Unit

Janel Caine

The purpose of this study was to examine the effects of music on selected stress behaviors, weight, caloric and formula intake, and length of hospital stay. Subjects were 52 preterm and low birthweight newborns in a newborn intensive care unit (NBICU) who were in stable condition and restricted to isolettes. Subjects in the experimental and control groups were matched for equivalency based on sex, birthweight, and critical level. Eleven males and 15 females were assigned to the control group and received routine auditory stimulation. The experimental group of 11 males and 15 females received music stimulation which consisted of approximately 60 minutes of tape recorded vocal music, including lullabies and children's music, and routine auditory stimulation. Thirty-minute segments of the recording were played alternately with 30 minutes of routine auditory stimulation 3 times daily. Exposure to music stimulation occurred only during the infants' stay in the NBICU.

Results suggest music stimulation may have significantly reduced initial weight loss, increased daily average weight, increased formula and caloric intake, significantly reduced length of the NBICU and the total hospital stays, and significantly reduced the daily mean of stress behaviors for the experimental group. Data analysis suggests the length of hospital stay may be correlated to the amount of stress experienced by the neonate and not to weight gains. Theoretical and practical aspects of these results are discussed.

Music Therapy Master's Thesis
The Florida State University
Fall 1989

Published: *Journal of Music Therapy* (1991), *28*(4), 180–192.

The Effect of Live Music on the Reduction of Negative Side Effects Experienced by Pediatric Patients During Onset, Final Thirty Minutes of Hemodialysis Treatment, and Removal of Needles

Julie E. Callaham

The purpose of this study was to investigate the effectiveness of music to alleviate negative side effects experienced by pediatric hemodialysis patients during three phases of treatment: cannulation of vascular access, the final 30 minutes of treatment, and removal of needles. Five subjects in a pediatric hemodialysis unit participated in the study. An ABAB reversal design was utilized with A being baseline (no music during hemodialysis) and B being live music interventions during cannulation of vascular access, the last 30 minutes of hemodialysis treatment, and needle removal. Subjects served as their own control with each condition being 1 week long, 3 treatments per week. Live music therapy interventions during the onset of treatment, during final 30 minutes of the procedure, and during needle removal were the independent variable. Dependent variables included self-report of pain, anxiety, and other side effects of hemodialysis treatment; behavior observation of subjects' body gestures and verbalizations in response to hemodialysis treatment; and physiological data: start and end weight and blood pressure.

Due to small sample size, only mean scores were tabulated and no statistical tests were applied. Group self-report of pain and anxiety during cannulation of vascular access indicated a pattern of decreased pain scores when the independent variable was applied. Similarly, group self-report of pain during needle removal indicated a trend of decreased pain score when music intervention was applied to the routine procedure. Group mean results from behavioral observation indicated a consistent decrease in pain and anxiety behaviors when music interventions were implemented in all three phases of treatment. Blood pressure fluctuations were not influenced by the independent variable. The group noted increased compliance to fluid intake on treatment days when music interventions were present. All patients ranked music interventions as highly effective during routine hemodialysis treatment.

Music Therapy Master's Thesis
The Florida State University
Spring 2004

თ

The Effect of Music Listening on Physiological Responses of Premature Infants in the NICU

Jane W. Cassidy & Jayne M. Standley

In this study 20 low birthweight infants of 24–30 weeks gestation age, who were being oxygenated in a Neonatal Intensive Care Unit (NICU), served as subjects during their first week of life. Ten infants listened to lullabies through Bio-logic insert earphones with ALGO Ear Couplers and 10 infants served as control subjects. All subjects passed an auditory brainstem response (ABR) procedure to ensure that audiological responses were consistent with normal hearing. Experimental treatment occurred across 3 days and was conducted in an ABABABABA design, with data collected during 5 segments of 4 minutes each of silence alternating with 4 segments of 4 minutes each of music. Oxygen saturation levels, heart rate, respiratory rate, and number of apnea/bradycardia episodes were recorded once per minute for the duration of baseline and treatment conditions (36 minutes). Results indicated that music was not contraindicated in the first week of life for these very low birthweight infants for whom sensory stimulation is usually restricted. In fact, music had noticeably positive effects on oxygen saturation levels, heart rate, and respiratory rate. No increase in apnea/ bradycardia episodes following music treatment were observed.

Published: *Journal of Music Therapy* (1995), *32*(4), 208–227.

თ

The Effect of Music Therapy in Reducing Fear and Anxiety in Preoperative Pediatric Patients

Helen Driskell Chetta

In this study, music was used as part of a comprehensive preoperative teaching session aimed at informing the pediatric patient about events pertaining to his surgery. The purpose of this study was to investigate whether music therapy can be useful in transmitting adequate information about the surgery experience to the pediatric patient to help reduce his anxiety and fear behaviors during induction of preoperative medication.

It seems to be the consensus of extra-musical literature on this subject that preoperative preparation of a child, that is, informing him concerning what will happen to him and how it will feel, is invaluable in reducing his fear and anxiety about the upcoming events. No music therapy research along these lines could be found.

Experimental design incorporated a three-sample method: Control group receiving only verbal preoperative instruction the evening before surgery, Experimental I group receiving the before mentioned verbal instruction with music being added, and Experimental II group receiving not only this treatment strategy but adding also music therapy immediately prior to induction of preoperative medication on the morning of surgery. Seventy-five subjects between the ages of 3 and 8 years and admitted for elective surgery were included. Data collection consisted of (1) time-sampling observation of the patient's behavior immediately preceding, during, and immediately following induction of preoperative medication and an overall behavior checklist of this same time period; (2) parent questionnaire of overall patient history as well as behaviors during hospitalization; (3) record of pulse rate the night before, immediately preceding and following induction of preoperative medication. The null hypothesis stated: There will be no significant differences in cumulative anxiety and fear behaviors during preoperative medication induction between those patients receiving verbal preoperative preparation the evening before surgery, those patients receiving verbal preoperative preparation and music therapy the evening before surgery, and those patients receiving verbal preoperative preparation and music therapy the evening before surgery as well as music therapy immediately prior to induction of preoperative medication on the morning of surgery. The time-sampling observational measurement, the observer-rating measurement, and the in-hospital behaviors measurement indicated significant differences between the groups and the null hypothesis was thus rejected. Consistently, the group receiving music therapy just prior to induction of preoperative medication was rated as indicating less anxiety before and during the procedure.

Music Therapy Master's Thesis
The Florida State University
Summer 1980

Published: *Journal of Music Therapy* (1981), *18*(2), 74–87.

ഗ

An Exploration of the Uses of Music in the Birthing Process

Peggy A. Codding

The purpose of this study was to investigate whether music can be used as a selective focus of attention by the birthing woman to facilitate relaxation, thereby reducing the fear, physical tension and pain associated with childbirth. A two-group posttest only design was used to test hypotheses concerning fear, tension, and pain. Twenty couples voluntarily participated in the study. Twenty women in the third trimester of pregnancy served as subjects. Subjects were matched on the basis of five variables and then assigned to two equal groups. Couples in the control and experimental groups participated in eight 2½ hour Lamaze-type childbirth preparation classes. Women in the control group used no music during childbirth and received no additional training outside of class. Women in the experimental group used client-selected music during childbirth and also received two 2½ hour training sessions with the music therapist prior to the onset of labor. All couples experienced routing hospital births.

Data were collected via eight self-report measures piloted in a previous study. Nonparametric statistics were used in data analysis. There was no significant difference in post hoc *fear* between groups; therefore, the fear hypothesis could not be rejected. There was no significant difference in post hoc reports of *tension* between groups; therefore, the tension hypothesis could not be rejected. There was no significant difference on post hoc measures of *pain* between groups; therefore, the pain hypothesis could not be rejected. Results of the study failed to indicate that music with training is an effective means of reducing the birthing mother's perception of fear, physical tension, and pain in childbirth. Further research is indicated.

Music Therapy Master's Thesis
The Florida State University
Fall 1982

ဟ

The Effects of Music Versus Guided Imagery and Progressive Muscle Relaxation Versus Guided Imagery and Progressive Muscle Relaxation With Music on the Pulse Rate and Peripheral Finger Temperature of Hemodialysis Patients Undergoing Treatment

Teresa Tyson Colgrove

The purpose of this study was to investigate the efficacy of music versus music with guided imagery and progressive muscle relaxation versus guided imagery and progressive muscle relaxation alone on the pulse rate and peripheral finger temperature of hemodialysis patients undergoing treatment.

The experimental design of the study utilized each subject as his or her own control. Each subject listened to three stimuli (music, music paired with guided imagery and progressive muscle relaxation, and guided imagery and progressive muscle relaxation alone during a hemodialysis treatment). The subjects' pulse rate and peripheral finger temperature were measured immediately prior to the onset of each stimulus and immediately following each stimulus. Each stimulus lasted 20 minutes followed by a 5-minute rest period. The subjects began listening to the stimuli 30 minutes after the onset of hemodialysis treatment.

Data collected during the experiment were beginning and ending pulse rates and peripheral finger temperature readings of each subject under each stimulus condition. Pulse rates were measured for 10 seconds on the wrist and multiplied by 6 for rate/minute. Peripheral finger temperature readings were measured for 25 seconds while the subjects held the thermometers between their thumb and index finger. The experimenter then read the thermometers and recorded the data.

The null hypothesis stated: H_0—There will be no statistically significant decrease between the beginning and ending pulse rates of the participants for any of the three conditions and $H2_0$—There will be no statistically significant increase between the beginning and ending peripheral finger temperatures of the participants for any of the three conditions. The study failed to reject either null hypothesis. There were no statistically significant differences for pulse rate or peripheral finger temperature under any stimulus.

Music Therapy Master's Thesis
The Florida State University
Fall 1991

∽

The Effects of Music on the Perceived Degree of Pain Relief, Physical Comfort, Relaxation, and Contentment of Hospitalized Terminally Ill Patients

Sandra Lynn Curtis

The purpose of the present study was to examine the effects of music on terminally ill patients' perceived degree of pain relief, physical comfort, relaxation, and contentment. The subjects were white, English- and French-speaking terminally ill patients; 4 males and 5 females participated in the study. The four dependent variables were self-recorded by the subjects on a modified Scott–Huskisson graphic rating scale under three conditions: (1) no intervention, (2) background sound, and (3) music. The order of condition presentation was ABACA for 5 subjects and ACABA for the remaining 4 subjects. Each condition was presented for 15 minutes, twice daily for 2 days. A Friedman two-way analysis of variance indicated no significant difference in the dependent variables under the experimental conditions; contentment score differences, however, approached significance ($p < .069$). A Kruskal–Wallis one-way analysis of variance indicated no significant difference according to severity of illness; however, graphic analysis of individual responses indicated that music may have been effective.

Music Therapy Master's Thesis
The Florida State University
Fall 1982

Published: *Journal of Music Therapy* (1986), *23*(1), 10–24.

∽

The Effects of Music and Relaxation Techniques on Pain and Anxiety of Women Undergoing In-Office Gynecological Procedures

Cynthia Allison Davis

The purpose of this study was to ascertain the effects of music and relaxation techniques on pain and anxiety of women undergoing in-office gynecological procedures.

The 22 subjects in this study ranged in age from 17 to 43 years. All were patients of the same gynecologist, undergoing procedures requiring instrumentation of the cervix: colposcopy (microscopic examination), punch biopsy (removal of tissue with punch action instrument), or cryosurgery (removal of tissue by freezing). There were two groups for the study, control and experimental. The experimental group received their choice of music through headphones combined with relaxation instructions.

Dependent variables measured were pulse rate, respiratory rate, behavioral observations, and self-reports of pain and anxiety during and 24 hours following the procedure. Data collection during the procedure occurred at five designated points: (1) baseline, (2) upon doctor's entrance, (3) moment of punch biopsy, (4) moment of cervical instrumentation, (5) upon doctor's exit.

Graphic analysis of the data revealed differences in scores between groups which were then statistically analyzed using a Mann–Whitney U test. The points analyzed were: pulse rates, respiratory rates, and behavioral observation score during points 3 and 4; self-report scores of anxiety during the procedure.

The results of the study showed a significantly higher respiratory rate ($U = 1.5$, $n_1 = 3$, $n_2 = 5$, $p = .05$) and behavioral observation score ($U = 2.5$, $n_1 = 4$, $n_2 = 5$, $p = .05$) for the control group during punch biopsy (point 3). Control subjects rated higher on pulse rate, respiratory rate, behavioral observations, and anxiety reports overall during the procedure; however, these scores were not significantly higher than those of the experimental group.

Music Therapy Master's Thesis
The Florida State University
Summer 1991

Published: *Journal of Music Therapy* (1992), *29*(4), 202–216.

ဟ

Stroke Patient Responses to a Variety of Stimuli During Music and Non-Music Conditions

Corey M. Domec

This study examines the responsiveness of stroke patients when exposed to multiple stimuli. The objective of this study was to examine the amount of responses to these stimuli when performed alone and paired with music, and to determine if one type of stimuli was more effective than others. The three types of stimuli tested were tactile, auditory, and olfactory. This research took place at a large community hospital located in the southeastern portion of the United States. The subjects were stroke patients on a long-term care unit of this hospital.

The research design consisted of alternating music and no music 2 days a week for a 3-week period. Subjects were exposed to the same three stimuli during every treatment with only music or the absence of music changing.

The number of responses by each subject with music and without music were summed independently. A Mann–Whitney U test revealed no significant differences between music and no music ($U = 32.5$, $p = .05$). Although no statistically significant differences were found, there were increases in the number of responses in 8 of the 10 subjects during the music sessions.

A chi-square two-tailed test revealed statistically significant differences in the number of responses when comparing the different types of stimuli ($\chi^2 = 10.69$, $df = 2$, $p < .01$). This significance appears to be found in higher responsiveness towards instruments (auditory) over tactile or olfactory stimuli.

Music Therapy Master's Thesis
The Florida State University
Summer 2000

ς

The Effect of Gender on One Day-Old Infants' Behavior and Heart Rate Responses to Music Decibel Level

Stephanie J. Dureau

The purpose of this study was to examine gender differences among full-term infants' responses to music played at a range of decibel levels. These responses were measured by physiological data (heart rate) and behavioral data (behavioral state score). All subjects ($N = 36$) were healthy, 24–48 hours old, and had passed a hearing screening at the time of testing. Heart rate and behavior state were recorded as male ($n = 18$) and female ($n = 18$) subjects listened to alternating 3-minute periods of silence and music for 21 minutes. The music—an excerpt of an instrumental lullaby—was presented via small speakers placed on either side of each subject's head and played at three different loudness levels: 55–60 dB, 65–70 dB, and 74–80 dB. Heart rate was measured using a pulse oximeter with a Y-sensor attached to each subject's great toe, and behavior state was measured using a scale adapted from the Neonatal Behavioral Assessment Scale (Brazelton & Nugent, 1995). A two-way analysis of variance with repeated measures computed for both order and gender found no significant difference in heart rate or behavior state during the three loudness levels. Possible reasons for this difference include enjoyment of the music regardless of intensity or physical inability to discriminate between the different levels.

Music Therapy Master's Thesis
The Florida State University
Fall 2003

The Effect of Music-Based Imagery and Musical Alternate Engagement on the Burn Debridement Process

R. B. Fratianne, J. D. Presner, M. J. Huston, D. M. Super, C. J. Yowler, and J. M. Standley

Management of pain is a primary concern in the treatment of burn patients. The intent of this study was to test the efficacy of music-based imagery and music alternate engagement in assisting burn patients in managing their pain and anxiety during debridement. Twenty-five patients, 7 years of age and older, who were admitted to the Comprehensive Burn Care Center, were enrolled in the study which used a repeated-measures design with subjects serving as their own control. Subjects were randomly assigned to one of two groups. Those placed in Group A received no music therapy intervention during their first dressing change, and no music therapy on the following day. Group B received no music therapy intervention during their first dressing change and music therapy during their dressing on the following day. Data were collected at four intervals in the medical procedure: in the patient's room before transfer to the treatment room, in the treatment room during debridement, in the treatment room after debridement, and upon returning to the patient's room. The measurements taken were pulse, patients' self-report of pain, patients' self-report of anxiety, and the nurses' observation of patients' tension. There was a significant reduction in the self-reporting of pain in those who received music therapy in contrast to those who did not receive music therapy ($p < .03$). Music therapy is a valuable noninvasive intervention for the treatment of pain after burn injury.

Published: *Journal of Burn Care and Rehabilitation* (2001), *22*(1), 47–53. Reprinted with permission from the American Burn Association, copyright 2005.

ω

The Effects of Music and the Somatron on the Physiological and Speech Responses of Head Injured and Comatose Subjects

Allison L. Grundy

Three studies were conducted to determine the effects of music and the Somatron, a vibro-tactile acoustic couch, on the physiological and speech responses of head injured and comatose subjects. Each study involved a single subject design with the subjects serving as their own control

Six males and two females, ages 13–77, served as subjects for Study 1. Six of the subjects had suffered closed head injuries, one a CVA, and one an aneurysm. The subjects participated in daily relaxation sessions that alternated treatment conditions of music listening, music with the Somatron, and no music. Data collected included electromyogram (EMG) measures of muscle activity; measurements of pulse, respiration, and blood pressure; and ratings of affect. The results of the study indicated that the music effected small increases in muscle activity and pulse rate, decreases in respiration, and changes in blood pressure. The changes were slight, however, and within baseline measures. Changes in affect was the most noticeable response with the subjects demonstrating calmer behavior following the sessions. No consistent effects were noted by the Somatron on physiological changes since classical music appeared more stimulating while New Age music appeared more relaxing when played on the Somatron.

One 53-year-old male who was comatose following a head injury served as a subject for Study 2. The subject participated in daily sensory sessions involving two music tapes and the alternate use of the Somatron over a period of 52 days. Data collected were similar to Study 1 with the addition of observations of reflexive and voluntary movements. Changes in EMG activity and pulse, respiration and blood pressure appeared to slightly increase during music. Observations of EMG activity as viewed on the biofeedback monitor indicated an initial increase in activity, which then reached a plateau. Voluntary movements increased and decerebrate posturing occurrences decreased over time in conjunction with the subject's improving condition and use of music. The Somatron was not effective in stimulating changes in the physiological measures; however, it did appear to promote voluntary movements during the second phrase of the study.

Two female subjects diagnosed as having expressive speech impairments as the result of cardiovascular accidents served as subjects for Study 3. The subjects participated in daily speech therapy sessions involving music and speech rehearsal formats. Each format was recorded with music and involved speech content pertinent to each subject. The subjects alternated listening to the tape alone and with the Somatron for three treatment cycles. No differences in performance or rate of speech were noted during the three treatment conditions of music alone, music with the Somatron, and no music for one subject, while the other increased across time on both variables and showed delayed response time to music alone and to the Somatron.

Music Therapy Master's Thesis
The Florida State University
Fall 1989

ഗ

The Effects of Music Therapy on Quality of Life and Length of Life of Hospice Patients Diagnosed With Terminal Cancer

Russell E. Hilliard

The purpose of this study was to evaluate the effects of music therapy on quality of life, length of life in care, physical status, and relationship of death occurrence to the final music therapy interventions of hospice patients diagnosed with terminal cancer. Subjects were adults who were living in their homes, receiving hospice care, and were diagnosed with terminal cancer. A total of 80 subjects participated in the study and were randomly assigned to one of two groups: experimental (routine hospice services and clinical music therapy) and control (routine hospice services only). Groups were matched on the basis of gender and age. Quality of life was measured by the Hospice Quality of Life Index-Revised (HQOLI-R), a self-report measure given every visit. Functional status of the subjects was assessed by the hospice nurse during every visit using the Palliative Performance Scale. All subjects received at least two visits and quality of life and physical status assessments.

A repeated measures ANOVA revealed a significant difference between groups on self-report quality of life scores for visits 1 and 2. Quality of life was higher for those subjects receiving music therapy, and their quality of life increased over time as they received more music therapy sessions. Subjects in the control group, however, experienced a lower quality of life than those in the experimental group, and without music, their quality of life decreased over time. There were no significant differences in results by age or gender of subjects in either condition.

Quality of life is divided into three subscales: functional, psychophysiological, and social/spiritual well-being. Two-way repeated measures ANOVA revealed a significant difference for the psychophysiological well-being between treatment conditions, but no significant difference for the functional well-being and social/spiritual well-being subscales. Subjects receiving music therapy had a higher degree of psychophysiological well-being.

Physical status was measured by the Palliative Performance Scale (PPS), a measure completed by the hospice nurses. Subjects in both treatment conditions exhibited physical status decline as their disease progressed. A repeated measures ANOVA analysis of PPS scores for visits 1 and 2 revealed no significant differences between groups. Even with the observed decline in physical status, quality of life scores for those receiving music therapy were consistently higher. Quality of life appeared unaffected by physical status for those in the music therapy group. The control group, however, showed a significant decline in quality of life over time as physical status declined.

Subjects' length of life and number of days from last scheduled visit by discipline (music therapist vs. counselor) to death were also measured. Independent t test analysis showed no significant difference in relationship to time of death from last scheduled visit by discipline and no significant difference in length of life in the hospice program by groups. Therefore, subjects' length of life in hospice care and time of death from the last scheduled visit by the music therapist and the counselor were not significantly affected by the music therapy treatment. Mean scores, however, showed subjects receiving music therapy lived longer in hospice care though not significantly (music therapy $x = 69.5$ days vs. control $x = 57.8$ days).

Care plan needs by discipline were analyzed, songs requested were documented, and the last music therapy notes prior to the subjects' deaths were transcribed. This study provides an overview of hospice/palliative care, explains the role of music therapy in providing care, and establishes clinical guidelines grounded in research for the use of music therapy in improving the quality of life among the terminally ill.

Music Therapy Doctoral Dissertation
The Florida State University
Summer 2002

Published: *Journal of Music Therapy* (2003), *40*(2), 113–137.

The Effect of Live Music on Anxiety Levels of Persons Waiting in the Surgical Waiting Room as Measured by Self-Report

Jennifer D. Jarred

The purpose of this study was to determine the effects of live music on anxiety levels in persons waiting in a surgical waiting room as measured by self-report. One hundred ninety-two (192) subjects over the age of 18 and waiting in a surgical waiting room participated in one of three groups: the direct music group ($n = 62$), the indirect music group ($n = 59$), or the control group ($n = 71$). Subjects in the direct music group were encouraged to request songs during approximately 20 minutes of live music and then asked to provide demographic data and to indicate their anxiety, stress, worry, relaxation and enjoyment levels, and to indicate the extent to which music helped their wait on a Visual Analog Scale. Subjects in the indirect music group were in the room for approximately 20 minutes of live music requested by the direct music group but had no control over music provision. They were asked the same questions, with the addition of whether or not they heard the music. Both groups were also asked if live music was a service the hospital should offer. Subjects in the control group received no live music during their wait in the surgical waiting room and were asked demographic data and to indicate their anxiety, stress, worry, and relaxation levels on a Visual Analog Scale. Results indicated no significant differences in anxiety, stress, and worry levels among the three groups. Subjects in the direct and indirect music groups indicated significantly greater relaxation levels than did the control group. Subjects in the direct music group indicated significantly greater enjoyment than the indirect music group. All subjects who answered the question of whether live music was a service the hospital should offer responded "yes."

Music Therapy Master's Thesis
The Florida State University
Summer 2003

ဿ

The Effect of Music Therapy on the Duration, Frequency, and Perceived Importance of Social Interactions Among Patients in a Physical Rehabilitation Setting

Amy M. Kemp

Research has repeatedly demonstrated that rehabilitation patients have a higher risk of becoming socially isolated and thus clinically depressed as they attempt to deal with the changes in their lives. The purpose of this study is to assess the role that music therapy can play in improving the socialization of rehabilitation patients in order to improve their overall quality of life. At a local inpatient rehabilitation facility, 46 patients volunteered to participate in either a music therapy group or a current events discussion group for 2 days. The participants were measured on the amount of time they socialized and quantity of interactions following each session. They also completed a pretest and posttest questionnaire that assessed their own perception of the importance of socialization. Results were not significant, but they did indicate a definite trend of improvement in all measures for the music therapy group. Additionally, questionnaire posttest responses and quantity of interactions were higher for the music therapy group as compared to the discussion group.

Music Therapy Master's Thesis
The Florida State University
Spring 2002

§

The Effect of Live Music on Exercise Duration, Negative Verbalizations, and Self-Perception of Pain, Anxiety, and Rehabilitation Levels of Physical Therapy Patients

Amy Renee Kendelhardt

The purpose of this study was to examine the effects of live contingent music on exercise duration, frequency of negative verbalizations, and self-perception of pain, anxiety, and rehabilitation of physical therapy patients. Subjects ($n = 30$) were patients in an extended care rehabilitation facility in northwest Florida receiving physical therapy for various conditions. The independent variable was live contingent music played during a physical therapy session on the Restorator. Dependent variables included subjects' exercise duration, negative verbalization frequency, and self-perception of pain, anxiety, and rehabilitation levels. Analysis of variance with repeated measures (ANOVA) statistical tests were conducted on all data. Subjects in the experimental group had significantly lower posttest pain and posttest anxiety levels and higher exercise duration percentages. Posttest rehabilitation levels and frequency of negative verbalizations produced no significant difference between groups. For all dependent variables, there were significant differences between sessions not differentiated by group, indicating general rehabilitative progress. This study confirmed that music decreased perceived pain and anxiety and increased exercise duration in physical therapy patients. This supports the need for further research regarding the use of music in physical therapy along with other types of therapies.

Music Therapy Master's Thesis
The Florida State University
Spring 2003

§

The Effect of Music on Non-Responsive Patients in a Hospice Setting

Sarah E. Kerr

The purpose of this study was to evaluate the effects of music on non-responsive patients in a hospice setting. Non-responsive was defined as those patients who were comatose or whose terminal illness had progressed to the point that the patient did not respond to verbal stimuli. A total of 10 subjects participated in the study on 2 consecutive days. Data were collected on subjects' heart rate and respiration rate at the beginning of each visit, after 10 minutes of silence, and then again after 10 minutes of music. Each subject listened to a classical selection and a New Age selection, but only one selection was played each day. A two-way repeated measures ANOVA revealed significant differences for both heart rate and respiration rate across trials but not for type of music. Heart rate and respiration rate data were also analyzed by day 1 versus day 2. Again, both physiologic measures were significantly lowered following music with no significant differences by day. Results of this study support the continued use for music therapy with hospice patients who are verbally non-responsive.

Music Therapy Master's Thesis
The Florida State University
Spring 2004

ς

The Effects of Music Assisted Relaxation on the Relaxation, Sleep Quality, and Daytime Sleepiness of Sheltered, Abused Women

Amy Lasswell

The purpose of this study was to examine the effects of music paired with progressive relaxation techniques on the relaxation, sleep quality, and daytime sleepiness of sheltered, abused women. Twenty women residing in six different domestic violence shelters participated in the study. Subjects were divided into two groups. Experimental subjects ($n = 12$) participated in one 15-minute session of progressive relaxation paired with music approximately 1 hour before going to bed. Control subjects ($n = 8$) did not receive a relaxation with music intervention prior to going to bed. Data were collected using a 7-point Likert scale for self-rated relaxation, a 7-question Sleep Quality Questionnaire for self-rated sleep quality, and the Epworth Sleepiness Scale for daytime sleepiness. Results revealed a significantly higher level of both relaxation and sleep quality for the experimental group. There was no significant difference in daytime sleepiness between groups.

Music Therapy Master's Thesis
The Florida State University
Summer 2001

ʊɔ

A Descriptive Analysis of the Music Therapy Assessment Technique for Hospitalized Children Ages Birth to Three Years

Deborah L. Layman

The purpose of this study was to investigate the generation and reliability of the music therapy developmental assessment tool for hospitalized children ages birth to 3 years. Twenty-nine hospitalized children ages 6 weeks to 3 years were given music therapy assessments at Health Hill Hospital for Children in Cleveland, Ohio. The patients were seen individually for one 30-minute assessment session. The assessment session included a greeting, hello song, selected musical activities designed to assess specific developmental milestones, and goodbye song. Twenty-six of these patients then received music therapy intervention and results were documented as case studies.

An alpha coefficient reliability test was completed on three selected assessment forms. Results indicated an overall high rate of reliability (0.814) for the music therapy assessment tool. Further research is encouraged to transfer and generalize findings to other settings, including early intervention programs.

Music Therapy Master's Thesis
The Florida State University
Fall 1998

ʊɔ

The Effect of Music Therapy on End-of-Life Patients' Quality of Life, Emotional State, and Family Satisfaction as Measured by Self-Report

Judy T. Nguyen

The purpose of this study was to examine the quality of life, anxiety level, and the family satisfaction of patients during their end-of-life experience within a medical setting. Any patient admitted to Tallahassee Memorial HealthCare that met the criteria of end-of-life intervention, as determined by the medical personnel, was considered as a potential subject. The end-of-life celebration included any or all of the activities listed: a "song" written about the patient and family, live music as a sing-along, patient preferred music to reminisce, and counseling to bring closure for the patient and family. The experimental and control groups were randomly assigned. The experimental group

($n = 10$), received two sessions of music therapy. The first music therapy session was used to gather family and patient information and also included singing patient preferred music, seeking information about patient's favorite song and preference, and assessing patient and family levels of coping. The second music therapy session for the experimental group was the end-of-life celebration that ended with patient and family providing self-report data on the Visual Analog Scale (VAS) (see Appendix B), Hospice Quality of Life Index (see Appendix D) questionnaire, and the Family Satisfaction Survey (see Appendix C). The control group ($n = 10$), agreed to participate in the study but received no music therapy services. However, each control subject completed the Hospice Quality of Life Index–Revised (see Appendix D) questionnaire, and a self-report using a Visual Analog Scale (VAS) (see Appendix B) that measured anxiety levels. There was no change in the usual procedure of hospital care for those subjects. The self-report questionnaire from the Visual Analog Scale (VAS) showed significantly lower anxiety scores for the experimental subjects than for the control subjects. The Family Satisfaction Survey, filled out only by the experimental subjects, also showed a 97% satisfaction of music therapy and its uses in the medical setting. There were no significant differences between groups for quality of life measure.

Music Therapy Master's Thesis
The Florida State University
Summer 2003

ꕔ

Pediatric Surgery Patients and Parent Anxiety: Can Live Music Therapy Effectively Reduce Stress and Anxiety Levels While Waiting to Go to Surgery?

Jurg Oggenfuss

When children submit to surgery, routine or otherwise, it can be a stressful time for all involved. Often families are asked to be at the surgery site early in the day only to have to wait at length before the procedure can be performed. The waiting becomes a time of growing apprehensiveness and uncertainty for both parents and child.

While past studies have examined the correlation between music therapy and child anxiety reduction in a medical setting, this study addressed reducing parent anxiety. Forty parents of children undergoing routine surgery participated in this research project. Subjects in the experimental group were given a questionnaire before and after their child participated in a 30-minute music therapy session. Parents were asked to rate their own anxiety level on a Likert scale pre- and postintervention. Subjects in the control group received no music and were free to structure their time for 30 minutes as they pleased. These participants were administered a pre- and posttest questionnaire. Anxiety pre- and posttest scores of parents were compared using the Mann–Whitney U to calculate significance. While some reduction was noted, results were not substantial enough to warrant significance. Although the null hypothesis was rejected, 95% of participants in the experimental group stated that the music therapy session they had observed inversely affected their anxiety levels. One hundred percent of all parents in the experimental condition found the music intervention to be of direct benefit to their child's well-being and stated that they would make use of this medium in the future where available. Pre- and posttest scores of the children were also analyzed for significance. While results did not indicate significant anxiety reduction, parents did find the live music therapy to be a benefit to their children. In future studies, the author suggests controlling for gender differences and limiting subjects to those whose children have had no prior surgeries.

Music Therapy Master's Thesis
The Florida State University
Spring 2001

ဟ

The Effects of Music on the Weight Loss, Crying, and Physical Movements of Newborns

Lynne Deason Owens

The purpose of this study was to determine the effects of music on the weight loss, crying, and physical movement of newborns. Twenty-nine normal newborns were exposed to routine auditory stimulation, and 30 normal newborns were exposed to taped musical auditory stimulation. The musical stimulation consisted of approximately 5 minutes of recorded lullabies played 12 times daily at an average of every 2 hours. No significant difference was found between the two groups in terms of weight loss, percentage of babies crying, or percentage of babies moving their arms, legs, or head.

Music Therapy Master's Thesis
The Florida State University
Fall 1978

Published: *Journal of Music Therapy* (1979), *16*(2), 83–90.

ဟ

The Effect of Music Therapy for Pain and Anxiety Versus Literature on Immediate and Future Perception of Cardiac Patients

Donna Parker

This study investigated the effects of music therapy on pain, anxiety, and present and future psychosocial perceptions of cardiac patients. Forty-eight men and women admitted to cardiac progressive care unit of a local regional medical center served as subjects for the study. Subjects were assigned to one of three groups. Sixteen subjects received relaxation and imagery paired with live music, 16 subjects received literature, and 16 subjects received no intervention. Pre- and postintervention data included pain medication intake and a self-report questionnaire concerning pain, anxiety, and present and future psychosocial perceptions. Patients in the music group were given a relaxation tape, which involved relaxation exercises and imagery, paired with music. Patients were called one week after discharge and given the questionnaire once more. Patients were also asked about their pain medication intake. Results from the study were collected and analyzed. The results revealed the music group scored significantly lower on the pre posttest questionnaire involving pain anxiety and present and future perceptions. A difference was found in the groups' pre/post medication intake but results were not significant. The analysis found that the music group had significantly lower scores on the questionnaire 1 week post discharge. The

music group also had a significantly lower level of pain medication 1 week post discharge. It was concluded that music therapy interventions are beneficial to subjects in a postoperative setting.

Music Therapy Master's Thesis
The Florida State University
Summer 2004

∽

The Effect of Music on Decreasing Arousal Due to Stress: A Meta-Analysis

Cory L. Pelletier

A meta-analytic review of research articles using music to decrease arousal due to stress was conducted on 22 quantitative studies. Results demonstrated that music alone and music assisted relaxation techniques significantly decreased arousal ($d = +.67$). Further analysis of each study revealed that the amount of stress reduction was significantly different when considering age, type of stress, music assisted relaxation techniques, musical preference, previous music experience, and type of intervention. Implications and suggestions for future research are discussed.

Published: *Journal of Music Therapy* (2004), *41*(3), 192–214.

∽

The Effect of Contingent Music With
Physical Therapy in Children Who Toe-Walk

Penny Roberts

The purpose of this study was to determine if physical therapy may be more efficacious with the addition of music than without. Nine subjects who toe-walked and were between the ages of 2–6 years were selected and recommended for participation in this study by a physical therapist. Subjects participated four sessions and served as their own control. Sessions were baseline, treatment, return to baseline, treatment. Sessions were videotaped and later analyzed by the music therapy researcher and an independent observer using a 5-second observe, 5-second record data collection process.

A one-way analysis of variance (ANOVA) test showed a statistically significant difference in the number of heel and toe scores when music was added to the physical therapy sessions. Though not significantly different, the number of complaints and noncooperation scores decreased as well. More extensive research is recommended to fully explore the most efficacious use of music in combination with children during physical therapy sessions.

Music Therapy Master's Thesis
The Florida State University
Fall 2002

∽

The Effect of Music on Reducing Preoperative Anxiety and
Postoperative Anxiety and Pain in the Recovery Room

Susan K. Sanderson

The purpose of this study was to investigate the effects of music on reducing preoperative anxiety and postoperative anxiety and pain in the recovery room. Sixty men and women, ages 18-70 years, admitted in a regional medical center for elective orthopedic surgery served as subjects for this study. Subjects were assigned to the control or experimental group on the basis of sex, age, inpatient/outpatient status, and major as opposed to minor surgery. Subjects in the music group listened to music preoperatively and postoperatively in the recovery room. Subjects in the control did not receive music.

Data were collected and six null hypotheses tested. Statistical analysis revealed that music group was significantly less anxious preoperatively, made fewer pain and anxiety verbalizations, was behaviorally less anxious, and used less pain and nausea medication in the recovery room than in the control group. There was no significant difference between the two groups in the length of time spent in the recovery or in the stabilization time. Results of this study indicate that music is effective in reducing preoperative anxiety and postoperative pain and anxiety in the recovery room. Further research is recommended.

Music Therapy Master's Thesis
The Florida State University
Summer 1986

ഗ

The Effect of Music Therapy Intervention on Preoperative Anxiety of Pediatric Patients as Measured by Self-Report

Andrea M. Scheve

The purpose of this study is to determine the effects of music therapy intervention on preoperative anxiety of pediatric patients as measured by self report. Sixty (60) subjects between the ages of 3–10 were randomly assigned to one of two groups: the control groups ($n = 30$) or the experimental group ($n = 30$). Subjects in the control group received no music intervention and were asked to rate their anxiety level prior to surgery on a 7-point Likert scale. The experimental group received approximately 20 minutes of music therapy intervention and were asked to rate their anxiety prior to surgery on the same 7-point Likert scale. Parents/guardians of all participants were asked for consent prior to subject participation in the study, and parents/guardians were asked to fill out a questionnaire concerning their anxiety, and their perception of their child's anxiety prior to surgery. Results indicate a statistically significant decrease in anxiety levels for the experimental group.

Music Therapy Master's Thesis
The Florida State University
Summer 2002

ഗ

The Effect of Music Listening on Blood Pressure Fluctuations in Adult Hemodialysis Patients

Betty Lynn Schuster

In this study, music was used as a treatment with hemodialysis patients. The purpose of the study was to investigate the efficacy of music therapy in reducing the amount of fluctuation in the blood pressures of patients undergoing hemodialysis treatment. It seems to be the consensus of extra-musical literature that hypertension and hypotension are of major concern to professionals working with hemodialysis patients. The music therapy research concludes that music affects the respiration rate, heart rate, blood pressure and Galvonic skin response (GSR). The experimental design incorporated a two-sample method: control group receiving measurement of blood pressure after each hour of dialysis, and experimental group receiving measurement of blood pressure after each hour of dialysis and music for 1 hour beginning 30 minutes after the onset of treatment and another hour of music after 2½ hours of treatment. Sixty-three adult dialysis patients between the ages of 22 and 81 years were included in this study.

Data collection consisted of blood pressure readings recorded daily from each patient's chart for a baseline period of 2 weeks and a treatment period of 3 weeks. The nurses completed a dialysis rating form on the final day of treatment on each patient concerning the exhibition of calmness or anxiety during the dialysis treatment. An attitude survey was given to each patient in the experimental group on the final day of treatment to obtain information regarding degrees of perceived anxiety and periods of relaxation. The null hypothesis stated: There will be no significant differences in the mean blood pressure readings between the group receiving music and the group not receiving music or in the mean blood pressure readings between the baseline and treatment sessions of the group receiving music. Statistical tests revealed no significant difference between the control group and the experimental group nor between the baseline and treatment sessions of the experimental group. Thus, the researcher failed to reject the null hypotheses. However, results for both groups were statistically significant for every blood pressure reading from onset to termination.

Music Therapy Master's Thesis
The Florida State University
Spring 1984

Published: *Journal of Music Therapy* (1985), *22*(3), 146–153.

ಉ

A Meta-Analysis of the Efficacy of Music Therapy for Premature Infants

Jayne M. Standley

This meta-analysis on music research with premature infants in neonatal intensive care units (NICU) showed an overall large, significant, consistent effect size of almost a standard deviation ($d = .83$) (Cohen, 1998). Effects were not mediated by infants' gestational age at the time of study, birthweight, or type of music delivery nor by physiologic, behavioral, or developmental measures or benefit. The homogeneity of findings suggests that music has statistically significant and clinically important benefits for premature infants in the NICU. The unique acoustic properties that differentiate music from all other sounds are discussed and clinical implications for research-based music therapy procedures cited.

ഗ

Clinical Applications of Music and Chemotherapy: The Effects on Nausea and Emesis

Jayne M. Standley

A summer music therapy program providing music listening opportunities to patients undergoing chemotherapy was initiated. Multiple data collection procedures were devised to determine the long-term effects of music on the frequency and degree of nausea and vomiting during chemotherapy, occurring posttreatment, and developing prior to treatment as anticipatory symptoms; the level of anxiety during chemotherapy administration as observed by peripheral finger temperature, verbal interaction, movement, and skin pallor; and attitudes about cancer and its treatment.

Data were collected on 15 people who completed four or more chemotherapy treatments under one of several conditions isolating the influence of music. One group ($n = 5$) listened to music during treatments 1 through 4, while another ($n = 5$) listened to music during treatments 2 through 5. There were two comparable no-music groups ($n = 2, 3$).

Throughout the project, patients and staff reacted very favorably to the benefits of music listening during chemotherapy. Data analysis showed that both music groups reported less nausea than the no-music groups. Data also demonstrated that the length of time before nausea began was much longer for the music groups than for the no-music groups. Other physiological and observed responses did not appear to be differentiated by music condition.

Published: *Music Therapy Perspectives* (1992), *10*(1), 27–35.

ഗ

Long-term Benefits of Music Intervention in the Newborn Intensive Care Unit: A Pilot Study

Jayne M. Standley

A 6-month follow-up study was conducted on 52 premature and low birth weight neonates who had previously participated in a music research project while restricted to isolettes in a

Newborn Intensive Care Unit. Mothers of these babies were surveyed approximately 6 months after the baby's hospital discharge to ascertain long-term health, behavioral, or developmental benefits of recorded music played in the isolette. Mothers of music babies had an unusually high return rate (76.9%), felt their children cried considerably less than other babies their age, and reported that their babies stopped crying or fell asleep in response to music. There was no difference between the music and non-music babies on rate of achievement of developmental milestones or on overall health/illness ratings.

Published: *Journal of the International Association of Music for the Handicapped* (1991), *6*(1), 12–22. Reprinted with permission.

ഗ

Music Research in Medical/Dental Treatment: Meta-Analysis and Clinical Applications

Jayne M. Standley

This article is a comprehensive analysis and application of music therapy research in the general field of music in medicine, and consists of a thorough review of the literature and a meta-analysis of all empirical studies using music in actual medical/dental treatments. It also transfers research results to clinical applications of music therapy techniques and program development in a general hospital setting.

Published: *Journal of Music Therapy* (1986), *23*(2), 52–122.

ഗ

Music Therapy in the NICU: Pacifier-Activated-Lullabies (PAL) for Reinforcement of Non-Nutritive Sucking

Jayne M. Standley

Today, very fragile infants as young as 23 weeks gestation or weighing less than a pound can survive their premature birth. Such infants spend many months in the neonatal intensive care unit (NICU) while completing their development. Music therapy research in the NICU has been highly successful for physiological, neurological, and developmental benefits. More importantly, music therapy has reduced length of hospitalization and subsequent medical costs for care of these infants. The purpose of this paper is to provide an overview of medical music therapy for the NICU, including an innovative mechanism, PAL, Pacifier-Activated-Lullabies for increasing non-nutritive sucking.

Published: *International Journal of Arts Medicine* (1999), *6*(2), 17–21. Reprinted with permission of MMB Music, Inc.

∽

Music Therapy Research and Applications in Pediatric Oncology Treatment

Jayne M. Standley and Suzanne B. Hanser

Music therapy is a profession which meets multiple physical, social, and psychological needs. Music therapists can facilitate health objectives by reducing the intensity or duration of pain, alleviating anxiety, and decreasing the amount of analgesic medication needed. Rehabilitative objectives can include activities which incorporate exercise, range of motion therapy, or gait training. Reduction of fear, anxiety, stress, or grief is a common psychological objective. Music therapy is particularly effective in promoting social objectives such as increased interaction, verbalization, independence, and cooperation; enhanced relationships with health care personnel and family members; and increased stimulation during long-term hospitalization or isolation. Counseling techniques are often paired with music to achieve emotional objectives such as expression, adjustment, stability, or locus of control. The purpose of this article is to synthesize the extant music/medical research literature and clarify how music therapy can provide a quintessential combination of physical, social, and psychological benefits to enhance the health care of pediatric oncology patients.

Published: *Journal of Pediatric Oncology Nursing* (1995), *12*(1), 3–8. Copyright 1995 by Sage Publications. Reprinted by permission of Sage Publications.

∽

Music Therapy With Pediatric Patients: A Meta-Analysis

Jayne M. Standley and Jennifer Whipple

This meta-analysis on 29 quantitative studies comparing music versus no-music conditions during medical treatment of pediatric patients showed an overall effect size of $d = .64$. The confidence interval did not include 0 so results were considered significant. All effects were in a positive direction for music except for one circumcision study comparing recorded background music to a placebo analgesic cream. The homogeneity Q value was significant ($p = .00$) indicating that results among the studies are inconsistent and not adequately explained by the overall effect size. Therefore, a quality analysis was conducted to try to identify the source of inconsistencies.

Studies were coded for nine qualities and analyzed. Results demonstrated that date of study did not differentiate results ($p = .64$) but publication source did ($p = .02$). The articles published in medical journals had significantly lower effect sizes. With regard to subjects, age was significant ($p = .00$) but gender of subjects was not ($p = .28$). The type of medical treatment affected results ($p = .00$). Children with major invasive procedures (debridement, bone marrow aspirations, post-surgery) and those with noninvasive procedures (newborn nursery, chest physiotherapy, pre-surgery) had significantly greater benefit from the music procedures than did those having minor invasive procedures (venipunctures, hypodermics, or circumcision). These results may be due to flawed definitions we chose for the subcategories since we operationally defined minor versus major invasive procedures. With regard to type of dependent variable measured in the studies, those with behavioral observation had significantly lower effect sizes than did those with physiological and self-report measures ($p = .02$).

Published: Robb, S. (Ed.). (2003). *Music therapy in pediatric healthcare: Research and best practice* (pp. 1–18). Silver Spring, MD: American Music Therapy Association.

ഗ

The Effect of Contingent Music to Increase Non-Nutritive Sucking of Premature Infants

Jayne M. Standley

This study assessed music as reinforcement for non-nutritive sucking of 12 premature infants born at an average gestation of 29.3 weeks and an average birth-weight of 1111.9 g. At the time of the study, the infants' average post conception age was 35.5 weeks, and their average weight was 1747.3 g. A pacifier was fitted with a pressure transducer so that a sufficient suck activated frequency and duration signals as well as 10 seconds of recorded music consisting of lullabies sung by female vocalists. A 14-minute ABAB study design included a silence baseline for 2 minutes, 5 minutes of contingent music, 2 minutes of silence, and 5 minutes of contingent music. Frequency data were recorded for each 5-second interval in which the duration light was activated for at least 3 seconds. Results demonstrated that sucking rates during the periods of contingent music were 2.43 times greater than baseline (silence) sucking rates. In this study, music contributed significantly to the development of non-nutritive sucking of premature infants.

Reprinted from *Pediatric Nursing* (2000), *26*(5), 493–499. Reprinted with permission of the publisher, Jannetti Publications, Inc., East Holly Avenue, Box 56, Pitman, NJ 08071-0056; (856) 256-2300; FAX (856) 589-7463; Web site: www.pediatricnursing.net.

ഗ

The Effect of Music and Multimodal Stimulation on Responses of Premature Infants in Neonatal Intensive Care

Jayne M. Standley

To assess the benefits of lullaby singing and multimodal stimulation on premature infants in neonatal intensive care, 40 infants in a Level III Newborn Intermediate Care Unit were divided into control ($n = 20$) and experimental ($n = 20$) groups by pair matching on the basis of gender, birthweight, gestational age at birth and severity of medical complications. Participants met these project criteria: (a) corrected gestational age >32 weeks; (b) age since birth >10 days; and (c) weight >1700 g. All participants had been referred for developmental stimulation by the medical staff. Experimental infants received reciprocal, multimodal (ATVV) stimulation paired with line singing of *Brahms' Lullaby*. Stimulation was provided for 15–30 minutes, one or two times per week from referral to discharge. Dependent variables were (a) days to discharge, (b) weight gain/day, and (c) experimental infants' tolerance for stimulation. Results showed that music and multimodal stimulation significantly benefited females' days to discharge and increased weight gain/day for both males and females. Both male and female infants' tolerance for stimulation showed marked and steady increase across the stimulation intervals with females' tolerance increasing more rapidly than males.

Reprinted from *Pediatric Nursing* (1998), *24*(6), 532–538. Reprinted with permission of the publisher, Jannetti Publications, Inc., East Holly Avenue, Box 56, Pitman, NJ 08071-0056; (856) 256-2300; FAX (856) 589-7463; Web site: www.pediatricnursing.net.

∽

The Effect of Music-Reinforced Non-nutritive Sucking on Feeding Rate of Premature Infants

Jayne M. Standley

Premature infants are fed by gavage tube before 34 weeks adjusted gestational age and when nipple feeding results in detrimental changes in respiration and heart rate. Nipple feeding skill must be developed and correlates with length of hospitalization and neurobehavioral development. This study provided music reinforcement for non-nutritive sucking and assessed nipple feeding rates pre- and posttreatment for 32 infants referred as poor feeders. A pacifier fitted with a pressure transducer activated 10 seconds of recorded music in a one-trial, 15-minute intervention given to experimental infants ($n = 16$) 30 to 60 minutes before the late afternoon bottle feeding. Feeding rates were collected for bottle feedings pre- and postintervention and for a similar interval for a no-contact control group ($n = 16$). Results showed that the intervention significantly increased feeding rates.

Music functioned as reinforcement and the sucking behavior transferred from a non-nutritive to a nutritive event.

ဌ

Therapeutic Effects of Music and Mother's Voice on Premature Infants

Jayne M. Standley and Randall S. Moore

Aversive environmental auditory stimuli is a common concern in neonatal intensive care. Recently, interest has developed regarding the use of music applications to mask such stimuli and to reduce the high risk for complications or failure to thrive. In this study of 20 oxygenated, low birth weight infants in a Newborn Intensive Care Unit of a regional medical center in the southeastern United States, 10 infants listened to lullabies and 10 infants to recordings of their mother's voice through earphones for 20 minutes across three consecutive days. Oxygen saturation levels and frequency of oximeter alarms were recorded. Results indicated a differential response to the two auditory stimuli as listening time progressed. On Day 1, the infants listening to music had significantly higher oxygen saturation levels, but these effects disappeared by Days 2 and 3. On Days 2 and 3, however, the babies hearing music had significantly depressed oxygen saturation levels during the posttest intervals after the music was terminated. Infants hearing music had significantly fewer occurrences of Oximeter alarms during auditory stimuli than did those listening to the mothers' voice. Implications for the therapeutic use of auditory stimuli in the Newborn Intensive Care Unit are discussed.

ဌ

The Role of Music in Pacification/Stimulation of Premature Infants with Low Birthweights

Jayne M. Standley

This article describes the problems of premature infants with low birth weights, reviews the literature on fetal and neonatal responses to auditory stimuli, and extrapolates and synthesizes research results for the development of effective early intervention techniques which incorporate music. Sample activities for both infant pacification/stimulation and parent training are given, and the role of music therapy in the development of comprehensive early intervention systems under PL 99-457 guidelines is discussed.

Published: *Music Therapy Perspectives* (1991), *9*, 19–25.

ᔑ

The Effect of Music Listening on Blood Pressure, Pulse Rate, Respiration Rate, and Anxiety State of Patients in the Preoperative Room

Shari Elizabeth Staples

This study was conducted to assess the effects of music on anxiety levels of patients waiting in the preoperative room of a regional medical facility. Anxiety was measured by physiological responses (blood pressure, pulse rate, and respiratory rate) and observable behaviors. Forty patients, age 18 to 86 years, served as the subjects for this study.

The 40 patients were randomly assigned to either the control group ($n = 20$) or the experimental group ($n = 20$). The patients in the experimental group listened with headphones to "Stillness in Motion" and "Shawntana's Peace" by Jim Oliver. The patients in the control group did not receive any music. Three sets of data were taken on each patient: (a) blood pressure, pulse rate, and respiratory rate were recorded when the patient arrived in the preoperative room; (b) after 10 minutes, a behavioral checklist indicating the patients anxiety level was completed; and (c) after the behavioral checklist was completed, a second reading of blood pressure, pulse rate, and respiratory rate was recorded.

The null hypothesis stated: There will be no significant differences between the diastolic blood pressure, systolic blood pressure, pulse rate, respiratory rate, and observable behavior of preoperative patients who listen to relaxing music and those of preoperative patients who do not listen to music. Although there was a noticeable difference between the data of the control group and those of the experimental group, the statistical analysis of the data failed to show a significant difference, and the null hypothesis failed to be rejected.

Music Therapy Master's Thesis
The Florida State University
Fall 1993

ᔑ

The Psychological and Physiological Effects of Vibrotactile Stimulation, Via a Somatron, on Patients Awaiting Scheduled Gynecological Surgery

Catherine L. Walters

This study investigated the effects of vibrotactile stimulation via a Somatron mattress on patients awaiting scheduled gynecological surgery. Thirty-nine women admitted to a local regional medical center between the ages of 19 and 65 years served as subjects for the investigation. Subjects were randomly assigned to one of three groups. Thirteen subjects received a vibrotactile intervention (VT), 13 subjects received a music only intervention (M), and 13 subjects comprised a nonintervention experimental control while in the surgical holding area. Pre- and postintervention psychological data included self-reported levels of tension, anxiety, relaxation, stress, and mood, which were also combined to produce pre and post levels of apprehension. Pre and post physiological data included measures of systolic and diastolic blood pressure, pulse rate, and temperature. Additional information regarding the specifics of the surgical procedure and patient recovery were also collected and analyzed. The results of the study revealed that both VT and M subjects demonstrated reductions in reported levels of tension, anxiety, and stress, increases in relaxation, and a general improvement in mood following the intervention. Statistical analysis utilizing one-way analyses of variance ($p < 0.05$) revealed that VT subjects demonstrated significantly less postintervention apprehension than the experimental control, VT and M subjects spent significantly less time in surgery and also in PACU than C subjects, and the VT and M groups were found to receive significantly less postoperative medication than the C group. No significant differences were observed with regard to pre- and postintervention physiological data, although VT and M subjects revealed a tendency for a reduction in pulse rate following the interventions. VT subjects were also found to consistently demonstrate the least fluctuation in both systolic and diastolic blood pressure throughout the surgical experience. It was concluded that both the VT and M interventions appeared to be beneficial to subjects in a preoperative setting, although the two appeared not to differ significantly from each other on any measure apart from the self-report data.

Music Therapy Master's Thesis
The Florida State University
Fall 1995

Published: *Journal of Music Therapy* (1996), *33*(4), 261–287.

The Effects of Live Music on Quality of Life Indicators for Brain Tumor Surgical Patients

Darcy DeLoach Walworth, Judy Nguyen, and Jennifer Jarred

The purpose of this study was to compare quality of life indicators, length of stay, and medications administered to patients undergoing surgical procedures for brain tumors at a regional medical hospital. Quality of life indicators included anxiety, relaxation, stress, pain, mood, and perception of hospitalization. Participants in the study were male and female and ranged in age from 8 years to 78 years old. Subjects were randomly assigned to either a music group ($n = 14$) or non-music group ($n = 12$). Subjects in the experimental music group received live music sessions daily, both preoperatively and during the recovery period and filled out questionnaires for quality of life measures using a visual analog scale (VAS). Live music sessions included singing patient preferred music accompanied by guitar, with patients and family members interacting through singing and playing rhythm instruments. Genres of music played included gospel, country, jazz, contemporary Christian, rock, pop, Motown, and American standards. Control subjects received no music and filled out the same questionnaire both preoperatively and daily during the recovery period. Results of the study show a significant difference of VAS scores between groups for relaxation ($p > .001$), stress ($p > .006$), pain ($p > .006$), and mood ($p > .004$). No significant differences were found between groups for anxiety, perception of hospitalization, or length of stay. Significant differences were also found for experimental subjects pre and post music sessions for anxiety ($p > .001$), relaxation ($p > .000$), stress ($p > .000$), pain ($p > .000$), and perception of hospitalization ($p > .007$). Presenters are currently tabulating comparison of medications administered to patients. The results of this study indicated the use of live music having a positive effect on quality of life indicators for patients undergoing surgical procedures for brain tumors.

Note: This study was funded by the National Brain Tumor Foundation and presented at the AMTA Annual Conference, Austin, 2004.

ഗ

The Use of Music and Relaxation Techniques to Reduce Pain of Burn Patients During Daily Debridement

Laura A. Ward

This study represents initial data based research in music therapy with burn patients. The purpose of this study was to ascertain the effect of music, paired with relaxation techniques, on the reduction of perceived pain, heart rate, behavioral characteristics of pain, and the burn technician's evaluation of patients' discomfort during daily debridement of burn patients.

There were 5 subjects in the study, whose ages ranged from 13–96 years. There were one male and four females. Subjects were consenting patients admitted to the Burn Center of The Delta Medical Center in Greenville, Mississippi, within a 2-month period.

Subjects were introduced to procedures prior to their next debridement. There were two experimental conditions: (a) Music/Progressive Muscle Relaxation (PMR), and (b) No Music Control. Each subject was his own control. The subjects received Music/PMR, every other treatment period, for 14 days. The number of treatments observed ranged from 9–14 times.

During conditions with Music/PMR, the subject was led through Progressive Muscle Relaxation, 20 minutes before debridement. Once debridement began, the music was started. The patient was instructed to concentrate on his breathing, letting the music help keep breathing steady. The patient's heart rate was taken before and after debridement. Results of the Wilcoxon matched-pair signed rank test of differences showed that without music, heart rates increased significantly after debridement, and that with music, heart rates stayed the same as before debridement ($p = .01$).

A chi-square test was computed for pain versus no pain. Results showed that there was a significant difference between pain and no pain, with levels of pain decreasing and levels of no pain increasing in conditions with music ($p = .05$).

There was no significant difference in the intensity of pain as computed by a chi-square test ($p = .05$). A chi-square test was also computed for the burn technician's evaluation of patients' pain level, and the patients' self-reporting measures. There were no significant differences in the perception of pain in conditions with Music/PMR, and conditions of No/Music ($p = .05$).

Music therapy could be a valuable contribution to burn centers. Further research in this area is needed to verify the results found in this study and to examine other possible areas of service that music therapy might have on a burn unit.

Music Therapy Master's Thesis
The Florida State University
Fall 1987

Published: Barker, L.W. (1991). In C. D. Maranto (Ed.), *Applications of music in medicine.* Washington, DC: National Association for Music Therapy.

ℒ

The Effects of Music with Abbreviated Progressive Relaxation Techniques on Occupational Stress in Female Nurses in a Hospital

Kumiko Watanabe

The purpose of this study was to investigate the effects of music paired with abbreviated progressive relaxation techniques on occupational stress of female nurses in a hospital. Forty subjects ($n = 40$) ranging in age approximately from 21 to 60 years participated in this study. All subjects were female full-time registered nurses (RNs) or licensed practical nurses (LPNs) in a hospital.

Only those who were scheduled to work for the first shift in 3 consecutive days were recruited to participate in this study.

The study utilized each subject as her own control in an $0_1 0_2 X 0_3$ design where $0 =$ observation and $X =$ treatment. The entire length of the experiment was 3 days per subject. Dependent variables utilized in this study were pulse rate, the emotional state form entitled "Emotions," and the Daily Nursing Stress Scale (DNSS) designed by the researcher based on the Nursing Stress Scale (Gary-Toft & Anderson, 1981), the Maslach Burnout Inventory (Maslach & Jackson, 1987), and the Nurse Stress Index (Williams & Cooper, 1997). Data collection during the research procedure occurred at seven designated points: (a) The Daily Nursing Stress Scale at the end of each subject's shift on Day 1 as a baseline, (b) pulse rate before the music trial on Day 2, (c) The "Emotions" before the music trial on Day 2, (d) pulse rate after the music trial on Day 2, (e) The "Emotions" after the music trial on Day 2, (f) The Daily Nursing Stress Scale at the end of subject's shift on Day 2, and (g) The Daily Nursing Stress Scale at the end of subject's shift on Day 3. The analysis of the Daily Nursing Stress Scale scores through the repeated measures analysis of variance (ANOVA) revealed no significant difference between all 3 days of the experiment; thus, it failed to reject the null hypothesis. However, a significant difference was found in means of pulse rate data collected pre and post music trial. A significant difference was also found in mean scores on the "Emotions." The results of this study suggest the effects of music paired with progressive relaxation decreased pulse rate and increased perceived positive emotions.

Music Therapy Master's Thesis
The Florida State University
Fall 2001

ဢ

The Effect of Parent Training in Music and Multimodal Stimulation on the Quality of Parent-Neonate Interactions and Infant Weight Gain and Length of Hospitalization in the Newborn Intensive Care Unit

Jennifer Whipple

This study examined the effects of parent training in music and multimodal stimulation on the quantity and quality of parent-neonate interactions and the weight gain and length of hospitalization of premature and low birthweight (LBW) infants in a Neonatal Intensive Care Unit (NICU). Twenty sets of parents and premature LBW infants participated in the study. Parents in the experimental group ($n = 10$) received approximately 1 hour of instruction in appropriate uses of music, multimodal stimulation including massage techniques, and signs of infant overstimulation and techniques for its avoidance. Parent-neonate interactions, specifically parent actions and responses and infant stress and nonstress behaviors, were observed for subjects in both groups. Infant stress behaviors were significantly fewer and appropriateness of parent actions and responses were significantly greater for experimental infants and parents than for control subjects. Parents in the experimental group also self-reported spending significantly more time visiting in the NICU than did parents of control infants. In addition, length of hospitalization was shorter and average daily weight gain was greater for infants whose parents received training, although these differences were not significant. A 1-month, postdischarge follow-up showed little difference between experimental and control group parent-infant interactions in the home.

Music Therapy Master's Thesis
The Florida State University
Spring 1999

Published: *Journal of Music Therapy* (2000), *37*(4), 250–268.

∽

The Effect of Music-Reinforced Nonnutritive Sucking on State of Preterm, Low Birthweight Infants Experiencing Heelstick

Jennifer Whipple

This study examined the physiologic and behavioral effects of music-reinforced nonnutritive sucking (NNS), using the Sondrex® Pacifier Activated Lullaby (PAL) System®, for preterm, low birthweight (LBW) infants experiencing heelstick. Research has shown NNS to be calming for infants during noxious procedures (Shiao, Chang, Lannon, & Yarandi, 1997) and varying types of music therapy intervention have documented reduction of infant stress behaviors (Standley, 2002). The Sondrex® Pacifier Activated Lullaby (PAL) System® uses a pacifier connected to a transmitter to receive a signal to play music contingent on infant sucking. While the PAL was originally designed and has FDA approval as a mechanism to facilitate poor feeding behaviors, the focus of this investigation was its application in soothing.

Subjects for this study were 60 preterm, LBW infants in a neonatal intensive care unit, aged 32 to 37 weeks post conceptional age, not receiving mechanical ventilation support, and experiencing a heelstick procedure. Infants were randomly assigned to one of three treatment groups, evenly divided for gender: PAL experimental ($n = 20$), pacifier-only control ($n = 20$), and no-contact control ($n = 20$). For all three groups, intervention and/or observation occurred on only one occasion. For experimental infants, intervention began approximately 3 minutes prior to the heelstick and continued throughout and approximately 3 minutes following the blood collection procedure. Infants were provided the Sondrex® PAL System® with which music was played contingent on sucking. A 10-second sound duration setting was used, meaning that music played for 10 seconds following each suck and then ceased until the infant sucked again. Music used was from a recording of traditional lullabies sung by a single female child's voice with piano accompaniment and maintained at 65 dB. Procedures were the same for infants in the pacifier-only control group, except that they did not receive music reinforcement for sucking. Infants in the no-contact control group were not provided a pacifier or music listening opportunities at any point during the heelstick procedure. Other standard care and pain management procedures such as swaddling, cuddling, and sucrose were not limited for infants in any of the groups. Stress level and behavior state based on the Assessment of Premature Infant's Behavior (Als, Lester, Tronick, & Brazelton, 1982) were assessed continuously and physiologic measures of heart rate (HR), respiratory rate (RR), and oxygen saturation (SaO_2) were recorded at 15-second intervals for all infants.

No meaningful gender differences were observed for physiologic measures, but standard deviations for behavior state and stress level were smaller for females than for males across time, indicating greater stability in responses. Some consistent group by gender interactions were evident for physiologic variables, though most physiologic data results were inconclusive. Examination of means and standard deviations revealed much more variability across time for HR and RR than for SaO2 and the behavioral variables. During-heelstick behavior state means were significantly lower, mean behavior state differences from the pre to during and during to post intervals were significantly smaller, and significantly less time was spent in undesirable Active and Crying states for the PAL and pacifier-only groups compared to the no-contact group. In addition, the PAL group had significantly lower pre, during, and post interval stress level means and significantly smaller mean stress level differences between the pre and during and the during and post intervals. Except for the pre interval mean, these differences also occurred for the pacifier-only control group compared to the no-contact control group. Although no significant differences were revealed between the PAL and pacifier-only groups, more and greater differences were evident between the PAL and no-contact groups than between the pacifier-only and no-contact control groups. Not only were behavior state and stress level means lower for all intervals and increases smaller during the painful stimulus for the PAL group than for the other two treatment groups, but the patterns of behavior state and stress level were more stable across time for the PAL group than for the other groups. Also, the pattern of changes in SaO_2 and in behavior state and stress level indicate that music-reinforced NNS may facilitate return to homeostasis following the completion of the heelstick procedure. Several significant correlations were found within all groups for physiologic and behavioral measures with infant acuity, initial behavior state, and heelstick procedure duration. Of those, less optimal behavior states were associated with an earlier point at which SaO_2 reached 95% or greater within the post interval for the PAL group, yet was also associated with the seemingly opposite result of a higher percentage of time in which SaO_2 was below 86% for the no-contact control group.

Based on results of this study, music-reinforced NNS seems to be effective in attenuating behavior state and stress level increases for preterm, LBW infants experiencing heelstick, documenting another method of nonpharmacologic pain management for the population of premature infants and identifying an additional benefit of the Sondrex® PAL System®. Limitations of this study and implications for future research regarding music-reinforced NNS for preterm, LBW infants are discussed, including its use in modulation of preterm infant behavior during non-painful conditions.

Music Therapy Doctoral Dissertation
The Florida State University
Fall 2004

သ

The Use of Music as an Audio-Analgesia During Childbirth

Marjorie A. Winokur

The purpose of this study was to investigate the effects of music on the perception of pain, fear, and physical tension. The effects of music on obstetric medication dosage were also investigated. Thirty-one women and their coaches, in the third trimester of pregnancy, voluntarily served as subjects for this study. All subjects were enrolled in Lamaze class and were randomly assigned to either the experimental or control group. Childbirth preparation classes met once a week for 7 weeks, 2 hours per class. Subjects attended a minimum of six classes. Couples in the control group received no music training during class and used no music during childbirth. Couples in the experimental group received music therapy training during the second hour of class and used individualized tapes during childbirth.

Data were collected on eight self-report measures and one observation measure. Nonparametric statistics were used to analyze data. There were no statistical differences on ad hoc measures of fear, tension, or pain between groups. Statistical differences were found on post hoc measures of fear, physical tension, pain, length of labor, and amount of medication accepted/rejected.

Results of this study indicate that music with training is an effective means of reducing the mother's fear, tension, and pain during childbirth. The findings of this study agree with the findings of Clark, McCorkle, and Williams (1981) and Hanser, Larsen, and O'Connell (1983). Further research is recommended.

Music Therapy Master's Thesis
The Florida State University
Summer 1984

သ

The Effect of Music Therapy on the Spirituality of Persons in an In-Patient Hospice Unit as Measured by Self-Report

Natalie Wlodarczyk

The purpose of this study was to determine the effect of music therapy on the spirituality of persons in an in-patient hospice unit as measured by self-report. Subjects ($N = 10$) were used as their own control in an ABAB design format. Session A consisted of approximately 30 minutes of music therapy, after which the patient/subject responded to a spiritual well-being questionnaire; session B consisted of approximately 30 minutes of a non-music visit, after which the patient/subject responded to a spiritual well-being questionnaire. The spiritual well-being questionnaire used in this study is an 18-item, religiously non-specific, self-report questionnaire using a Likert scale of 6 degrees adapted from the Spiritual Well-Being Scale (Ellison & Paloutzian, 1982). All subjects gave written consent prior to participation in the study. Data results were graphically and statistically analyzed after four visits and four spiritual well-being questionnaires were completed for each subject. Results indicate a statistically significant increase in scores on music days.

Music Therapy Master's Thesis
The Florida State University
Fall 2003

Reference

Madsen, C. K., & Madsen, C. H. (1997). *Experimental research in music.* Raleigh, NC: Contemporary Publishing.

Note: References in reprinted abstracts can be found by accessing the original document.

Section III

The Organization of MT Clinical Services at TMH: Treatment Protocols and Case Studies

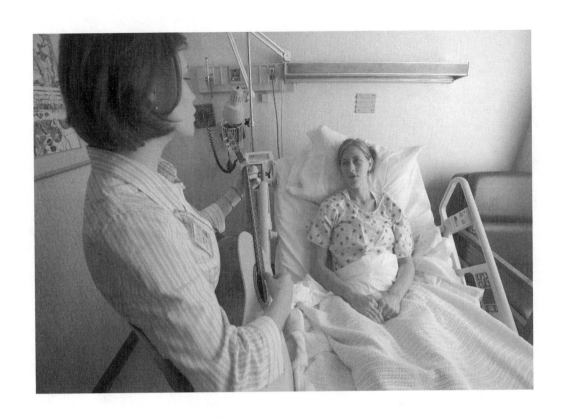

Chapter 7

Music Therapy Clinical Services

∽

Judy Nguyen, M.M., MT-BC,
Jennifer Jarred, M.M., MT-BC,
Darcy Walworth, M.M., MT-BC,
Kristen Adams, M.M., MT-BC,
and Danielle Procelli, MT-BC

MUSIC THERAPY CLINICAL SERVICES

Referrals

The current music therapy referral system used at Tallahassee Memorial HealthCare has generated many referrals throughout the hospital for all types of patients. Music therapy services are provided to benefit patients for multiple reasons: to reduce anxiety, to increase coping skills, to increase relaxation, to teach stress management, to provide cognitive stimulation, to increase quality of life, to establish reality orientation, to eliminate the need for sedation, to teach pain management, to elevate mood, to increase socialization, to increase sensory stimulation, to increase motivation, to increase communication, or to normalize environment.

There are three types of referrals differentiated by the priority and patient need for services. The first type, the medical referral, has top priority. These are referrals that contain written orders from physicians, nurses, therapists, social workers, and other medical staff personnel. These referrals can be made during a patient care conference or individually via phone, e-mail, or entered into the hospital database. The music therapy staff strives to conduct individual sessions for all medical referral patients at least three times a week.

Another form of medical referral is the "appointment only" referral. These are accomplished in two ways. Patients receiving echocardiograms are scheduled with the physician up to a week in advance. This type of "appointment only" referral requires all music therapy staff members to be "on-call" at some time during the mornings and early afternoons. The therapist is notified the morning of the procedure by receiving a faxed referral and a telephone call. The faxed referral form contains the patient's name, age, and appointment time. When the patient arrives for the procedure, the therapist is then paged. The other type of "appointment only" referral includes CT scans, EEGs, EKGs, IV starts, and bone/renal scans. Medical staff personnel within the radiology, nuclear medicine, and neurodiagnostics department contact the music therapy staff several days in advance to ensure that a therapist is available to assist. Occasionally, if the music therapy staff is unable to assist, the medical staff personnel will reschedule the procedure for when music therapy is available.

The second type of referral is identified as "rounds." This "open referral" system was created with each nurse manager's input and was established so that any and all patients that were deemed appropriate on each unit would have the opportunity to receive music therapy services. During rounds, a therapist finds a medical staff person and determines which patients are appropriate for music therapy services that day. The therapist then takes these referrals and makes "rounds" on the unit providing MT to all patients who are available. After receipt of music therapy services, patients are assessed as to whether they require continuous music therapy services. If so, that patient is moved up to the top priority of the referral system and therefore becomes a first level medical referral. When patients meet their music therapy objectives during rounds and no longer require music therapy services, one of two possibilities can occur. The individual patient will be seen again only during the next rounds opportunity or will be discharged from music therapy services.

The pediatric outpatient surgery referral system has its own unique form of rounds. Music therapy services are attempted at least twice weekly. A surgery census is printed out the afternoon before the actual surgical procedure. This census contains surgery times, surgical procedure, age, the patient's name, and the name of the physician performing the procedure. Music therapy services are provided to those patients between the ages of 2–8 years. The day of the surgery, the therapist arrives 30–40 minutes prior to the patient's scheduled surgery time. To increase success, the therapist might choose surgery times that contain those patients whose age ranges are similar.

The third referral type is the SFA (Social Functional Assessment). During the initial hospital admission, a medical staff person is responsible for taking a history and physical. At that time a nurse inquires about the patient's overall need for care, which includes a myriad of questions pertaining to the patient's well being. Pre-determined music therapy objectives are "triggered" upon admission if a patient answers "yes" or displays evidence of any of the following: young maternal age (15 years old or younger), increased anxiety, increased depression, cognitive decline duration greater than 48 hours, decreased coping/stress tolerance, increased pain greater than 48 hours, abuse suspected, and comfort measures only needed. Due to the numerical magnitude of SFA requisitions printed out daily, the music therapy department would require significantly increased staff in order to see all of these patients. Therefore, SFA referrals are seen if and when time permits.

The music therapy staff must possess the ability to educate other medical staff about the benefits of music therapy, in order to further the use of services throughout the hospital. Due to the fast-paced nature of the hospital, the medical staff personnel are usually working hard to care for their patients and only have time to hear a brief description of how music therapy would benefit their patients. Occasionally, music therapy referrals are made because a "patient is down and would enjoy some entertainment." In discussing the referral, the MT can take the opportunity to briefly educate medical personnel about the physiological, psychological, emotional, and cognitive issues that music therapy can address. Thus, it is essential that the music therapist make his/her own assessment of the patient to determine the validity and appropriateness of the referral.

Patient Care Conferences and Documentation

Patient Care Conferences are interdisciplinary team meetings that review patient diagnosis, treatments, and status. Patient care conferences can occur weekly or bi-weekly. These team meetings include physicians, physician's assistants, nurses, social workers, music therapists, physical therapists, occupational therapists, speech therapists, recreational therapists, and occasionally administrators. The team approach is an important factor during these meetings, as referrals are discussed and agreed upon as a group.

Other hospital units have daily team meetings with a "triad." The triad consists of a clinical nurse specialist, a social worker, and a utilization manager. The triad meets daily to maintain continuity of care for all patients. During these meetings if a patient fits the criteria for music therapy or any of the other hospital services, a referral is made.

Using the Cerner computer system, the music therapist documents every patient session. This "e-charting" is a paperless system that gives all medical staff members immediate access to necessary patient information. This electronic chart stores all patient information, records physician's orders, enables all staff members to schedule patient appointments, assists nurses with medication administration, and updates staff members by allowing access to all information and documentation written by other staff members.

One of the features of this program is called the "interdisciplinary patient plan of care." In addition to the free text documentation in SOAP format, the therapist is also responsible for documenting in the interdisciplinary plan of care. In this section, the therapist identifies the goals/objectives of the session and comments on the patient's ability to meet them.

The SOAP format mentioned above is a common format to document sessions within the medical setting. Social workers, occupational therapists, speech therapists, and physical therapists also utilize this method. The S stands for subjective, the professional impression of the patient upon entering the room. The O stands for objective, treatment goals and objectives for the session. The A stands for assessment, actions taken by the therapist during the session and how the patient responded. The P stands for plan, the intent for the patient in future sessions.

The music therapy department also records the number of those in attendance in sessions where documentation does not take place, such as Adult Day Services, support groups, Parkinson's voice program and choir, and public presentations. In cases where patients do not have individualized medical charts, those in attendance are counted and then recorded. These data are used in regular reports to demonstrate the impact of music therapy to hospital administrators and for funding purposes.

Administrative Committees and Community Outreach

The partnership between the Florida State University and the Tallahassee Memorial HealthCare provides the music therapy staff access to Care Conferences whose membership is otherwise restricted to TMH's administrators. With these privileges, the music therapy coordinator is able to participate in policy making, implementation of new projects, and communication with other medical staff professionals about patient issues. The MT staff is a part of the following Care Conferences: the Brain Tumor conference, the Bereavement conference, the Palliative Care conference, the Cancer Care conference, and the Complimentary Alternative Medicine conference.

The music therapy staff also contributes to the TMH community outreach programs by providing services to the following support groups: Caregivers 101, Stroke, Parkinson's, Traumatic Brain Injury, and Mended Hearts. In addition, we provide music therapy services to community retirement centers and assisted living facilities and provide services in conjunction with the Multiple Sclerosis Society.

The affiliation between the university and the hospital also enables the therapy staff regular opportunities to educate students about the benefits of music therapy in other degree programs. Every semester we address the FSU School of Nursing, the FSU School of Social Work, and participate in the university health fairs.

Ongoing Research

The music therapy department works diligently to augment the status of music therapy services in the medical setting by conducting research, providing research consultations, and becoming the liaison between the university and the hospital in establishing new research projects. This is particularly helpful to graduate students desiring to conduct a medical study for their thesis. The MT staff assists them in contacts with key personnel to facilitate the design and implementation of research of their choice. Music therapy research projects conducted in 2004 at TMH have included music in the following areas: elective craniotomy and stereotactic radiosurgery, Pacifier Activated Lullaby with premature infants, live music effects in the NICU, counseling with cardiac patients, and reduction of sedation/anesthesia in gynecological procedures.

Inpatient Music Therapy Programs and Goals

Newborn Intensive Care Unit (NICU)

- Multimodal Stimulation for neurological development
- Parent Training in Multimodal Stimulation to reduce incidents of overstimulation
- Music reinforcement of non-nutritive sucking for feeding enhancement (PAL)
- Counseling for parents to reduce distress
- Recorded lullabies in incubator to mask aversive sound stimuli

Related Clinical Cases Documented in SOAP Format:

Patient: premature infant

Therapist: Judy Nguyen, MM, MT-BC

Referral Objective: MT to increase tolerance to multimodal stimulation

Results/Post Treatment Record:

S: Pt lying in open crib.
O: Pt received MT services to increase tolerance to multimodal stimulation, including auditory, tactile, visual, and vestibular stimulation.
A: Pt responded positively to MT session aeb cuddling and making eye contact. Pt displayed halt hand and facial grimace 1x during tactile stimulation of the back. Tactile stimulation ceased until pt return to homeostasis. Stimulation continued and pt able to tolerate auditory, tactile, and vestibular stimulation throughout session. Session lasted about 20 minutes.
P: Will attempt to return to address above goals.

Comments:

Patient: 3 week old, male infant born prematurely, adjusted gestational age of 32 weeks

Therapist: Jennifer Jarred, MM, MT-BC

Referral Objective: MT to increase tolerance to multimodal stimulation

Results/Post Treatment Record:

S: Pt lying in incubator.
O: Pt received MT services to increase tolerance to multimodal stimulation, including auditory, tactile, visual, and vestibular stimulation.
A: Pt responded positively to music aeb smiling, head orientation, and eye contact. Pt displayed signs of overstimulation aeb halt hand (x2) and grimace (x1) during session. With each sign of overstimulation, stimulation ceased until Pt returned to homeostasis. Pt tolerated stimulation progression down to legs with rocking in 20 minutes.
P: Will attempt to return to address above goals.

Comments:

On the following two pages are two forms. The TMH NICU/NBICU Music Therapy Patient Information form is currently used by music therapists attending the NICU Patient Care Conference to record information about infants referred for MT. The NICU Patient Progress Documentation form is used to record results of MT intervention and is then placed in the infant's medical record.

Pediatrics / Pediatric Intensive Care Unit

- MT during CT scans / Echocardiograms to anxiety and decrease need for sedation
- MT during IV sticks to distract child and reduce anxiety
- MT training in pain management to reduce physiological distress
- Counseling for coping skills
- Family assistance in dealing with special needs
- MT for normalization of physical and emotional environment
- MT for environmental stimulation and to elevate mood and improve quality of life
- "Surgery Buddies." musical play during preoperative preparations for small children to reduce anxiety

TMH NICU/NBICU Music Therapy Patient Information

Date: _____ **HR I**

Initial Patient Information	Family Information	Patient Status	Current Patient Information	Medications/ Complications

MM PAL new_____
 	
 _____
 	
 _____
 	
 M / F   Twin A / B
    Triplet A / B / C
 DOB: _____
 Dr. _____
 Discharge: _____
	Town
	 _____
	 Mother
	 _____
	 Age
	 _____
	 Gr/Pa _____ Ab _____
	 Father
	 _____
	 Call / Visit
		Dub. Apgar
		 _____ _____
		 Delivery: CS VD BR ABR
		 _____D_____ W
		    (CGA)
		 ___ ___ ___ _____
		 Kg Lb oz
		 Bed: OW I OC co-bed RW
		 Complications:
			NC RA CPAP Hood
			 O2= Vent ____ % ____ L
			 Nutrition: OG PO Q ____
			 G-tube TPN/L NPO PICC
			 IV Fluids UA/UVC
			 Cranial:
			 _____
			 Photo_____ A/B _____
				aldactone / amp / aminoph.
				 arthro / ativan / acyclovir
				 claforan / diflucan / diuril
				 drisdol / decadron / fent. drip
				 fortez / gent / morphine drip
				 NaCl / neosporin / nystatin
				 polyvisol / phenobarb
				 reglan / theoph. / tylenol
				 vanco / vt. E D / zantac

MM PAL new ____
 	
 _____
 	
 _____
 	
 M / F   Twin A / B
    Triplet A / B / C
 DOB: _____
 Dr. _____
 Discharge: _____
	Town
	 _____
	 Mother
	 _____
	 Age
	 _____
	 Gr/Pa _____ Ab _____
	 Father
	 _____
	 Call / Visit
		Dub. Apgar
		 _____ _____
		 Delivery: CS VD BR ABR
		 _____D_____ W
		    (CGA)
		 ___ ___ ___ _____
		 Kg Lb oz
		 Bed: OW I OC co-bed RW
		 Complications:
			NC RA CPAP Hood
			 O2= Vent ____ % ____ L
			 Nutrition: OG PO Q____
			 G-tube TPN/L NPO PICC
			 IV Fluids UA/UVC
			 Cranial:
			 _____
			 Photo_____ A/B _____
				aldactone / amp / aminoph.
				 arthro / ativan / acyclovir
				 claforan / diflucan / diuril
				 drisdol / decadron / fent. drip
				 fortez / gent / morphine drip
				 NaCl / neosporin / nystatin
				 polyvisol / phenobarb
				 reglan / theoph. / tylenol
				 vanco / vt. E D / zantac

MM PAL new_____
 	
 _____
 	
 _____
 	
 M / F   Twin A / B
    Triplet A / B / C
 DOB: _____
 Dr. _____
 Discharge: _____
	Town
	 _____
	 Mother
	 _____
	 Age
	 _____
	 Gr/Pa _____ Ab _____
	 Father
	 _____
	 Call / Visit
		Dub. Apgar
		 _____ _____
		 Delivery: CS VD BR ABR
		 _____D_____ W
		    (CGA)
		 ___ ___ ___ _____
		 Kg Lb oz
		 Bed: OW I OC co-bed RW
		 Complications:
			NC RA CPAP Hood
			 O2= Vent _____ % ____ L
			 Nutrition: OG PO Q_____
			 G-tube TPN/L NPO PICC
			 IV Fluids UA/UVC
			 Cranial:
			 _____
			 Photo_____ A/B _____
				aldactone / amp / aminoph.
				 arthro / ativan / acyclovir
				 claforan / diflucan / diuril
				 drisdol / decadron / fent. drip
				 fortez / gent / morphine drip
				 NaCl / neosporin / nystatin
				 polyvisol / phenobarb
				 reglan / theoph. / tylenol
				 vanco / vt. E D / zantac

MM PAL new ____
 	
 _____
 	
 _____
 	
 M / F   Twin A / B
    Triplet A / B / C
 DOB: _____
 Dr. _____
 Discharge: _____
	Town
	 _____
	 Mother
	 _____
	 Age
	 _____
	 Gr/Pa _____ Ab _____
	 Father
	 _____
	 Call / Visit
		Dub. Apgar
		 _____ _____
		 Delivery: CS VD BR ABR
		 _____D_____ W
		    (CGA)
		 ___ ___ ___ _____
		 Kg Lb oz
		 Bed: OW I OC co-bed RW
		 Complications:
			NC RA CPAP Hood
			 O2= Vent ____ % ____ L
			 Nutrition: OG PO Q ____
			 G-tube TPN/L NPO PICC
			 IV Fluids UA/UVC
			 Cranial:
			 _____
			 Photo_____ A/B _____
				aldactone / amp / aminoph.
				 arthro / ativan / acyclovir
				 claforan / diflucan / diuril
				 drisdol / decadron / fent. drip
				 fortez / gent / morphine drip
				 NaCl / neosporin / nystatin
				 polyvisol / phenobarb
				 reglan / theoph. / tylenol
				 vanco / vt. E D / zantac

NICU Patient Progress Documentation

Patient Name: _____ **FIN #:**_____**Date:** _____

Multimodal Stimulation: increases tolerance to auditory (singing/guitar), tactile (massage), visual (eye contact/lights), and vestibular (rocking) stimulation

Date:						
Stimulation Progression: *check*						
Auditory only						
Add Scalp: linear						
Back: linear						
Back: circular						
Throat: linear						
Arms: linear or circular						
Abdomen & linea alba: linear						
Legs: linear or circular						
Cheeks: linear						
Forehead: linear						
Nose to ear: linear						
Add Rocking						
Positive responses: *check*						
Head orientation						
Eye contact						
Smiling						
Vocalization						
Snuggling						
Negative responses: *frequency*						
Halt hand						
Grimace / red face						
Crying						
Startle reflex						
Other *(specify)* tongue protrusion, finger splay, hiccups, etc.						

PAL (Pacifier Activated Lullaby): increases the suck/swallow reflex for patients with feeding difficulties

Date:						
Start time:						
Stop time:						
Sucking duration (in sec.)						
Sucking frequency (#sucks)						
None						
Poor / infrequent						
Moderate						
Strong / steady						
Frantic with fatigue						

TMH – FSU Infant and Child Medical Music Therapy Institute ©

- MT to increase socialization including group interactions, verbalizations, family/sibling interactions, and fun interactions with medical staff
- MT to increase relaxation using guided imagery and progressive muscle relaxation exercises
- MT to increase autonomy and control through the exercise of choices
- MT to increase fine and gross motor skills
- MT to improve perception of hospitalization

Related Clinical Cases Documented in SOAP Format:

Patient: 13 year old female in PICU

Therapist: Darcy Walworth, MM, MT-BC

Referral Objective: MT to assist with ventilator extubation

Results/Post Treatment Record:

S: Pt lying in bed awake and alert. Pt surrounded by family members. Pt failed two previous ventilator extubation attempts. Pt stated thinking she could not breathe on own without machines.

O: MT used iso-principle technique and played guitar and sang live music to assist Pt with successful ventilator extubation to prevent Pt from receiving a tracheotomy.

A: At beginning of session Pt appeared anxious about procedure aeb statements of feeling scared, and muscle tension seen in face, arms, and hands. Pt's family members also appeared anxious aeb pacing in room, statements to Pt and MT, and facial tension. Pt immediately requested songs from MT and mouthed words to songs. In between songs Pt and family verbalized positive statements about procedure and being happy MT was assisting with procedure.

During procedure Pt coded and MT was asked by staff to leave room until Pt stabilized. After Pt was stabilized, MT returned to Pt room and used the iso-principle technique to lower Pt's anxiety level and breathing rate. MT stayed until Pt was successfully breathing off of ventilator. At end of session, Pt was sleeping peacefully and had a 97% oxygen saturation level.

P: Pt's family and staff thanked MT for assistance. MT will return to see Pt.

Comments:

Patient: Pediatric female diagnosed with juvenile osteochondrosis, leg (de-calcification of the bone)

Therapist: Kristen Adams, MT-BC

Referral Objective: MT to normalize environment and to increase upper body movement

Results/Post Treatment Record:

S: Pt sitting on bed being bathed by nurse tech and mother.

O: Pt receiving MT services to normalize environment.

A: Pt responded positively to music aeb engaging in instrument playing, puppets, and reading. Pt able to choose activities and engaged in turn taking. Pt, Pt's mother, and Pt's father engaged in boomwhacker activity requiring all to work together to form a song. Pt and family successfully performed song and made positive comments. Pt engaged in scarf activity aeb imitating gross and fine motor movements of MT.

P: Will attempt to see Pt again.

Comments:

Patient: 5 yr. old male post-surgical patient

Therapist: Judy Nguyen, MM, MT-BC

Referral Objective: MT to normalize environment and increase compliance

Results/Post Treatment Record:

S: Pt lying in bed with mother.

O: Pt receiving MT services to normalize environment.

A: Pt responded positively to MT services aeb smiling, laughing, singing, playing instruments, and making choices in the beginning of session with minimal prompts, pt requiring no prompts at end of session. During session, pt's mother insisting pt drink entire glass of juice due to recent surgery. MT able to encourage pt to drink juice using contingent music. Pt able to participate in music activity then would drink approximately 2 tablespoons of juice and music would resume. MT and pt engaged in this activity until entire glass of juice was empty. Pt's mother and father making positive comments throughout session, stating that pt would not drink any juice all morning. Session lasted about 40 minutes.

P: Pt and pt's family requesting MT return. Will try to do so tomorrow.

Comments:

Patient: Pediatric male pre-surgery patient

Therapist: Jennifer Jarred, M.M., MT-BC

Referral Objective: MT to reduce pre-op anxiety

Results/Post Treatment Record:

S: Pt sitting in mother's lap in pediatric pre-op waiting room.
O: Pt received MT services to decrease preoperative anxiety, elevate mood, and normalize the environment.
A: Pt responded to MT positively aeb making eye contact, smiling, laughing, playing with instruments and puppets, making appropriate verbalizations in songs, singing, verbalizing choices of activities, interacting with group members, and making positive comments about the music. Pt focused attention on MT and MT activities while doctor talked with parents. Pt stated not wanting to leave MT when it was time to go to surgery, and doctor requested MT accompany Pt down the hall to the operating room. Pt sang with MT while walking down the hall and music continued as Pt hugged mother and went into room with doctors. Pt's mother and doctor thanked MT for coming.
P: Pt outpatient, no further contact indicated.

Comments:

Patient: Pediatric male patient

Therapist: Jennifer Jarred, M.M., MT-BC

Referral Objective: MT for procedural support: IV stick and CT scan

Results/Post Treatment Record:

S: Pt in process of IV stick procedure.
O: Pt received MT services for distraction during IV start and to eliminate the need for sedation during CT scan.

A: Pt responded to MT positively aeb focusing attention on MT and MT activities during IV stick, going to sleep afterwards, and remaining asleep and still during CT. Procedures were successfully completed without sedation.

P: Pt outpatient, no further contact indicated.

Comments:

Patient: Pediatric female diagnosed with reflux

Therapist: Kristen Adams, MT-BC

Referral Objective: MT for procedural support: CT scan

Results/Post Treatment Record:

S: Pt sitting in waiting room.

O: Pt received MT services for procedural support during CT scan to eliminate the need for sedation.

A: Pt responded positively to MT aeb engaging with puppets and instruments, singing, smiling, and choosing activities. Pt focused attention on puppets and music activities during procedure and imitated puppets holding their breath at appropriate times. Procedure completed with no sedation.

P: Pt outpatient. No further contact indicated.

Comments: Young patients are instructed by radiology staff to hold their breath during each scan (approximately 3 seconds) to facilitate lack of movement and remaining still. MTs are able to position themselves in a place where Pt can see MT at all times. Imitation of puppets holding their breath is effective in cuing needed behavior during procedure.

Oncology

- Counseling for coping skills
- MT for pain reduction
- Family bereavement counseling
- Music therapy during chemotherapy
- MT for outpatient surgery patients to reduce use of post-operative medications and to relieve side-effects of anesthesia

Related Clinical Cases Documented in SOAP Format:

Patient: Middle-aged female patient diagnosed with cancer

Therapist: Judy Nguyen, M.M., MT-BC

Referral Objective: Music Therapy (*MT*) to improve Quality of Life (*QOL*) during
                       prolonged bed rest

Results/Post Treatment Record:

S: Patient (*Pt*) lying in bed.
O: Pt received MT services to increase QOL.
A: Pt responded positively to MT session as evidenced by (*aeb*) smiling, making song
         choices, singing along, making positive statements throughout session and requesting
         songs. Pt able to discuss current illness and told MT about being newly enrolled in
         Hospice in Perry. Pt stated that "my spirits are very high today." Pt expressed
         gratitude to MT for music. Pt made positive statements about future plans and
         possible actions steps to increase positive outcome. Pt spoke much about
         family/church family support.
P: Will attempt to return to address above goals.

Comments:

Patient: Middle-aged female diagnosed with bone cancer

Therapist: Jennifer Jarred, M.M., MT-BC

Referral Objective: MT to decrease nausea and elevate mood

Results/Post Treatment Record:
Session 1
S: Pt lying in bed, family present.
O: Pt received MT services to decrease nausea and elevate mood.
A: Pt responded to MT positively aeb making and maintaining eye contact, choosing
         songs, engaging family members in session, singing minimally without prompting,
         smiling, and making positive comments about the music. Pt stated at start of session
         that Pt was nauseated and hoped that music would help. Pt made no other
         verbalizations about nausea throughout the session. Pt stated much frustration with
         not understanding or being informed of recent diagnosis or treatment. Pt stated

looking forward to speaking with doctor so Pt would be educated about Pt's situation. MT informed Pt that MT can help Pt cope with diagnosis and discussed music interventions. Pt displayed positive affect immediately after this comment and verbalized, "That would be very helpful, thank you." Pt stated enjoyment of music and thanked MT for visit.

P: Will attempt to return to increase coping skills and increase stress/pain management strategies.

Session 2

S: Pt lying in bed, nurse adjusting IV.

O: Pt received MT to increase relaxation and induce sleep.

A: Pt greeted MT upon arrival and told MT that Pt just wanted to take a nap when the nurse finished with the IV. MT played soft, slow music at Pt's request. Pt responded to MT positively aeb closing eyes, breathing heavily, relaxing facial muscles, and making occasional positive comments between songs. Pt appeared to fall asleep during music aeb above behaviors.

P: Will attempt to return to address coping skills and pain management strategies.

Comments:

Patient: Geriatric female diagnosed with malignant neopl stomach NOS

Therapist: Jennifer Jarred, M.M., MT-BC

Referral Objective: MT to reduce pain

Results/Post Treatment Record:

S: Pt lying in bed groaning.

O: Pt received MT services to decrease pain and increase relaxation.

A: Pt responded positively to MT aeb verbalizing music preference with maximum prompting, reduced groaning, more relaxed facial muscles, and decreased erratic arm movement. Pt displayed pain at beginning of session aeb grimacing, erratic and rigid arm movement, groaning and sighing. Pt required moderate to maximum prompting for verbal responses during first half of session. During music, Pt relaxed aeb decreased facial tension, groaning, and arm movement, and appeared to briefly fall asleep aeb heavy breathing, eyes closed, and slight snoring. Music remained constant throughout session and when music stopped, Pt immediately requested more music without prompting. Pt's responses at end of session required no prompting and were much more coherent than at beginning of session. Pt requested MT to return.

P: MT will attempt to return to address above goals.

Comments:

Heart and Vascular Institute / Cardiac Outpatient

- Stress reduction and life management for cardiac patients
- Counseling for anxiety reduction
- MT for pain management
- MT and relaxation training for stress reduction

Related Clinical Cases Documented in SOAP Format:

Patient: Middle-aged female diagnosed with pulmonary edema

Therapist: Danielle Procelli, MTI, & Janna Branning, MTI

Referral Objective: MT to reduce anxiety

Results/Post Treatment Record:

Session 1: Danielle Procelli
S: Pt lying in bed.
O: Pt received MT services to elevate mood and reduce anxiety.
A: Pt responded positively to MT aeb smiling, singing, initiating conversation with Music Therapy Intern (*MTI*), and making positive comments about music. During first song, Pt elevated bed, sat up, and made eye contact with MTI. Pt talked about previous work experience, childhood memories, and family. Pt expressed enjoyment of educating and caring for other people. Pt stated that Pt wished that Pt could still partake in activities that Pt used to do. With minimum prompting, Pt verbalized that staying in the hospital until Pt is healthier is better than going home sick and having to return to the hospital. Pt thanked MT for coming and asked for MT to return.
P: Will attempt to return to address above goals.

Session 2: Janna Branning
S: Pt lying in bed.
O: Pt received MT services to increase socialization.
A: Pt responded positively to MT aeb smiling, nodding head to music, making positive comments about music and conversing with MTI. Pt was able to talk with MTI about being in the rehabilitation (*rehab*) facility and talked about going home. Pt told MTI

that Pt would have to take it easy in order to take care of heart. Pt reminisced about a childhood doctor that told Pt that obesity would weaken Pt's heart and how it had finally happened. Pt talked of action steps in order to lessen stress on Pt's heart, including quitting job and not taking care of nephew as often. Pt told MTI that Pt was not afraid of death, that Pt was ready because of Pt's health. Pt thanked MTI for coming and asked MT to return.

P: Will attempt to return to address above goals.

Comments:

Geriatric / General Inpatients

- Reality orientation for patients with confusion
- "Life Celebration" for those of whom death is imminent
- MT for pain management
- MT to reduce agitation
- MT for coping skills
- Family assistance and special needs
- MT to improve quality of life

Related Clinical Cases Documented in SOAP Format:

Patient: Geriatric male, diagnosis not recorded

Therapist: Janna Branning, MTI

Referral Objective: MT to reduce agitation

Results/Post Treatment Record:

S: Pt sitting in gerichair at bedside.

O: Pt received MT to decrease agitation and increase reality orientation.

A: Pt responded positively to MT aeb singing. At beginning of session, Pt was trying to get out of gerichair and was talking of having to go to the window. With moderate prompting, Pt was able to sing with MTI. Pt was then able to lie back in chair and make eye contact with MTI. Pt showed signs of confusion aeb asking for a hat to be taken off head (indicating a pillow) and trying to get to window to "make sure everything was ok." Pt was able to answer simple questions between songs. Pt would remain on topic for about 1 minute after song. Pt required maximum cuing to keep feet in the gerichair. When MTI left room, Pt was lying back in chair and singing.

P: Will attempt to return to address above goals.

Comments:

Patient: Geriatric male diagnosed with L CVA, R paralysis, CAD, DVT, IDDM

Therapist: Jennifer Jarred, M.M., MT-BC

Referral Objective: MT to decrease agitation

Results/Post Treatment Record:

S: Pt lying in bed, groaning.

O: Pt received MT services to decrease agitation.

A: Pt responded to MT positively aeb making brief eye contact with MT, choosing songs by nodding head "yes/no" with minimal to moderate prompting, nodding head during music, and decreasing agitation behaviors. Pt displayed signs of agitation aeb groaning, moaning, pulling at bed rail and sheets, and biting gown. MT gradually slowed music and decreased volume of music. Pt appeared to fall asleep aeb closed eyes, relaxed muscles, ceasing of agitation behaviors, and heavy, even breathing. MT ceased guitar and continued to sing softly as MT left room.

P: Will attempt to return to address above goals.

Comments:

National Brain Tumor Foundation Grant (Elective Craniotomy and Stereotactic Radiosurgery)

- MT for preoperative anxiety reduction
- MT to reduce hospital length of stay
- MT for postoperative pain reduction
- MT to elevate mood and increase quality of life

Related Clinical Cases Documented in SOAP Format:

Patient: 53 yr old female surgical pt with brain tumor

Therapist: Darcy Walworth, M.M., MT-BC

Referral Objective: MT to decrease stress and pain

Results/Post Treatment Record:

S: Pt sitting in bed awake and alert.

O: Pt received MT services to decrease stress, increase relaxation, increase QOL, decrease pain, and improve perception of hospitalization.

A: Pt completed visual analog scale (VAS) at beginning of session for quality of life indicators. MT played guitar and sang Pt preferred music. Pt responded positively throughout session aeb by participating actively through singing along and requesting specific songs. Pt's daughter and husband were present and participated throughout session as well. Pt made positive comments about MT throughout session. Pt reported feeling less pain, less stress, and increased relaxation and improved perception of hospitalization through self-report (VAS) at end of session. Pt reported being cleared for discharge home earlier that morning but decided to stay for one last MT session. Pt thanked MT for sessions during the hospitalization stating they helped Pt improve.

P: Pt discharged home today.

Comments:

Patient: 62 yr old male surgical pt with brain tumor

Therapist: Judy Nguyen, M.M., MT-BC

Referral Objective: MT to decrease anxiety and length of stay

Results/Post Treatment Record:

S: Pt sitting up in gerichair.

O: Pt receiving MT services as an experimental craniotomy subject to decrease anxiety and length of stay.

A: Pt responded positively to MT session aeb making positive comments after each song, indicating music preferences, making song choices, and smiling. Pt showed little facial affect throughout session and made eye contact. Pt displayed some confusion during session aeb asking off-topic questions. Pt's family present throughout session and redirected pt to sing-along with MT, pt easily redirected. Pt's family participated in session and made many song choices throughout session.

P: Will attempt to return to address above goals.

Comments:

Rehabilitation Center

- Reality orientation for those with confusion
- MT for environmental stimulation
- MT to improve socialization /communication
- MT to increase range of motion
- Physical activity paired with MT to increase motor skills
- MT for memory enhancement
- Counseling for anxiety reduction or life management issues

Related Clinical Cases Documented in SOAP Format:

Patient: Geriatric male diagnosed with L Hemorrhagic CVA, R hemi paresis

Therapist: Kristen Adams, MT-BC, & Brett Miller, MT Practicum Student

Referral Objective: Music to increase functional use of R side of body and to improve
              speech

Results/Post Treatment Record:

Session #1
S: Pt lying in bed.
O: Pt received MT services to increase expressive communication and movement of right
     side of body.
A: Pt making mostly incoherent, incongruent statements when MT and student entered
     room. Pt smiled during songs and tapped left foot. Pt able to tap right foot to music
     when prompted. Pt sang some words to songs with no prompting. Pt able to repeat
     line of lyrics when cued by MT and able to initiate next line of song with no prompting
     from MT. Pt able to verbalize song preference when given two titles, with mostly
     correct words.
P: Will attempt to return to address above goals.

Session #4
S: Pt lying in bed.
O: Pt received MT services to increase coherent statements and to increase movement of
     both sides of body.
A: Pt smiled during songs and tapped left hand and foot. Pt made positive comments after
     each song and made coherent statements while reminiscing about music. Pt able to

choose song when given two choices by stating title with minimal word replacement. Pt engaged in left hand movement activity with Q-chord aeb strumming and responding to prompts by MT student. Pt engaged in right hand movement activity aeb playing shaker instrument with music. Pt stated enjoyment of playing Q-chord and reported playing guitar in the past.

P: Will attempt to see Pt again.

Comments: Throughout sessions it was noted that patient's statements were more coherent immediately following song and when statement pertained to previous song. As conversation would move away from music, statements became increasingly incoherent.

Patient: 57 yr. old male with gait impairment

Therapist: Erin Rink, MTI and Judy Nguyen, MM, MT-BC

Referral Objective: MT gait training

Results/Post Treatment Record:

S: Pt in wheelchair in PT gym.

O: Pt receiving MT services for gait training paired with Physical Therapy.

A: At the begining of session, pt was evaluated to determine the appropriate tempo for music during walking. Pt then walked for 20 seconds and PT counted the number of heels strikes completed. The tempo was then determined to be 54bmp. The pt was able to tap hands, tap toes, and do body shifting to the set beat. Pt then walked with the music the entire length of the hall and back to the wheelchair. The music tempo was then increased to 63bmp, approximately 10% increase. The pt was then able to correctly tap toes and march to the beat while seated. Once standing the pt was able to do body shifting and walked the entire length of the hall and back to the increased beat. At the end of the session the pt sat in wheelchair and sang one song with the MTI.

P: Will attempt to return to address above goals.

Comments:

Orthopedic / Neurology

- MT for cognitive stimulation
- MT to increase communication skills
- MT to increase physical activity / Gait training
- MT to increase respiration rate or to stabilize respiration
- MT for memory enhancement
- MT for pain management
- MT for anxiety reduction

Related Clinical Cases Documented in SOAP Format:

Patient: Geriatric female diagnosed with MVC

Therapist: Danielle Procelli, MTI

Referral Objective: MT counseling for coping skills

Results/Post Treatment Record:

S: Pt lying in bed.

O: Pt received MT to increase alertness, elevate mood and increase coping skills.

A: Pt responded positively to MT aeb initiating and engaging in conversation, minimally singing, maintaining eye contact, and making positive comments about music. Pt's daughter verbalized desire for MTI to help wake patient up and become more alert. MTI stood on Pt's right side so Pt was able to see due to inability to turn neck. Pt reminisced about music selections and previous music experiences, deceased spouse, daughter and life experiences. Pt told MTI about car accident and stated that the driver (Pt's best friend) acquired no injuries. Pt also told MTI that Pt forgave friend and friend is very ashamed of self. Pt showed decreased coping skills through comments made and stated, "I will never walk again." With moderate prompting, however, Pt was able to state desire to get better at the rehab center. Pt and pt's daughter both smiled and thanked MTI for coming.

P: Will attempt to return to address above goals.

Comments:

Patient: Geriatric female diagnosed with L CVA, R Hemi paresis, R hip fx

Therapist: Judy Nguyen, M.M., MT-BC

Referral Objective: MT to improve speech

Results/Post Treatment Record:

S: Pt lying in bed.
O: Pt received MT services to increase communication and socialization.
A: Pt responded positively to MT session aeb smiling and singing along. Pt able to respond to MT questions verbally yes/no. Pt pointed and moved head to indicate music preference and to answer other questions. Pt's husband participating and relaying information to patient. Pt able to use communication board, pointing to "home," "now," and "yes, play." Pt able to verbally fill in words during a song with minimal prompting. Pt maintained eye contact during most of session. Pt's husband discussed reason for admission.
P: Will attempt to return to address above goals.

Comments:

Patient: Middle-aged female diagnosed with subarachnoid hemorrhage

Therapist: Danielle Procelli, MTI, & Kristen Adams, MT-BC

Referral Objective: MT to improve memory

Results/Post Treatment Record:

S: Pt sitting in gerichair.
O: Pt received MT to improve reality orientation and memory.
A: Pt responded positively to MT aeb interacting with roommate, shaking instruments, following verbal and gestural cues, smiling, clapping hand, stomping feet, and making moderate eye contact with prompting. Pt involved roommate in MT session by telling MTI roommate's name and asking if roommate would like to have MT also. Pt was able to participate in MT sign language and movement activities by following gestural and verbal cues from MT. Pt was not able to name the title of specific songs before or immediately after singing with maximum prompting from MTI as Pt did in previous session. Pt responded appropriately to greetings and specific questions. Pt could not answer open ended questions. Pt thanked MT and MTI for coming and agreed to have MT return.
P: Will attempt to return to address above goals.

Comments:

Patient: Post-surgical geriatric female diagnosed with ankylosis L Knee

Therapist: Kristen Adams, MT-BC

Referral objective: MT to reduce pain

Results/Post Treatment Record:

S: Pt lying in bed.
O: Pt received MT services to reduce pain.
A: Pt reported being in pain due to removal of stitches in left leg earlier in the day and so experiencing nausea. Pt's right hand was clenched in a fist and left arm was pressed against forehead. Pt responded positively to music aeb moving right foot to music at the beginning of the session, then moving both feet, relaxing hand, and moving arm to side of body by the end of the MT session. Pt smiled throughout session and reported feeling better and that pain had decreased.
P: Will attempt to return to check on patient later in the day.

Comments:

Patient: 45 yr. old female with aphasia from CVA

Therapist: Jennifer Jarred, M.M., MT-BC

Referral Objective: MT to increase reality orientation and increase verbal communication

Results/Post Treatment Record:

S: Pt lying in bed and visiting with father.
O: Pt received MT services to increase reality orientation and increase verbal communication.
A: Pt responded to MT positively aeb making eye contact, singing with moderate prompting, requesting songs, smiling, engaging father in session, making positive comments about the music, and conversing with MT. Pt was able to answer open-ended questions, and hold congruent conversation with MT. Pt required less prompting to sing than in previous sessions. At the end of session, Pt was able to recall

2 song titles of songs sung during session with no prompting, and 2 song titles with minimal prompting, which is an improvement from prior sessions. Pt was also able to recall bands' names of songs sung in prior sessions. Pt thanked MT for music and stated "see you next time."

P: Will attempt to return to address above goals.

Comments:

Patient: 57 yr. old male with aphasia from intracerebral hemmorrhage

Therapist: Jennifer Jarred, MM, MT-BC

Referral objective: MT to elevate mood and increase verbal accuracy

Results/Post Treatment Record:

S: Pt lying in bed.
O: Pt received MT services to elevate mood and increase verbal accuracy.
A: Pt responded to MT positively aeb making eye contact, smiling minimally, stating music preference, singing along with MT with no prompting, filling in accurate words of songs with minimal to moderate prompting, and nodding head after songs. Most of Pt's speech was incoherent during session. Pt stated liking the music and that words were easier to get out during songs than in talking. Pt agreed for MT to return.
P: Will attempt to return to check on patient later in the day.

Comments:

Labor and Delivery / Antenatal Care Unit

- MT to facilitate difficult or extended labor
- MT for childbirth education
- MT for relaxation and coping with extended hospitalization

Related Clinical Cases Documented in SOAP Format:

Patient: Middle-aged female antenatal patient

Therapist: Jennifer Jarred, M.M., MT-BC, & Danielle Procelli, MTI

Referral Objective: MT to increase QOL during prolonged bed rest

Results/Post Treatment Record:

Session #1: Jennifer Jarred
S: Pt lying in bed.
O: Pt received MT assessment for preference and goals.
A: Pt responded to MT positively aeb smiling, laughing, tapping hands and feet to music, singing, requesting songs, and making positive comments about the music. Pt talked openly with MT about situation and trying to forestall premature labor. Pt displayed positive coping skills aeb positive statements and discussion regarding faith. Pt verbalized enjoyment of session and thanked MT for visit.
P: Will attempt to return to increase relaxation and improve QOL.

Session #8: Danielle Procelli
S: Pt lying in bed.
O: Pt received MT to increase QOL.
A: Pt responded positively to MT aeb smiling, singing, engaging in conversation with MTI and making positive comments about music. Pt requested songs throughout session and talked about family and pregnancy. Pt stated not feeling as good as other days but was looking forward to seeing children during upcoming weekend. Pt closed eyes and sang during every song. Pt and family members thanked MTI for coming.
P: Will attempt to return to address above goals.

Comments:

Emergency Services

- MT to calm agitated mental health patients and medical patients experiencing severe anxiety
- MT to facilitate emergency services to children

Related Clinical Cases Documented in SOAP Format:

Patient: 11 yr old female

Therapist: Judy Nguyen, M.M., MT-BC

Referral Objective: MT to decrease agitation and increase coping skills

Results/Post Treatment Record:

S: Pt sitting in treatment room.

O: Pt receiving MT services to increase coping skills.

A: Upon entering treatment room pt jumping up and down in bed, was wearing medical gloves on both hands and throwing teddy bear up in the air. Pt responded positively to MT session aeb smiling, laughing, singing along, moving body to music, engaging in all activities with no prompts. Pt displayed appropriate behavior aeb making eye contact, answering "yes ma'am," and sitting still in bed. Pt openly discussed family situation and displayed negative facial expression when MT mentioned friends and school. Pt explained that school was hard and pt does not have many friends. Pt discussing current reasons for admission into hospital and reason for being Baker Acted. Pt able to discuss action steps needed to leave current facility. Pt and MT able to discuss actions steps after discharge from next facility. Pt needing minimal cues and able to verbalize plan for self when pt returns home.

P: Will attempt to return to address above goals.

Comments:

In-Hospital Staff Morale Boosters—All Units

- Weekly music serenade/interaction to increase motivation, mood, and staff rapport
- MT given to staff to educate them about benefits and referral guidelines

A recent addition to the assortment of music therapy services offered includes employee "morale boosters." Morale boosters are weekly music interactions intended for all staff members working on that floor/unit. At this time, all staff members are encouraged to gather around the nurse's station, play a rhythm instrument, sing, and even dance. One designated staff member chooses the unit's "theme song" for the day. The staff members usually start to sing, dance, laugh, bring patients out to join in, and engage patients or family members who show interest. These interactions not only increase staff motivation, mood, and rapport, but also facilitate the therapists' opportunity to educate the staff on music therapy referral objectives and guidelines. The morale booster usually lasts 5–7 minutes, and the therapists are then available to interact with and receive referrals from staff members, as well as briefly discuss music therapy concerns with nurse managers who might otherwise be tied up in meetings and other responsibilities.

A feedback form is distributed after these musical interactions. Table 11 shows the mean ratings on this feedback form from five hospital units served during 1 week. Five is the highest possible rating.

Table 11. Staff Perception of Weekly MT Morale Booster Interactions

N	My Anticipation	My Benefit	Thoughts of Patient Referral
25	4.76	4.84	4.64

It is obvious that staff perceive major benefits for themselves and their work environment. The lowest rating is for the question regarding the musical interlude's effect to cue staff to think about the possibility of referring their patients to MT. As most research shows, such transfers are seldom made. The rating of 4.64 is high enough to be encouraging, however, and shows a strong connection between the musical interlude and recognition of patient need for MT services.

Outpatient Music Therapy Programs and Goals

NeuroScience Center Parkinson's Voice Program

- MT to improve speech and to augment Speech Therapy exercises
- MT to improve vocal intensity, breath support, and pitch range

NeuroScience Center Support Groups

- MT to increase coping skills
- MT to increase group relationships
- MT to increase motivation of Parkinson's patients

Pediatric Rehabilitation

- MT in co-treatment with ST, PT, OT to augment their therapeutic goals
- Counseling for special needs, coping skills
- MT to increase attention to task
- MT to increase communication and appropriate socialization, including increased verbalization and communication of wants, intelligibility and prosody of speech, increased play skills, increased compliance with directions and treatment, increased eye contact, increased cooperation, sharing, and turn taking
- MT for pain Management
- MT for cognitive development including increased decision making, initiating, and ability to simultaneously attend to multiple stimuli
- MT to increase gross and fine motor skills
- MT to increase tolerance to transition or interruption
- MT for increased spatial orientation
- MT to enhance auditory discrimination and listening skills

Related Clinical Cases Documented in SOAP Format:

Patient: 6 yr. old male

Therapist: Brett Miller, MTI and Judy Nguyen, M.M., MT-BC

Referral Objective: MT to increase use of R side and socialization

Results/Post Treatment Record:

S: Pt entered treatment room with therapist and parent.
O: Pt receiving MT services to increase use of R side and appropriate socialization.
A: Pt responded positively to MT session aeb smiling, laughing, making eye contact, following verbal commands with minimal prompts, engaging in all activities, making appropriate choices, and initiating activities. Throughout session pt using R and L hands/arms to engage in activities.
P: Will attempt to return to address above goals.

Comments:

Patient: 6 yr. old female

Therapist: Jennifer Jarred, M.M., MT-BC

Referral Objective: MT to increase appropriate socialization.

Results/Post Treatment Record:

S: Pt entered treatment room.
O: Pt receiving MT services to increase appropriate socialization.
A: Pt responded to MT positively aeb making eye contact with and without prompting from MT, verbalizing activity preferences, making appropriate verbalizations in songs and books, smiling, laughing, and singing goodbye song at increased volume than in previous sessions.
P: Will attempt to return to address above goal.

Comments:

Adult Day Services

- MT for memory enhancement
- MT to increase physical activity
- MT for socialization
- MT for anxiety reduction

Innovative Medical MT Services at TMH

Some MT clinical services at TMH are so innovative that more detail is necessary to understand their rationale, evidence-base, and effects. The NICU program is one example. It is a research-based, evolving demonstration project to develop innovative early intervention programs for the premature infant. Clinically, it integrates identification of patient problems (medical, social, and educational), awareness of developmental milestones and patterns of premature infant growth and needs, and scientific rationale for music therapy procedures.

NICU Music Therapy Services at TMH

Problems of Premature Birth

Incidence and Survival

- 50% of infants born @ 23 weeks gestation survive; 44% survive who are born weighing less than 1 lb; 97% survive who are born weighing (@ 2.5–3 lbs. (1997–99).
- Incidence of low birthweight (LBW) births is increasing: 7.6% of live births (2001). Premature is defined as less than 37 wks. gestation, while LBW is less than 2500g (5 lbs., 8 oz.). Prematurity and LBW are 2nd leading cause of infant mortality.

Long-term Problems of Premature Birth

- LBW children are twice as likely to be hospitalized during early childhood and will spend longer in hospital. Avg. cost/child for initial hospitalization is $50,000 for 22-day stay (up to $500,000 for very LBW) vs. $2,800 for term infant.
- LBW children are 50% more likely to be enrolled in special education. The most common neurological problem is cerebral palsy with incidence increasing as birthweight decreases. Other problems are hyperactivity, SLD, or ADHD learning problems.
- Most common medical problems are asthma, upper and lower respiratory infections, and ear infections. Growth attainment is decreased. Other medical problems include respiratory immaturity, organ immaturity (heart, lungs, kidneys, bowels). The provision of oxygen can cause retrolental fibroplasia (visual impairment), while ototoxic drugs can cause hearing loss.

Developmental Issues

Premature Infant Development

- Faster habituation to stimuli equates to greater maturation. Interruption of neurological development decreases habituation.
- The premature infant is hypersensitive to stimuli and stimulation is cumulative; therefore, stimuli must be restricted and controlled. Overstimulation disrupts neurological development.
- Suck-swallow-breathe coordinated response develops @ 34 weeks. At this time, the infant must be taught to suck if he/she was tube fed for an extended period.
- Stroking promotes breathing in neonate; therefore, massage and kangaroo care are excellent therapies.
- Language development is faster if the language is directed to the infant in "parentese" (song-like qualities), i.e., live lullabies are most effective.

Rationale for Early Intervention in the NICU

- In the 3rd trimester the fetus is adding 250,000 neurons/min. in the developing brain, all the individual will get for a lifetime. Cells compete to hook up after birth. Greatest neurological development occurs from 3rd trimester to 2 yrs. The infant is self constructing and his/her experiences create the connections. Early learning is cause/effect learning.
- If the infant is premature, the necessary medical procedures create pain and distress. During stress, cortisol floods the brain, and this creates a damaged cell network resulting in a constant hyper-alert state. Up to 8 yrs. later, severely premature infants show reduced brain volume. The good news is that some of this damage can be neutralized by nurturing.

Meta-Analysis of Music Therapy Research with Premature Infants

Reference: Standley, J. M. (2002). A meta-analysis of the efficacy of music therapy for premature infants. *Journal of Pediatric Nursing, 17*(2), 107–113.

Meta-Analysis Criteria

1. Quantitative studies using group or individual subject experimental designs
2. Subjects who were premature or low birth-weight infants in a NICU
3. Music as an independent variable
4. Research report (in English) meeting criteria for replication and data analysis.

Table 12. Effect Size Results by Study and Type of Dependent Variable

Study	Study *n*	Dependent Variable	Effect Size Cohen's *d*
Caine (1991)	52	Days in hospital	.5045
		Weight gain	.8375
		Behavior state	.7283
Cassidy & Standley (1995)	20	Oxygen saturation	1.1885
Coleman, Pratt, Stoddard, Gerstmann, & Abel (1997)	66	Heart rate	.9190
		Oxygen saturation	.8636
		Behavior state	1.9528
		Days in hospital	.4915
		Weight gain	.4915
Collins & Kuck (1991)	17	Oxygen saturation	.6971
		Behavior state	1.2559
		Heart rate	.4555
Flowers et al. (1999)	9	Oxygen saturation	1.0503
		Behavior state	.8809
Moore, Gladstone, & Standley (1994)	22	Oxygen saturation	1.2887
Standley (1998)	40	Days in hospital	.5489
		Weight gain	.8102
Standley (2000)	12	Non-nutritive sucking rate	.7334
Standley (2003)	32	Feeding rate	.8726
Standley & Moore (1995)	20	Oxygen saturation	1.0280

Summary of Results

1. All effect sizes were in a positive direction for the effects of music, ranging from .4915 to 1.9528.
2. Overall $d = .83$, the difference between the music and non-music results in standard deviation units, which is statistically significant.
3. The Q-value was not significant ($p = .1752$) which means that the effect sizes of music studies in the NICU were consistent and adequately explained by the single, mean effect size. Effects were not mediated by infants' gestational age at the time of study, birth-weight, or type of music delivery nor by physiological, behavioral, or developmental measures of benefit.

Evidence-Based Practice in NICU MT

Benefits of Music

1. Recorded lullaby music in the infant's isolette (beginning @ 28 wks aga):
   • improves oxygen saturation levels
   • increases weight gain
   • shortens hospital stay
2. Live singing and multimodal stimulation (@ 31–32 wks aga):
   • shortens hospital stay
   • increases tolerance for stimulation
3. Parent training in the multimodal stimulation program:
   • reduces overstimulation
   • increases visitation time in the NICU
   • empowers parents and promotes bonding
4. The PAL (Pacifier-Activated-Lullaby system):
   • reinforces non-nutritive sucking (@ 30 wks)
   • increases feeding rate of poor feeders (@ 34–36 wks)

Guidelines for Use of Music

• Can begin around 28 weeks
• Sounds in the NICU should be soothing, constant, stable, and relatively unchanging to reduce alerting responses. The least alerting music styles would have these characteristics:
   – voice alone or only 1 accompanying instrument
   – light rhythmic emphasis, constant rhythm, slow tempo
   – constant volume
   – melodies in the higher vocal ranges which infants hear best and prefer
   – female vocalists since normally developing fetuses hear in the womb and develop a preference for women's voices
   – children's voices since infants attend to and learn from other children

- Volume level for music in the low 70's dB (C) range is recommended (never > 75–80 dB(C)). Note: Male hearing acuity is less developed than female acuity.
- Maximum time/day for continuously playing music: 1.5 hours (alternating ½ hr. on and ½ hr. off).
- Daily approval of the nurse providing care to the infant should be obtained for provision of music stimulation.
- Musical or sound generating toys and mobiles should be prohibited as they are usually repetitive and the volume can seldom be controlled.
- Live singing is excellent when it is steady, constant, quiet, soothing, higher pitched, at slower tempi, and infant directed.
- Lullabies promote language development with emphasis on vowels, rising/falling phrases, and the recognition of soothing sounds and can be provided in the native language of the infant's family.

Meta-Analysis References

Caine, J. (1991). The effects of music on the selected stress behaviors, weight, caloric and formula intake, and length of hospital stay of premature and low birth weight neonates in a newborn intensive care unit. *Journal of Music Therapy, 28*(4), 180–192.

Cassidy, J. W., & Standley, J. M. (1995). The effect of music listening on physiological responses of premature infants in the NICU. *Journal of Music Therapy, 32*(4), 208–227.

Coleman, J. M., Pratt, R. R., Stoddard, R. A., Gerstmann, D. R., & Abel, H.-H. (1997). The effects of the male and female singing and speaking voices on selected physiological and behavioral measures of premature infants in the intensive care unit. *International Journal of Arts Medicine, 5*(2), 4–11.

Collins, S., & Kuck, K. (1991). Music therapy in the neonatal intensive care unit. *Neonatal Network, 9*(6), 23–26.

Flowers, A. L., McCain, A. P., & Hilker, K. A. (1999). *The effects of music listening on premature infants.* Paper presented at the biennial meeting, Society for Research in Child Development, April 15–18, Albuquerque, NM.

Moore, R., Gladstone, I., & Standley, J. (1994, November). *Effects of music, maternal voice, intrauterine sounds and white noise on the oxygen saturation levels of premature infants.* Unpublished paper presented at the National Conference, National Association for Music Therapy, Orlando, FL.

Standley, J. M. (1998). The effect of music and multimodal stimulation on physiological and developmental responses of premature infants in neonatal intensive care. *Pediatric Nursing, 24*(6), 532–539.

Standley, J. M. (2000). The effect of contingent music to increase non-nutritive sucking of premature infants. *Pediatric Nursing, 26*(5), 493–499.

Standley, J. M. (2003). The effect of music-reinforced non-nutritive sucking on feeding rate of premature infants. *Journal of Pediatric Nursing, 18*(3), 169–173.

Standley, J. M., & Moore, R. S. (1995). Therapeutic effects of music and mother's voice on premature infants. *Pediatric Nursing, 21*(6), 509–512, 574.

Using the PAL with Premature Infants

by Andrea M. Cevasco, MMEd, MT-BC

Behaviors premature infants must evince prior to discharge:
(The American Academy of Pediatrics Proposed Guidelines):
- Infants must coordinate the suck, swallow, and breathe responses while feeding
- Infants must gain weight and grow across time

Recent research efforts have determined that NNS:
- provides physiological benefits
- improves behavior states
- prepares infants for nipple feeding, and
- improves early bottle feedings

Major goals for premature infants in NICU:
- strengthen the suck and
- increase the rate of nutritional intake.

Evidence of Benefits of PAL:
- increases sucking endurance
- increases feeding rate
- develops sucking bursts of 10–12 sucks before pause
- reduces pain perception

Characteristics of Infants who Might Benefit from the PAL:
- Medically stable
- Has begun gavage feeding
- Demonstrates apnea during nipple feeding
- Evinces early fatigue and frantic short bursts followed by fatigue. (PAL is used to lengthen sucking pattern.)
- Still receiving gavage feedings at 34 weeks GA or greater
- Medically able to receive a pacifier following painful procedures (PAL is used to teach NNS for pain relief.)

PAL Procedures
- Consult primary nursing caregiver for daily approval of PAL use.
- Set music volume at approximately 60–65 dB (Scale C) on the PAL, or 1 bar line on the machine's read out.
- Duration of use is 10–15 minutes once or twice a day. PAL should be stopped when infant experiences overstimulation or ceases to suck for 1-minute duration despite stimulation of pacifier in mouth.
- Initial use settings include lowest level pressure criteria, music reinforcement of 10 seconds, and suck criterion of 1.

- Select pacifying music. (Usually lullabies are selected due to the constant rhythm and volume level as well as for language development.)
- Insert pacifier into the infant's mouth from side assuring that the nipple is on top of the tongue. If infant does not suck immediately move pacifier in and out of mouth or stroke the cheek to stimulate a suck.
- If the infant is sucking consistently and demonstrating progress, then increase PAL criteria for music reinforcement by gradually increasing sucking pressure and the sucking criteria to desired burst level of 10–12 sucks.
- Continue PAL opportunities until infant completes 10–15 minutes of NNS and demonstrates improvements in feeding.

Recommended Books on NICU MT

Standley, J. (2004). *Music therapy with premature infants: Research and developmental intervention.* (175 pp.). Available from American Music Therapy Association at www.musictherapy.org

Robb, S. L. (Ed.). (2003). *Music therapy in pediatric healthcare: Research and evidence-based practice.* Silver Spring, MD: American Music Therapy Association.

Ongoing NICU Research: How Do Premature Infant Physiologic Responses Differ According to Music Variation?

Introduction

Wharrad and Davis (1997) demonstrated that premature infants react differently to sound than do term infants. Premature infants' heart rates increased and respiration rates decreased significantly more to sound stimuli than did those of term infants. Lecanuet, Granierre-Deferre, Jacquet, and DeCasper (2000) found that 90% of fetuses 36–39 gestational weeks reacted to changes in low pitches with cardiac deceleration. They also determined that spontaneous decreases in cardiac decelerations in the absence of auditory changes were rare.

High ambient noise levels in the NICU raise stress levels, disrupt sleep cycles, cause startle responses reflected in highly variable physiological measures, and reduce growth and development of premature infants (Perlman, 2001). Higher levels of noise are associated with "busyness" of staff activities and show little diurnal variation (Kenner & McGrath, 2004). The American Academy of Pediatrics (1997) recommends that ambient noise levels be kept below 55 dB (Scale A) for the general welfare of these fragile infants. Concern has been expressed about adding music to the NICU environment on the assumption that additional sound might exacerbate the problem.

Research with music in the NICU has shown that premature babies thrive when provided with musical auditory stimuli. Physiologic measures such as heart rate and respiration rate stabilize and oxygen saturation levels increase (Cassidy & Standley, 1995; Standley & Moore, 1995). Music infants gain weight and are discharged sooner than those not receiving such stimulation (Caine, 1992). The majority of these studies have provided music to individual infants with tape players or speakers placed directly in the incubator to avoid sound pollution of the entire NICU environment (Cassidy & Ditty, 2001).

Kemper, Martin, Block, Shoaf, and Woods (2004) surveyed NICU physicians and nurses about their expectations for music provision in the NICU. The majority (68%) agreed that they would like to have music played throughout the NICU and that their preference was for recorded rather than live music. One study has examined the effect of recorded music played free field at 62 dB (Scale C) throughout the entire NICU environment (Standley, 2003). In this 7-week study, speakers were placed at each end near the ceiling of the NICU. Decibel levels were measured in the room under no music and recorded music conditions across 7 weeks. It was determined that overall dB levels in the room dropped from a baseline mean of 64.5 dB to 63.6 dB during the addition of music. Observational data revealed that the dB decrease resulted from staff speaking more quietly with each other and from infants crying less.

Few research studies have incorporated live singing in the NICU. A 1998 study by Standley demonstrated major benefits for premature infants by using humming to elicit and maintain homeostasis during increasing levels of multimodal stimulation. This approach began as a research study but was so successful it was initiated as a clinical service in the Tallahassee Memorial HealthCare NICU by the Music Therapy Department of the Florida State University. On a daily basis, several premature infants were given multimodal stimulation simultaneously by multiple therapists with unison humming of the same lullaby. Infants thrived but after several years, the repetitiousness of the music began to irritate the nurses who worked long-term in the setting.

To deal with the staff's auditory satiation, it was determined that a variety of music should be adapted to lullaby style for the multimodal stimulation clinical program and provided live to the entire NICU environment thereby meeting infant needs while also having a more positive response on the attending staff. The purpose of this series of studies was to determine what types of live music were least obtrusive to all infants in the NICU as measured by physiological responses, specifically heart rates and respiration rates displayed on infants' monitors.

Method

Subjects for these studies were all infants housed in the 12-bed intermediate Neonatal Intensive Care Unit at the Tallahassee Memorial HealthCare. The majority of these infants were premature; however, there were occasionally term neonates with serious illnesses included. No effort was made to control the population in the room since turnover was minimal during a 1-week period, the duration of each segment of this series of studies.

Each study used a repeated measures design with subjects as their own control during a week-long contrast of musical elements. Stimulation was provided for 20 minutes/day for 3 days during the 5-day workweek between 4–5 p.m. The dependent measures were heart rate and respiration rate collected from each infant's monitor.

Study 1: Ambient Noise vs. Humming

This 3-week study observed 8 infants and measured baseline conditions of ambient noise across 3 days for 20 minutes/day during the first week. No stimuli were added to the usual ambient noise in the room. Two researchers divided the room in half and recorded HR and RR for each subject every 2 minutes. Monitors were scanned and data recorded in the same direction for each collection interval. Results were combined for each interval across the 3 days and mean group responses were calculated.

A second week contrasted this baseline condition with the humming condition taken from the multimodal research protocol for 20 minutes/day for 3 days. The song, "Brahm's Lullaby," was used repetitiously throughout these 3 days for 20 minutes/day. It was hummed a cappella without words by one singer. Data were measured in 2-minute intervals as before with the first interval being a no-music baseline.

A third week contrasted these two conditions with a cappella singing of a variety of songs in lullaby style for 20 minutes/day for 3 days. The songs in presentation order can be found in Table 13. Again, the music was provided by one singer positioned in the center of the room. Data were measured in 2-minute intervals as before with the first interval being a no-music baseline.

Table 13. A Cappella Songs in Lullaby Style in Order of Presentation

Day 1	Day 2	Day 3
"A Dream Is a Wish"	"Twinkle, Twinkle"	"Baby Mine"
"When You Wish Upon a Star"	"The Farmer in the Dell"	"Mary Had a Little Lamb"
"Baby Mine"	"Six Little Ducks"	"I'm Forever Blowing Bubbles"
"Candle on the Water"	"Mary Had a Little Lamb"	"London Bridge"
"I'm Forever Blowing Bubbles"	"Old MacDonald's Farm"	"A Dream Is a Wish"
"Can You Feel the Love Tonight"	"Itsy, Bitsy Spider"	"This Old Man"
"This Old Man"	"Hush Little Baby"	"When You Wish Upon a Star"
"Down by the Bay"	"London Bridge"	"Twinkle, Twinkle"

Results are shown in Figures 1 and 2. Figure 1 shows the 3-day group mean heart rate across 2-minute intervals for baseline ambient noise conditions in the NICU ($n = 25$), for the humming procedure traditionally used to accompany multimodal stimulation ($n = 25$), and for the a cappella singing condition ($n = 27$). It is clear that the humming that we added to the ambient noise in the NICU environment had a calming and stabilizing influence on heart rate and the a cappella singing had a calming effect in the majority of intervals. Figure 2 shows respiration rate for the measures as above and, again, documents the more calming influence of the live music condition.

Figure 1
Heart Rate: Humming & Singing
vs. Ambient Noise

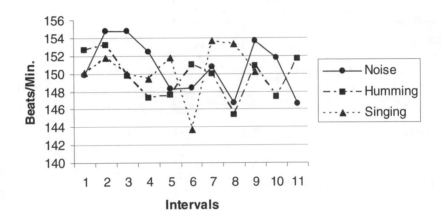

Figure 2
Respiration Rate: Humming & Singing
vs. Ambient Noise

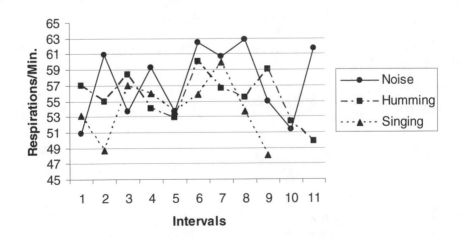

Study 2: Simple vs. Complex Guitar Accompaniment

This 1-week study consisted of 3 days within a 5-day workweek that contrasted a baseline interval with 4 simple versus 4 complex accompaniment selections beginning with simple and alternating for a total of 8 songs. The songs for simple/complex contrasts in order of presentation are listed in Table 14. These contrasting conditions consisted of live singing by one singer using words and guitar accompaniment. All music was performed in lullaby style: quiet singing, finger-picking pattern matched to song meter, and monotonous and consistent volume and tempi. Simple accompaniment was operationally defined as having 3 or fewer major chords and complex accompaniment as using more than 3 chords, some of which were minor. Heart rate and respiration rate data were collected as previously described on all infants in the NICU at the conclusion of each song, approximately 2 minutes in length.

Table 14. Simple/Complex Accompaniment Comparisons

Accompaniment	Day 1	Day 2	Day 3
Simple	"Mary Had a Little Lamb"	"You Are My Sunshine"	"Itsy, Bitsy Spider"
Complex	"Try to Remember"	"Baby Mine"	"A Dream Is a Wish Your Heart Makes"
Simple	"Wheels on the Bus"	"Home on the Range"	"Twinkle, Twinkle, Little Star"
Complex	"I Can't Help Falling in Love"	"Over the Rainbow"	"I'm Forever Blowing Bubbles"
Simple	"Skip to My Lou"	"Peace Like a River"	"If You're Happy and You Know It"
Complex	"I Will"	"What a Wonderful World"	"Candle on the Water"
Simple	"The Farmer in the Dell"	"Blowin' in the Wind"	"Old MacDonald Had a Farm"
Complex	"In the Still of the Night"	"When You Wish Upon a Star"	"Circle of Life"
Simple	"Six Little Ducks"	"The Way You Do the Things We Do"	"Willoughby, Wallaby"
Complex	"Someone to Watch Over Me"	"Moon River"	"Beauty and the Beast"

Results are shown in Figures 3 and 4. Figure 3 shows 3-day group mean heart rate responses to song selections alternating simple vs. complex accompaniment styles ($n = 21$). This graph demonstrates a stronger alerting response to the complex accompaniment that also maintained heart rate at a higher level throughout the experiment. Figure 4 shows similar data and results for respiration rates, though not quite as consistent. It seems obvious from these two graphs that simple accompaniment style has the most calming influence on the infants.

Figure 3
Heart Rate: Simple vs. Complex
Accompaniment

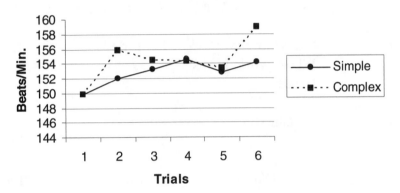

Figure 4
Respiration Rate: Simple vs. Complex
Accompaniment

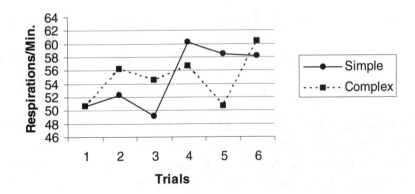

Study 3: Songs in Minor vs. Major Keys

This one week study contrasted a baseline interval with 4 minor and 4 major song selections beginning with minor and alternating for a total of 8 songs. Table 15 shows songs in order of presentation used for each of 3 days during a 5-day workweek. Data were collected at the conclusion of each song as previously described.

Table 15. Major/Minor Accompaniment Comparisons

Accompaniment	Day 1	Day 2	Day 3
Minor	"Scarborough Fair"	"Sunrise, Sunset"	"Scarborough Fair"
Major	"He's Got the Whole World in His Hands"	"Let It Be"	"Itsy, Bitsy Spider"
Minor	"Summertime"	"My Favorite Things"	"Ain't Gonna Let Nobody"
Major	"This Old Man"	"Edelweiss"	"I Will"
Minor	"And I Love Her"	"Greensleeves"	"House of the Rising Sun"
Major	"I'm A Little Teapot"	"Beautiful Dreamer"	"You Are My Sunshine"
Minor	"Sunrise, Sunset"	"Summertime"	"If I Could"
Major	"London Bridge"	"The Rose"	"A Dream Is a Wish"

Results are shown in Figures 5 and 6. Figure 5 shows 3-day group mean heart rate responses to alternating songs in minor and major keys ($n = 30$). The first music interval shows infants had an alerting/listening response with a heart rate increase of about 6 beats/minute. This alerting response quickly dissipated with the major key having a slightly greater decrease in heart rate than did the minor key selections. However, there is little difference between the two types of music according to heart rate.

Figure 6 shows respiration rate responses to these same selections. Respiration rate for the selections in major keys is more stable and lower than for selections in minor keys. Therefore, songs in major key seem slightly preferable for calming infants.

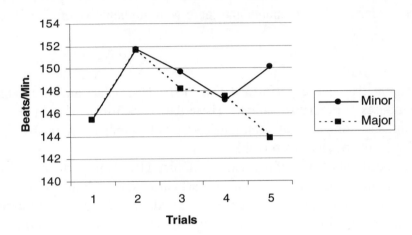

Figure 5
Heart Rate for Minor vs. Major Accompaniment

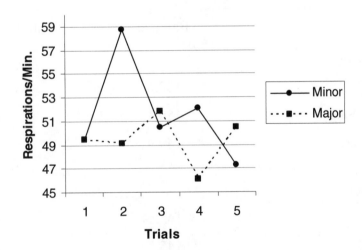

Figure 6
Respiration Rate:
Minor vs. Major Accompaniment

Results

Overall results of all musical variations are shown in the following tables. Mean heart rates (Table 16) and mean respiration rates (Table 17) are recorded for baseline intervals and intervention intervals by each study's contrasting conditions. It is apparent that the hummed music ("Brahm's Lullaby") was the only condition which reduced both heart and respiration rates from baseline measures though a cappella singing of songs in lullaby style left heart and respiration rates unaffected. The songs using major keys increased heart rates only slightly while showing stability in respiration rates. All other conditions increased heart rates and respiration rates by more than 3 beats/minute but these increases represent a relatively mild effect. It should be noted that all physiological responses to all of the music variations performed were within normal parameters for premature infants and there were no negative effects observed.

Discussion

It is apparent that music performed live in the NICU has an observable impact on physiologic responses of premature infants. These data demonstrate that in order to elicit the most calming influence on heart rate, the music should be hummed in lullaby style in a major key with the fewest chord changes possible.

There are anecdotal reports of harpists petitioning NICUs to perform calming music for the infants and reports of music therapists using earth drums, xylophones, or other instruments in NICU performance. Such creative, but undocumented, uses of music are contraindicated until data can be established for each new auditory stimulus proposed for the NICU sound environment. It is apparent that premature infants have immediate and sometimes contraindicated physiological responses to some types of music. Ongoing data collection is crucial to understanding the most medically appropriate and therapeutic musical selections.

Table 16. Three-Day Group Mean Heart Rates by Music Variation

	Baseline	Intervention Intervals
Noise vs. Humming		
Humming	152.6	149.4
A Cappella Singing	150.1	150.5
Ambient Noise	149.9	150.8
Major/Minor Mode Alternating		
Major	145.5	147.8
Minor	145.5	149.7
Simple/Complex Accompaniment Alternating		
Simple	149.8	153.5
Complex	149.8	155.4

Table 17. Three-Day Group Mean Respiration Rates by Music Variation

	Baseline	Intervention Intervals
Noise vs. Humming		
Humming	57.0	55.3
A Cappella Singing	53.2	54.1
Ambient Noise	50.9	58.1
Major/Minor Mode Alternating		
Major	49.5	49.4
Minor	49.5	52.1
Simple/Complex Accompaniment Alternating		
Simple	50.7	57.4
Complex	50.7	55.7

Study References

American Academy of Pediatrics. Committee on Environmental Health. (1997). Noise: A hazard for the fetus and newborn. *Pediatrics, 100*(4), 724–727.

Caine, J. (1992). The effects of music on the selected stress behaviors, weight, caloric and formula intake, and length of hospital stay of premature and low birth weight neonates in a newborn intensive care unit. *Journal of Music Therapy, 28*(4), 180–192.

Cassidy, J., & Ditty, K. (2001). Gender differences among newborns on a transient otoacoustic emissions test for hearing. *Journal of Music Therapy, 38*(1), 28–35.

Cassidy, J.W., & Standley, J. M. (1995). The effect of music listening on physiological responses of premature infants in the NICU. *Journal of Music Therapy, 32*(4), 208–227.

Kemper, K., Martin, K., Block, S., Shoaf, R., & Woods, C. (2004). Attitudes and expectations about music therapy for premature infants among staff in a neonatal intensive care unit. *Alternative Therapies, 10*(2), 50–54.

Kenner, C., & McGrath, J. (2004). *Developmental care of newborns and infants: A guide for health professionals.* St. Louis, MO: Mosby.

Lecanuet, J., Graniere-Deferre, C., Jacquet, A., & DeCasper, A. (2000). Fetal discrimination of low-pitched musical notes. *Developmental Psychobiology, 36,* 29–39.

Perlman, J. (2001). Neurobehavioral deficits in premature graduates of intensive care—Potential medical and neonatal environmental risk factors. *Pediatrics, 108*(6), 1339–1348.

Standley, J. (1998). The effect of music and multimodal stimulation on physiologic and developmental responses of premature infants in neonatal intensive care. *Pediatric Nursing, 21*(6), 532–539.

Standley, J. (2003). *Music therapy for premature infants: Research and developmental interventions..* Silver Spring, MD: American Music Therapy Association.

Standley, J., & Moore, R. (1995). Therapeutic effects of music and mother's voice on premature infants. *Pediatric Nursing, 21*(6), 509–512, 574.

Wharrad, H., & Davis, A. (1997). Behavioural and autonomic responses to sound in pre-term and full-term babies. *British Journal of Audiology, 31*(5), 315–329.

NICU Recommended Song Lists

As a result of our research, we recommend these songs for general NICU use. Songs should be performed a cappella or with the simplest accompaniment possible and using as few chord changes as possible. If the NICU infant is critically sick, greater care should be taken in song selection according to results documented previously.

Least Alerting Songs

These songs are considered to be "least alerting songs" for the following reasons: three chords or less, major chords, lullaby style (repetitious, no separate melody for a chorus or bridge), and all are played slowly and softly.

A-Hunting We Will Go
Alphabet Song
Are You Sleeping
Baby Bumble Bee
Barney Song
The Bear Went Over the Mountain
Bingo
Blowin' in the Wind
Boom Boom (Ain't It Great to Be Crazy)
Cold, Cold Heart
Down by the Bay
Down in the Valley
Farmer in the Dell
Five Green and Speckled Frogs
God Bless America
Going Over the Sea
Head, Shoulders, Knees, and Toes
He's Got the Whole World
Hush Little Baby
I Fall to Pieces
I Know an Old Lady Who Swallowed a Fly
If All the Raindrops
If You're Happy and You Know It
I'm a Little Teapot

Itsy Bitsy Spider
London Bridge
Looby Loo
Mary Had a Little Lamb
The More We Get Together
The Muffin Man
Old MacDonald's Farm
On Top of Old Smokey
Peace Like a River
Red River Valley
Row, Row, Row Your Boat
Shake My Sillies Out
Sing a Song of Sixpence
Sing, Sing a Song
Singing in the Rain
Six Little Ducks
Skinnamarink
Skip to My Lou
This Old Man
Twinkle, Twinkle Little Star
Wheels on the Bus
Willoughby Wallaby
You Are My Sunshine
Zip-a-dee-doo-dah

Other Acceptable Songs

The following list contains examples (not exclusive) of other acceptable songs for use in the NICU. These songs meet the following criteria: in a major key, all chords are major or minor (no diminished or augmented), there are no more than four chords within a lyrical phrase, and all may be played slowly and softly.

A Dream Is a Wish Your Heart Makes
Accentuate the Positive
America the Beautiful
Annie's Song (You Fill Up My Senses)
Baby Mine
Beautiful Dreamer
Blue Moon
Blueberry Hill
Brahms Lullaby
Candle on the Water
Can't Help Falling in Love
Could I Have This Dance
Country Roads
Dream Dream Dream
The Dance
Edelweiss
From This Moment On
Getting to Know You
Have You Ever Seen the Rain
Hey, Jude
Home on the Range
I Can See Clearly Now
I Hope You Dance
I Will
I'm Forever Blowing Bubbles

In the Sill of the Night
Kiss the Girl
Lean on Me
Leaving on a Jet Plane
Let It Be
Let Me Call You Sweetheart
Love Me Tender
Moon River
My Heart Will Go On
Oh, What a Beautiful Morning
Old Folks at Home (Swanee River)
Over the Rainbow
Peaceful, Easy Feeling
The River
The Rose
Shenandoah
Simple Gifts
Simple Man
Stand by Me
Try to Remember
Unchained Melody
Under the Boardwalk
What a Wonderful World
When You Wish Upon a Star
Wonderful Tonight

Pediatric Procedural Support:
CT Scans, Echocardiograms, IV Sticks, Electroencephalographs,
X-rays, Ventilator, and Emergency Procedures

A second highly innovative clinical MT program is the service provided during pediatric procedural support. It is so effective that it negates the need for sedating children, thereby reducing the time of the procedure from more than 2 hours to approximately 15 minutes and precluding the need for nursing supervision during the procedure. It saves the hospital money; releases RNs for other duties; increases the probability of a successful procedure; and reduces parental, child, and staff trauma.

Several pediatric procedures in the health care setting have historically required sedation for successful completion. Music therapy assisted procedures have demonstrated the ability to eliminate or lower the amount of sedation administered. Areas currently receiving MT procedural support at Tallahassee Memorial Hospital (TMH) include CT scan, EKG/echo, EEG, X-Ray, IV starts, ventilator extubation trials, and some emergency services. Due to the non-invasive status of most of these procedures, music is able to function as a distraction to lower anxiety or a catalyst to begin the sleep process in patients unable to sleep.

Patients are administered sedation to successfully complete non-invasive procedures due to increased patient anxiety about procedures. Sometimes a patient will have an adverse reaction to the sedation and become extremely irritable. Traditionally the patient procedure is rescheduled when this happens. Music therapy has been able to assist with these cases as well, resulting in the patient successfully completing the procedure, even after having an adverse reaction to sedation. To improve patient care, TMH implemented a hospital-wide initiative to decrease the amount of sedation administered to patients. Also, the current Joint Commission on Accreditation of Healthcare Organizations (JCAHO) standards require at least an RN trained professional to be present from the time sedation is administered until the patient is cleared from the sedative effects. Eliminating the need for increased staff interaction benefits the entire hospital system. Patients appropriate for music therapy assisted procedures range from birth through adulthood. Music therapy staff members are available to provide live music interventions to eliminate the need for sedation and the techniques for completion of this goal vary according to the procedure and each patient. The iso-principle is employed in every situation discussed.

For a CT scan the patient is required to lay completely still for an image to be captured successfully. In pediatric patients this generally requires the patient to be asleep. In an unfamiliar, noisy, and brightly lit environment, a pediatric patient usually has difficulty going to sleep, even after sleep deprivation. The music therapy staff member acts as the patient advocate in this situation, assessing all variables causing increased patient anxiety resulting in interference with the patient falling asleep. Environmental variables include number of people in the waiting room and the activity/noise level in room and hallway. Emotional variables include previous negative medical procedures and quality of family support. Physiological variables include age of child and amount of sleep deprivation, if any. When a patient requires an IV for the CT scan, the increased anxiety due to perception of pain also becomes a factor for the music therapist to consider. Since no two patients are the same when combining all of the previously mentioned variables, fine-tuned assessment skills are a necessity.

Electroencephalogram (EEG) patients are often required to be sleeping for administration of the test. Pediatric patients receiving this test also experience increased anxiety due to the leads placed on the patient's head to transmit data as well as the other variables mentioned above. Some patients completing this procedure are still given a mild sedative and music therapy services resulting in lowering the amount of sedation needed for the patient to fall asleep.

Echocardiograms/electrocardiograms, X-rays, IV starts, and ventilator extubation trials all require distraction from patient anxiety to successfully complete the procedure. Each of these procedures is completed while the patient is awake and fully conscious, and therefore, the patient can attend to whatever live music stimulus is present. All live music played is each patient's preferred genre or song. Due to the same patient and environmental variables discussed earlier, every session varies as it progresses and as the music therapist assesses each situation. An echocardiogram is a sonogram/ultrasound of the heart. Pictures are captured at different angles with the same type of device used for pregnant women. Emergency center services can include any of the discussed procedures and can differ in the amount of time before notification of the procedural support needed and the baseline level of patient anxiety prior to procedure.

The establishment of this type of music therapy program is dependent on medical staff approval, open communication between staff members and the music therapist, and a working pathway. Finding colleagues who support music therapy services and can encourage other staff members to try new techniques in patient care is invaluable to setting up a new program area such as this. Educating medical staff through in-services, presentations, and even hallway greetings can impact the acceptance and enthusiasm staff members have about music therapy in the medical setting. Once staff members see music therapy work, through video clippings or observing an interaction, most form a new appreciation and understanding of the value a music therapist provides to the team.

Referral processes vary from unit to unit due to the leadership and communication style differences of each unit. Finding the optimal way to fit within the existing communication network is highly recommended. Music therapists at TMH are notified of patient procedures by fax, paging, scheduling in advance, and phone calls, depending on which unit is making the contact. Also, how far in advance the music therapist arrives before the start of the procedure varies according to the patient intake system of each unit. All procedural support at TMH has an approved policy and procedure document for medical staff reference and standard practice guidelines. When writing a protocol for a new program area, sometimes general versus specific guidelines are beneficial. The high degree of variance involved in procedural support music therapy lends itself better to a protocol with room for change. Once a new program is in place, be visible in the area you need referrals. The more exposure you receive, the higher number of referrals usually come in!

Specific Music Therapy Procedures

CT Scans: Patient Asleep

- Prerequisites: sleep and food deprivation
- Music to establish rapport and capture focus of attention
- Iso principle for sleep induction
- Music during transport and scan
- Parent's role: Nurturing and reinforcement of relaxation responses
- If it doesn't work, try feeding patient then start again or schedule another day

CT Scans: Patient Awake and Still

- Establish rapport and trust
- Capture focus of attention and gain participation
- Reinforce child following musical directions
- Explain scan procedure to child
- Use iso principle during scan to promote relaxation
- Parent's role: Nurturing and reinforcement of relaxation responses
- If it doesn't work, sedate or re-schedule another day

CT Scans with Contrast

- IV start
- Barium swallow
- Contingent music

Echocardiograms

- Establish rapport and trust
- Use wide variety of music and participatory activities, including puppets, instrument playing, manipulation of objects
- Explain procedure to child
- Use successive approximations to get started with the procedure: distraction and involvement in music
- Use the iso principle during procedure
- Continue music through four picture positions
- Parent's role: Nurturing and reinforcement of relaxation responses
- If it doesn't work, try other music activities or schedule another day

IV Starts and EEGs

- Establish rapport and trust
- During procedure: iso principle, participation, and distraction
- Parent's role: Nurturing and reinforcement of relaxation responses

Music Therapist's Role

- Patient advocate
- Patient/family educator
- Relieve patient/family anxiety
- Reduce need for sedation of children
- When frustrated, remember the end result—even if it's not an ideal response, if the child wasn't sedated, the goal was achieved

Rationale for Music Therapy

- Too much sedation is harmful for children
- *Moderate Sedation/analgesia* is defined as: A drug induced depression of consciousness during which patients respond purposefully to verbal commands, either alone or accompanied by light tactile stimulation. No interventions are required to maintain a patent airway, and spontaneous ventilation is adequate. Cardiovascular function is usually maintained.
- Because sedation-to-anesthesia is a continuum, it is not always possible to predict how an individual patient receiving medication with the intent to achieve moderate or deep sedation will respond.
- Only credentialed and privileged physicians or competency validated RNs may administer the medications used for sedation. JCAHO sedation standards require that a RN be present for the entire time that a child is sedated. For these procedures, the average dose results in a 2-hr. time interval requiring individualized nursing intervention.
- The most common side effects of chloral hydrate, the most common sedative used with children, are nausea, vomiting, stomach pain, mild respiratory depression, irritability, and hyperactivity (Greenberg, Faerber, Aspinall, & Adams, 1993; Sifton, 1998).
- Although guidelines exist for using conscious sedation, adverse outcomes still occur in multiple venues with different medications and for various reasons (Cote, Alderfer, Notterman, & Fanta, 1995). Adverse outcomes include seizures, respiratory failure requiring bag ventilation, laryngospasm, significant increases in middle ear pressure, oxygen desaturation/hypoxemia, sinus arrhythmia, and/or death (Abdul-Baqi, 1991; Biban, Baraldi, Pettenazzo, Filippone, & Zacchello, 1993; Cote et al., 1995; Munoz et al., 1997; Polaner et al., 2001; Sing, Erickson, Amitai, & Hryhorczuk, 1996).
- Non-invasive procedures are scary but not harmful

Overcoming Hurdles

- Gain staff approval through inservice presentations—RNs, MDs, medical technicians.

- Educate through inservices and presentations. Use cost benefit analysis in Chapter 3 to educate administration about cost savings.
- A picture is worth 1,000 words. Let the staff see music therapy work either in live demonstrations or through a video-taped session.

Agreeing on a Referral Pathway

- Referral process differs for different teams.
- Timing is critical—If children need to be asleep before procedure versus awake, then they need to arrive at different intervals prior to the scheduled test.
- Try, try again . . . not every child is the same.

The Final Hurdle

- Establish a protocol (move from general to specific principles).
- Be visible in your area (the more exposure the more referrals).

References

Abdul-Baqi, K.J. (1991). Chloral hydrate and middle ear pressure. *Journal of Laryngol Otolaryngology, 105*, 421–423.

Biban, P., Baraldi, E., Pettenazzo, A., Filippone, M., & Zacchello, F. (1993). Adverse effect of chloral hydrate in two young children with obstructive sleep apnea. *Pediatrics, 92*(3), 461–463.

Cote, C. J., Alderfer, R. J., Notterman, D. A., & Fanta, K. B. (1995). Sedation disasters: adverse drug reports in pediatrics—FDA, USP, and others. *Anesthesiology, 83*(3A), 1183.

Greenberg, S. B., Faerber, E. N., & Aspinall, C. L., & Adams, R. C. (1993). High-dose chloral hydrate sedation for children undergoing MR imaging: Safety and efficacy in relation to age. *American Journal of Roentgenology, 161*, 639–641.

Munoz, M., Gomez, A., Soult, J. A., Marquez, C., Lopez-Castilla, J. D., Cervera, A., et al. (1997). Seizures caused by chloral hydrate sedative doses (letter). *Journal of Pediatrics, 131*(5), 787–788.

Polaner, D. M., Houck, C. S., Rockoff, M. A., Mancuso, T. J., Finley, G. A., Maxwell, L. G., et al. (2001). Sedation, risk, and safety: Do we really have data at last? *Pediatrics, 108*(4), 1006–1008.

Sifton, D. W. (Ed.). (1998). *PDR® Generics™*. Montvale, NJ: Medical Economics.

Sing, K., Erickson, T., Amitai, Y., & Hryhorczuk, D. (1996). Chloral hydrate toxicity from oral and intravenous administration. *Clinical Toxicology, 34*(1), 101–106.

Patient and Medical Staff Perceptions
of Medical Music Therapy Clinical Services

The Medical Music Therapy program regularly requests feedback from patients receiving in-hospital clinical services. A form is left with the patient at the termination of the music therapy session. The clients or a member of their families fill out the form and return it to their nurse who places it in a central file for the MT staff to retrieve. The Table 18 shows mean satisfaction ratings for enjoyment of MT, perceived therapeutic benefit of MT, and MT improvement of patients' perception of their stay at TMH. Each feedback question was rated on a 5-point Likert scale with 5 being the highest rating possible.

Table 18. Mean Patient Perceptions of Medical Music Therapy

	N	Enjoyment	Therapeutic Benefit	Improved TMH Stay
Pediatric Procedural Support	43	5.00	4.88	4.93
Other Medical MT Services	35	4.97	4.91	4.70
Combined Services	78	4.99	4.89	4.83

The data show that medical MT services have extremely high ratings in all categories. The perceptions are highest for enjoyment of the session, which speaks to the quality of music competencies of the therapists and to their interaction skills with patients of all ages. It is also apparent that patients and their families recognize the therapeutic value of MT. This indicates that TMH MTs are perceived as a medical service, which is reassuring since they practice in the same facility with AIM volunteer musicians. Additionally, the mean ratings reveal that medical music therapy serves a useful function in improving patient perceptions of their hospital stay. This is important to document since many hospitals strive to improve their satisfaction ratings. Tallahassee Memorial HealthCare conducts regular surveys of patient satisfaction with services using the Press Ganey Satisfaction Survey. Results from over 170 patients surveyed following their TMH hospitalization in mid-2004 show approval ratings decidedly lower than those for medical MT. Table 19 shows n and mean percent agree response for the highest rated questions on the 84-item survey which used a 0–5 Likert scale. The best ratings at TMH are for ICC skill and for friendliness of the childbirth unit. All medical services evaluated had lower agreement ratings than those for MT. Given this contrast in approval levels, it is important that administrators understand that music therapy offers a skilled, relatively low-cost clinical service with both therapeutic and patient satisfaction benefits.

Table 19. Mean Percent Approval on Press Ganey

Question	% Approval	n
Skill of ICU/CCU nurses	95.6	17
Friendliness/courtesy of childbirth unit	92.9	32
Skill of physician	91.9	167
Skill of nurses	86.5	166
How well pain was controlled	84.2	161
Overall rating of care given	**83.5**	**168**
Staff provided care in safe manner	83.3	159
Re-admission process	81.8	122
Skill of person starting IV	81.0	159
Helpfulness of people at info desk	79.8	140
Speed of discharge process	79.4	169
Skill of person that took blood	79.2	160

Following is the survey form that is used at the hospital for collecting music therapy feedback. Results are shared with administration on a regular basis concerning the impact music therapy is having on patient perceptions of the hospital and of MT.

Music Therapy Satisfaction Survey

Please feel free to answer any or all of the questions. Completion of this survey (or any question on it) is optional. We value your opinion about our services.

Please circle your response to each question.

You are a: Patient   Patient's family member   Patient's friend/visitor

Did you enjoy the music therapy services you received?

  Yes, very much   Yes   No opinion   Not really   Not at all

Did you benefit from music therapy?

  Yes, very much   Yes   No opinion   Not really   Not at all

Did music therapy services improve your perception of your stay at TMH?

  Yes, very much   Yes   No opinion   Not really   Not at all

Have you received or experienced music therapy services prior to this hospitalization?

  Yes   No   If yes, where?

_____

Would you like to receive music therapy services again if you return to TMH?

  Yes   Maybe   No

Comments:

Date: _____ Room number: _____ Name (optional): _____

PLEASE ASK YOUR NURSE TO RETURN THIS SURVEY TO THE MUSIC THERAPY ENVELOPE AT THE NURSE'S STATION. THANK YOU FOR YOUR FEEDBACK!

If you have any questions regarding this survey or music therapy services, please contact Judy Nguyen at 431-7468.

Section IV

National Institute for Allied Health Professionals

Chapter 8

Infant and Child Medical Music Therapy Institute

∽

Jayne M. Standley, Ph.D., MT-BC,
Jennifer Jarred, MT-BC,
Judy Nguyen, MT-BC,
Darcy Walworth, MT-BC,
and Andrea Cevasco, MT-BC

THE INFANT AND CHILD MEDICAL
MUSIC THERAPY INSTITUTE

Mission Statement

The mission of the *Tallahassee Memorial HealthCare—The Florida State University Infant and Child Medical Music Therapy Institute* is to provide an international site for the most progressive in vitro education and training in the use of research-based music therapy in pediatric medical settings. Its purpose is two-fold: (a) to train music therapists in the specialty of medical music therapy for children, and (b) to teach medical and allied health personnel about the benefits, uses, and inclusion of music therapy in medical treatment programs for children. The institute provides demonstration of professional knowledge, clinical skills, and applications with pediatric and premature infants in intensive care, pediatric rehabilitation, pediatric inpatient care, and pediatric procedural support.

Learning Objectives

As a result of the training provided in this institute, the learner will be able to:

- Relate issues of neurological development and maturation in the third trimester of fetal development to implications for clinical treatment of the premature infant;
- Cite problems and needs of pediatric patients and premature infants and their families;
- Adhere to NICU/Pediatric Unit protocols for interacting with premature infants and pediatric patients;
- Assess medical and music therapy needs and develop objectives for premature infants and other pediatric patients;
- Relate music therapy NICU/pediatric research results to clinical applications with hospitalized children;
- Train parents in the use of music and recommended interactions with their hospitalized children;
- Recommend early intervention music therapy objectives and activities to parents for use upon discharge to further the health and well being of the child;
- Develop and use music therapy protocols for procedural support during pediatric patients' medical tests;
- Interact with medical personnel in planning and implementing medical programs with children;
- Document cost benefits of music therapy medical protocols for children.

Design and Funding

A formal proposal was submitted to TMH administration in order to initiate the institute (see Appendix A). The hospital agreed to fund a music therapy position for 1-year as a demonstration project. All funds generated by institute registrations returns to the hospital as reimbursement for the start-up funding. The 2-day institute was designed to maximize the expertise of faculty, doctoral students, TMH music therapists, and hospital personnel. Other funding requirements have been kept to a minimum. All persons participating in the Institute do so as volunteers except Jennifer Jarred, M.M., MT-BC, who was funded by the hospital and manages institute arrangements.

The intended audience for the institute includes music therapists, music therapy students and interns, NICU nurses, pediatric nurses, pediatric physicians, pediatric healthcare administrators, child life specialists, and other allied health personnel. The institute provides 12 CEUs and is an advanced certification course approved by the Certification Board for Music Therapy.

Schedule

The institute is a 2-day experience observing clinical music therapy services with pediatric patients and is designed to allow small groups of people entry to actual medical services. Two institutes per month are scheduled with a maximum of 4 persons/institute. Each institute is unique depending upon actual medical services being provided on that date. Therefore, live observations are scheduled as possible with video taped MT services shown as an alternative if a particular medical procedure does not occur during the participants' stay in Tallahassee. An additional day may be added at the option of the participant to observe the comprehensive clinical MT services to adults.

SAMPLE INSTITUTE SCHEDULE

GROUP 1

Thursday

8:00 – 8:15	Holiday Inn Select Shuttle departs for TMH
9:00 – 10:00	Presentation: Orientation and TMH Policies
10:00 – 10:30	Presentation: Beyond Patient Interaction
10:30 – 11:00	Presentation: Pediatric Goals and Objectives
11:00 – 12:00	Presentation: NICU Music Therapy
12:00 – 1:00	Lunch
1:00 – 2:30	Observation: Pediatric Rehabilitation
2:30 – 3:00	Travel time
3:00 – 3:30	Presentation: Pediatric Rehabilitation Goals and Objectives

3:30 – 4:30	Presentation: NICU Multimodal Stimulation Training
4:30 – 5:30	Hands-on Experience: NICU Multimodal Stimulation
5:30 – 5:45	Holiday Inn Select Shuttle departs TMH

Friday

7:00 – 7:15	Holiday Inn Select Shuttle departs for TMH
7:45 – 8:00	Brief introduction to 8:00 activity
8:00 – 9:00	CT scan or Surgery Buddies if available
9:00 – 10:00	Presentation: Pacifier Activated Lullaby
10:00 – 11:00	Presentation: Music Therapy at TMH
11:00 – 12:00	Observation: Pediatrics, PICU, echo
12:00 – 1:00	Lunch
1:00 – 3:00	Presentation: Pediatric Procedural Support
	CT and echo tour
3:00 – 4:00	Observation: Pediatrics, PICU
4:00 – 5:00	Hands-on Experience: NICU Multimodal Stimulation
5:00 – 5:30	Evaluations
5:30 – 5:45	Holiday Inn Select Shuttle departs TMH

GROUP 2

Thursday

7:00 – 7:15	Holiday Inn Select Shuttle departs for TMH
7:45 – 8:00	Brief introduction to 8:00 activity
8:00 – 9:00	CT scan or Surgery Buddies if available
10:00 – 10:30	Presentation: Beyond Patient Interaction
10:30 – 11:00	Presentation: Pediatric Goals and Objectives
11:00 – 12:00	Presentation: NICU Music Therapy
12:00 – 1:00	Lunch
1:00 – 1:30	Presentation: Pediatric Rehabilitation Goals and Objectives
1:30 – 2:30	Presentation: NICU Multimodal Stimulation Training
2:30 – 3:00	Travel time
3:00 – 4:30	Observation: Pediatric Rehabilitation
4:30 – 5:30	Presentation: Music Therapy at TMH
5:30 – 5:45	Holiday Inn Select Shuttle departs TMH

Friday

8:00 – 8:15	Holiday Inn Select Shuttle departs for TMH
9:00 – 10:00	Presentation: Pacifier Activated Lullaby
10:00 – 11:00	Hands-on Experience: NICU Multimodal Stimulation
11:00 – 12:00	Observation: Pediatrics, PICU, echo

12:00 – 1:00	Lunch
1:00 – 3:00	Presentation: Pediatric Procedural Support
	CT and echo tour
3:00 – 4:00	Observation: Pediatrics, PICU
4:00 – 5:00	Hands-on Experience: NICU Multimodal Stimulation
5:00 – 5:30	Evaluations
5:30 – 5:45	Holiday Inn Select Shuttle departs TMH

Content Outline of Presentations and Observations

Orientation
Jennifer Jarred, MM, MT-BC
- Get acquainted with attendees, their backgrounds, and their expectations of the institute
- Review TMH policies and procedures
- Sign confidentiality agreements and collect proof of liability insurance

Presentation: Beyond Patient Interaction
Judy Nguyen, MM, MT-BC
- Music therapy referral system
- Patient care plan conferences
- Documentation
- Administrative committees and responsibilities
- Community outreach
- Medical music therapy research

Presentation: Pediatric Inpatient Techniques
Jennifer Jarred, MM, MT-BC
- Review of music therapy goals and objectives for pediatric inpatients and "Surgery Buddies"

Presentation: NICU Music Therapy
Jayne Standley, Ph.D., MT-BC
- NICU/NBIMCU research
- Rationale and guidelines for music therapy with premature infants
- Multimodal stimulation and PAL
- Parent education and training

Presentation: Pacifier Activited Lullaby (PAL) in the NICU
Andrea Cevasco, MMEd., MT-BC
- PAL research and development
- Rationale for and purposes of the PAL
- How to use the PAL in a NICU

Presentation: Pediatric Procedural Support
Darcy Walworth, MM, MT-BC, and Jennifer Jarred, MM, MT-BC
- Rationale for using music therapy during pediatric procedures
- How to start a pediatric procedural support program
- Cost analysis
- Demonstrations and how to succeed using music therapy during procedures (CT scans, echocardiograms, IV starts, EEGs)

Presentation: NICU Multimodal Stimulation
Jennifer Jarred, MM, MT-BC
- Familiarity with NICU monitors, terms, and interventions
- Signs of infant overstimulation
- Simulated specialized training in multimodal stimulation
- Guidelines for music to use in the NICU
- Parent education and training

Observation with an MT-BC in the areas of:
- "Surgery Buddies:" preoperative music therapy with outpatient pediatric surgical patients
- Inpatient pediatrics
- Pediatric procedural support: CT scan, echocardiogram
- Pediatric Rehabilitation: pediatric outpatients with autism, Down's syndrome, cerebral palsy, developmental delays, visual impairments, speech/communication impairments

Hands-on Specialized Training with an MT-BC in:
- NICU multimodal stimulation
- PAL

References

Jarred, J. (2003). Music assisted surgery: Preoperative and postoperative interventions. In S. L. Robb (Ed.), *Music therapy in pediatric healthcare: Research and evidence-based practice* (pp. 147–162). Silver Spring, MD: American Music Therapy Association.

Standley, J., & Whipple, J. (2003a). Music therapy with pediatric patients: A meta-analysis. In S. L. Robb (Ed.), *Music therapy in pediatric healthcare: Research and evidence-based practice* (pp.1–18). Silver Spring, MD: American Music Therapy Association.

Standley, J., & Whipple, J. (2003b). Music therapy for premature infants in the neonatal intensive care unit: Health and developmental benefits. In S. L. Robb (Ed.), *Music therapy in pediatric healthcare: Research and evidence-based practice* (pp. 19–30). Silver Spring, MD: American Music Therapy Association.

Walworth, D. (2003). Procedural support: Music therapy assisted CT, EKG, EEG, X-ray, IV, ventilator, and emergency services. In S. L. Robb (Ed.), *Music therapy in pediatric healthcare: Research and evidence-based practice* (pp. 137–146). Silver Spring, MD: American Music Therapy Association.

Institute Policies and Procedures

Participant Requirements

There are no prerequisites to enroll in the workshop, which is open to music therapy students, music therapy interns, professional music therapists (MT-BCs, RMTs), child life specialists, NICU and pediatric nurses, pediatric physicians, and pediatric healthcare administrators. CMTE credits can be given only to MT-BCs.

Reservation Policy

- Reservations must be made at least 6 weeks prior to the desired workshop dates.
- Workshops will only be hosted for two or more attendees; therefore, you will be contacted via email or phone call and given a confirmation number 5 weeks prior to the workshop dates.
- Do not finalize your airfare and/or travel plans until you have received your confirmation number.
- *Reservations are not complete without full payment and a confirmation number.*
- Email application information to jennifer.jarred@tmh.org and send registration fee to:
    TMH Music Therapy
    Infant and Child Medical Music Therapy Institute
    c/o TMH Neuroscience Center
    1401 Centerville Road, Suite 504
    Tallahassee, Florida 32308

Payment Policy

- Full payment ($200) is required in order to receive confirmation number to secure your workshop reservation.
- $200 registration fee can be paid via money order or check made payable to:
    TMH Music Therapy
    Infant and Child Medical Music Therapy Institute
    c/o TMH Neuroscience Center
    1401 Centerville Road, Suite 504
    Tallahassee, Florida 32308
- $200 registration fee can be paid via credit card by contacting:
    Dean Dawkins
    TMH Neuroscience Center
    (850) 431-7005
- Checks and money orders will be deposited after confirmation numbers are given.

Cancellation and Refund Policy

- Workshop attendees will be allowed to change reservations until 30 days prior to the workshop dates, contingent upon minimum enrollment, with no financial penalty.
- Once you have received your confirmation number, your workshop dates are secure and will not be cancelled by us. If you cancel before 30 days prior to your confirmed dates you will be entitled to a 50% refund. No refunds will be given for cancellation notices after 30 days prior to confirmed dates.
- Workshop attendees are responsible for hotel reservations, alterations, cancellations, and any penalties that may accompany these changes.

Confidentiality Policy

- All participants will be required to read and sign the Confidentiality Agreement and Statement of Responsibility.
- All participants will adhere to the policies outlined in the Confidentiality Agreement and Statement of Responsibility.

Liability Insurance Policy

- All workshop attendees who desire to participate in the hands-on training in the NICU will be required to show proof of professional/student liability insurance before holding a neonatal patient at TMH. Workshop attendees who fail to show proof of liability insurance will only be allowed to observe in the NICU. Participants can either bring proof of liability insurance with them to the workshop or fax it to:
    TMH Music Therapy at (850) 431-4483
- To obtain professional or student liability insurance, please contact:
    Marsh Affinity Group Services (a service of Seabury & Smith)
    1440 Renaissance Drive
    Park Ridge, IL 60068-1400
    1-800-323-2106

Other Policies

- Due to the unpredictablity of the hospital census, the Tallahassee Memorial HealthCare—The Florida State University Infant and Child Medical Music Therapy Institute cannot guarantee that participants will observe all areas outlined in the workshop schedule.
- All participants are responsible for their own transportation to, from, and during the workshop dates.
- All participants are responsible for their own hotel/lodging arrangements during the workshop dates.
- All participants are responsible for their own meals during the workshop dates.

- All particpants will adhere to the Tallahassee Memorial HealthCare policies and procedures, including confidentiality, personal responsibility, practice of universal precautions, program unit procedures, and grooming standards.

Grievance Policy and Procedure

- Participants have the right to file a grievance within 30 days of workshop completion.
- Content of a grievance should include aspects of the workshop as covered by the policies and procedures.
- Participants wishing to file a grievance should submit it in writing to:
  Judy Nguyen
  1331 East 6th Avenue
  Tallahassee, FL 32303
  judy.nguyen@tmh.org
- All grievances will be presented to a grievance committee and a written response will be sent to the participant within 30 days of receipt of the grievance.

Grievance Appeal Policy and Procedures

- Participants have the right to appeal decisions made by the grievance committee.
- Participants wishing to file an appeal should submit it in writing to:
  Judy Nguyen
  1331 East 6th Avenue
  Tallahassee, FL 32303
  judy.nguyen@tmh.org
- All appeals will be presented to a grievance appeal committee and a written response will be sent to the participant within 30 days of receipt of the appeal.
- Participants have the right to have an unresolved grievance addressed by CBMT's Continuing Education Committee. (NOTE: This should occur only after the Tallahassee Memorial HealthCare—The Florida State University Infant and Child Medical Music Therapy Institute Grievance Procedure has been exhausted.)

TMH Grooming Standards

Dress Code

Visitors must wear their identification badge whenever on hospital grounds. Attire should be professional in appearance. No sleeveless shirts, open-toed shoes, denim, corduroy, or shorts are permitted. Skirt length should fall below the knee.

Hair

All hair styles should be clean, neat and conservatively styled and in good taste. The length and/or bulk of the hair will not be excessive or present a ragged, unkempt, or extreme appearance. It should be neatly cut. No rattails or spike hairdos are permitted. Men's hair styles should be conservative and businesslike and not excessively long. Sideburns should not extend downward beyond the upper part of the exterior ear opening. Sideburns should also be straight and not flared. Women's hair falling below the shoulder should be contained and back. Hairpieces can be worn if they are conservative and in good taste. No hair glitter or sparkling jewelry is to be worn either in the hair or on the hairpiece. Beards and mustaches are permitted if they are short and neatly trimmed.

Hands and Nails

Hands should be clean and neatly manicured. Nail polish should be in keeping with the hospital's conservative image. When working in the Newborn Intensive/Intermediate Care Units, acrylic and other artificial fingernails are prohibited and natural fingernails should not extend beyond the fingertip, in order to prevent the spread of bacteria.

Jewelry and Accessories

Jewelry should be in good taste, not lavish or overly ornate. Only moderate amounts should be worn. Multi-colored garnish beads or heavy chunky style beads are not permitted. Single strands of one color are allowed. Dangling earrings of one inch or less are permitted, with one earring in each ear. Males are not allowed to wear earrings. Pins are limited to wear on scarves, collars, or lapels. Rings are limited to the third and fourth fingers of each hand, with no more than one ring per finger (wedding rings and engagement rings are considered one), and with no more than three total rings. Neck chains and necklaces should be tasteful and not too thick. Students may not wear a hat, cap, visor, scarf, or headband unless used as part of a costume. However, it is acceptable to wear those items to and from the hospital.

Cosmetics

Makeup should be subdued, without heavy or dramatic effects. Perfumes, colognes, and scents should be minimal and should not be a heavy fragrance that dominates a room.

Isolation Precautions

1. *Airborne Isolation:* Utilized to prevent transmission of tuberculosis due to M. tuberculosis, M. bovis or M. africanum.

What to Do: a. Wear respirator mask to enter room.

b. Keep door closed.

c. Utilize Standard Precautions for all of aspects of patient care.

2. *Stop Sign Isolation:* Utilized to prevent transmission of communicable diseases which pose a risk ONLY to susceptible (non-immune) individuals.

What to Do: a. Nursing personnel are to screen personnel and visitors for susceptibility before they enter the room.

b. If a person is susceptible to the communicable disease, s/he **is not to enter the room**.

c. If a person is immune, s/he may enter. Utilize Standard Precautions for all other aspects of patient care.

3. *Respiratory Isolation:* Utilized to prevent transmission of micro-organisms which may be transmitted by droplets generated by the patient during coughing, sneezing, talking, or the performance of procedures. (Note: Transmission by droplets requires relatively close contact with the source because droplets generally do not remain suspended in the air for extended periods and travel only short distances through the air.)

What to Do: a. Wear mask/eyeshield protection when entering the room.

b. Utilize Standard Precautions for all other aspects of patient care.

4. *Contact Isolation/Strict Contact Isolation:* Utilized to prevent transmission of micro-organisms which may be transmitted by direct contact with the patient (i.e., hand or skin-to-skin contact that occurs when performing patient-care activities that require touching the patient's intact skin) or indirect contact (i.e., touching) with environmental surfaces or patient-care items in the patient's environment, to heighten awareness of the need for strict adherence to Standard Precautions.

What to Do: a. Wear gloves to enter room.

b. Wear gown whenever contact of clothing with patient or environment is likely.

c. Perform hand hygiene immediately after removal of gloves and/or gown.

d. Utilize Standard Precautions for all other aspects of patient care.

Standard Precautions: For the care of all patients, the consistent application of infection control precautionary measures to prevent exposure to the blood/body fluids of all patients is practiced.

Hand Hygiene

How to Wash Your Hands

- Turn on water and adjust temperature.
- Dispense soap.
- Wash thoroughly and with vigor for at least 10 seconds.
- Dry hands with paper towel.
- Turn off water with paper towel.
- Dispose of towel without touching waste container.

When to Wash Your Hands

- Hands look dirty or feel dirty
- After contamination—known or possibly—by body secretions or excretions
- Before eating or handling food
- When caring for sick people

Other Precautions

- Remember not to re-contaminate hands by touching handles and doorknobs.
- It is important to wash well. Excess jewelry and long sleeves may get in the way, so be sure to remove them.

Infant and Child Medical Music Therapy Institute at TMH
Participant Satisfaction Survey

Please rate the workshop you have completed: (Circle one number for each item.)

	Strongly Disagree				Strongly Agree

1. I was satisfied with the instructor's presentation on:
   a. pediatric procedural support.   1   2   3   4   5
   b. pediatric inpatient techniques.   1   2   3   4   5
   c. NICU multimodal stimulation/parent
      training.   1   2   3   4   5
   d. PAL research and instruction.   1   2   3   4   5
   e. TMH Music Therapy and Arts in
      Medicine.   1   2   3   4   5
2. The workshop met my expectations for:
   a. quality of relevant information.   1   2   3   4   5
   b. type of relevant information.   1   2   3   4   5
   c. amount of relevant information.   1   2   3   4   5
3. The registration fee was reasonably priced.   1   2   3   4   5
4. The workshop was well organized.   1   2   3   4   5
5. I was satisfied with the schedule.   1   2   3   4   5
6. I would like to attend a similar workshop
   on more aspects of medical music therapy. 1   2   3   4   5
7. What I learned enhances my music therapy
   practice.   1   2   3   4   5 N/A
8. I was satisfied with the length of the workshop.   1   2   3   4   5
9. Objectives of the workshop were adequately met.   1   2   3   4   5

The best aspect of this workshop was:

Describe how you will incorporate what you learned from this workshop into your clinical practice:

Additional comments:

Adapted from CEC Sample Assessment of Participant Satisfaction

Confidentiality Agreement

The undersigned hereby acknowledges his/her responsibility under Federal and State Law to keep confidential any information regarding all patients at Tallahassee Memorial HealthCare. The undersigned agrees, under penalty of law, not to reveal to any person or persons, except authorized clinical staff and associated personnel, any specific information regarding any patient.

Dated this _____ day of _____ year _____

Participant Signature _____

Participant Name _____

Witness Signature _____

Witness Signature _____

Statement of Responsibility

For and in consideration of the benefit provided the undersigned in the form of experience in evaluation and treatment of patients of Tallahassee Memorial HealthCare, the undersigned, and his/her heirs, successors, and/or assigns does hereby covenant and agree to be solely responsible for any injury or loss sustained by the undersigned while participating in programs jointly entered into between Tallahassee Memorial HealthCare and The Florida State University if such injury or loss results from the undersigned's negligence.

Dated this _____ day of _____ year _____

Participant Signature _____

Participant Name _____

Witness Signature _____

Witness Signature _____

Appendix A. Proposal to TMH to Establish the Institute

The Music Therapy Infant and Child Medical Institute: Developmental Interventions and Enhancement of Hospital Care

A Cooperative Partnership Between Tallahassee Memorial HealthCare and The Florida State University Music Therapy Department

Purpose: The partnership between TMH and FSU music therapy has resulted in the development of the most comprehensive and progressive use of music in the medical treatment of children currently existing in the world. It is a research-based clinical program with the thrust for this research coming directly from the Florida State University Music Therapy Department. In the last 25 years, 47 medical research studies have been completed by FSU students and faculty. Twenty-five of these are studies with procedures for infants and children with 20 of these being published in refereed nursing and music therapy journals. The purpose of this institute will be to establish an international site for demonstration and training in the use of research-based music therapy with infants and children. The Institute will provide workshops to music therapists and nursing personnel in the uses of music for developmental intervention and enhancement of medical treatment of young children. The American Music Therapy Association is in the process of implementing a certificate program for specialized training in NICU music therapy and has requested a demonstration project to accompany the planned classroom content. The first training program is being presented in November 2003 by Dr. Jayne Standley of FSU to over 100 people. The NICU music therapy program at TMH is the only site in the world capable of providing such training. We propose implementing this phase of the Institute training immediately and phasing in the development of an educational/information program for nursing personnel within 4 months. All funds emanating from this Institute will accrue to TMH with the priority for use being the funding of the music therapy position required to staff the Institute.

Program: The institute program will have two major thrusts:
- A. Training music therapists in research based music therapy procedures pioneered at TMH and demonstrating their use in clinical practice
- B. Educating nursing personnel about the benefits of NICU/pediatric music therapy

Content will include:
1. NICU MT:
   - a. music listening to increase oxygen saturation and stabilize RR of oxygenated infants;
   - b. music and multimodal stimulation to facilitate tolerance to stimuli in premature infants;

    c. parent training in music and multimodal stimulation to reduce overstimulation of infants and increase visiting time in the NICU; and

    d. use of the FDA approved device (PAL) invented by Dr. Standley and tested at TMH that uses music to reinforce non-nutritive sucking of premature infants learning to nipple feed. This device will be distributed by early 2004 in Ohmeda Medical.

2. Pediatric Music Therapy:

    a. music therapy protocol to reduce infant and toddler anxiety during venipuncture;

    b. music to increase appetite of infants and toddlers;

    c. music to soothe infants and toddlers for sleep;

    d. music and progressive relaxation for older children as a distraction and coping strategy for painful procedures;

    e. music to reduce amount of pain medication used;

    f. music to reduce boredom and dissatisfaction of teenagers; and

    g. music therapy procedures to help children reduce fear, connect with, and communicate with medical personnel.

3. Pediatric Rehabilitation Music Therapy:

    a. music to facilitate physical therapy rehabilitation exercises;

    b. music to facilitate short-term memory;

    c. music to increase heel strikes in children with Autism who toe-walk music to increase bi-lateral strength in upper extremities;

    d. music to facilitate speech and language responses of children with Developmental Delays;

    e. music to teach socialization skills to children with Autism.

4. Procedural Support Music Therapy:

    a. music therapy to eliminate the need for sedation and RN supervision during CT scans and echocardiograms;

5. Surgery Buddies/Kids Korner:

    a. training in the music therapy protocol to reduce anxiety during preoperative preparation and separation from parents;

    b. training in the music therapy protocol for reducing anxiety of parents in the surgical waiting room.

6. Craniotomy Surgery with Pediatric Patients:

    a. Training in music therapy protocol developed for the National Brain Institute Grant to reduce preoperative anxiety and use of pain medication following this surgical procedure.

7. Collaboration between Arts/Medicine volunteer program and Music Therapy for Pediatric units.

Personnel: The Coordinator of the Institute will be a MT-BC with Master's degree, position to be established by November 1, 2003 and supervised by Judy Nguyen, Coordinator of TMH Music Therapy.

Guest instructors in the Institute will include the following people as available:

> Dr. Jayne Standley, Ph.D., MT-BC, Director of FSU MT Degree Programs
> Christy Harrison, RN, Director of TMH Neuroscience Department
> Judy Nguyen, M.M., MT-BC, Director of TMH Music Therapy
> Music therapy interns and FSU MT practica students
> Cindy Quackenbush, RN, Director of TMH Neonatal Services

Schedule: The 2-day, 14-hour training program will include classroom training and in situ observation of each technique outlined above. Institute programs will be scheduled on Thursday and Friday 2 times/month. Trainees will by cycled in small groups through observations on hospital units to control the number of people visiting a particular medical setting. The schedule for observations will be developed in consultation with nursing personnel on each unit.

Budget: The cost of the program in the first year will be the salary for one Board Certified Music Therapist with a Master's degree at an annual rate of $30,000 plus benefits (22% = $6,600), a total cost of $36,600. It is proposed that the TMH Foundation provide upfront funds of $15,600 to begin the program and that the remaining $21,000 be generated through Institute income at a rate of $200 per person for a 2-day program. This formula would require training 105 people during fiscal year 2003. Other funds generated will accrue to the TMH NICU and Pediatric Programs budgets.

Advertising: Advertising will include the following at no expense to TMH:
1. Development of an internet website describing and advertising available dates for the program linked to the websites of the American Music Therapy Association, The Florida State University, and the World Federation of Music Therapy. We will seek alliances with appropriate and similar nursing associations.
2. Distribution of flyers at the AMTA annual conference in November, 2003, the European Congress of Music Therapy in Finland in Summer 2004, and the World Congress of Music Therapy in Brisbane, Australia in Summer 2005. Christy Harrison and Institute personnel will submit a proposal for an AACN presentation in 2005 and, if accepted, distribute information there.
3. We will seek alliance with the Vermont Oxford Network through contacts of Cindy Quackenbush and attempt a presentation at their annual training institute in December 2005.

References

MEDICAL RESEARCH WITH MUSIC REFERENCES

Aldridge, K. (1993). The use of music to relieve pre-operational anxiety in children attending day surgery. *The Australian Journal of Music Therapy, 4,* 19–35.

Alvarez, R. (2003, June 30). *Florida Legislative FTE Appropriation for 2002-2003.* Personal interview with Florida State University Associate Vice President for Administrative Affairs, Budget Analysis.

American Music Therapy Association. (1998). *Reimbursement primer: The ABC's of health care reimbursement for music therapy services.* Silver Spring, MD: Author.

American Music Therapy Association. (2002). *AMTA member sourcebook 2002.* Silver Spring, MD: Author.

Ammon, K. J. (1968). The effects of music on children in respiratory distress. *American Nurses' Association Clinical Sessions,* 127–133.

Armatas, C. (1964). *A study of the effect of music on postoperative patients in the recovery room.* Unpublished master's thesis, The University of Kansas.

Arts, S., Abu-Saad, H., Champion, G., Crawford, M., Fisher, R., Juniper, K., & Ziegler, J. (1994). Age-related response to Lidocaine-Prilocaine (EMLA) emulsion and effect of music distraction on the pain of intravenous cannulation. *Pediatrics, 93*(5), 797–801.

Atterbury, R. (1974). Auditory pre-sedation for oral surgery patients. *Audioanalgesia, 38*(6), 12–14.

Augustin, P., & Hains, A. (1996). Effect of music on ambulatory surgery patients' preoperative anxiety. *AORN Journal, 63*(4), 750, 753–758.

Bailey, L. (1983). The effects of live music versus tape-recorded music on hospitalized cancer patients. *Music Therapy, 3*(1), 17–28.

Bailey, L. (1984). The use of songs in music therapy with cancer patients and their families. *Music Therapy, 4*(1), 5–17.

Bailey, L. (1986). Music therapy in pain management. *Journal of Pain and Symptom Management, 1*(1), 25–28.

Bampton, P., & Draper, B. (1997). Effect of relaxation music on patient tolerance of gastrointestinal endoscopic procedures. *Journal of Clinical Gastroenterology, 25*(1), 343–345.

Barker, L. (1991). The use of music and relaxation techniques to reduce pain of burn patients during daily debridement. In C. D. Maranto (Ed.), *Applications of music in medicine* (pp. 163–178). Washington, DC: National Association for Music Therapy.

Barnason, S., Zimmerman, L., & Nieveen, J. (1995). The effects of music interventions on anxiety in the patient after coronary artery bypass grafting. *Heart and Lung, 24*(2), 124–132.

Barrera, M., Kykov, M., & Doyle, S. (2002). The effects of interactive music therapy on hospitalized children with cancer: A pilot study. *Psycho-Oncology, 11,* 379–388.

Barrickman, J. (1989). A developmental music therapy approach for preschool hospitalized children. *Music Therapy Perspectives, 7,* 10–16.

Bason, P., & Celler, B. (1972). Control of the heart rate by external stimuli. *Nature, 238,* 279–280.

Batson, A. (1994). *The effects of live music on the distress of pediatric patients receiving intravenous starts, venipunctures, injections, and heel sticks.* Unpublished master's thesis, The Florida State University, Tallahassee.

Beck, S. (1991). The therapeutic use of music for cancer-related pain. *Oncology Nursing Forum, 18*(8), 1327–1336.

Behrens, G. (1982). *The use of music activities to improve the capacity, inhalation, and exhalation capabilities of handicapped children's respiration.* Unpublished master's thesis, Kent State University, Kent, OH.

Berlin, B. (1998). Music therapy with children during invasive procedures: Our emergency department's experience. *Journal of Emergency Nursing, 24*(6), 607–608.

Beyer, J., Villarruel, A.M., & Denyes, M. (1993). *The Oucher: The new user's manual and technical report.* Denver: Health Sciences Center, School of Nursing, University of Colorado.

Blankfield, R., Zyzanski, S., Flocke, S., Alemagno, S., & Scheurman, K. (1995). Taped therapeutic suggestions and taped music as adjuncts in the case of coronary-artery-bypass patients. *American Journal of Clinical Hypnosis, 37*(3), 32–37.

Bob, S. (1962). Audioanalgesia in podiatric practice, a preliminary study. *Journal of American Podiatry Association, 52,* 503–504.

Boldt, S. (1996). The effects of music therapy on motivation, psychological well-being, physical comfort, and exercise endurance of bone marrow transplant patients. *Journal of Music Therapy, 33*(3), 164188.

Bolwerk, C. (1990). Effects of relaxing music on state anxiety in myocardial infarction patients. *Critical Care Nursing, 13*(2), 63–72.

Bonny, H. (1983). Music listening for intensive coronary care units: A pilot project. *Music Therapy, 3*(1), 4–16.

Boyle, M., & Greer, R. (1983). Operant procedures and the comatose patient. *Journal of Applied Behavioral Analysis, 16*(1), 3–12.

Bradt, J. (2001). *The effects of music entrainment on postoperative pain perception in pediatric patients.* Unpublished dissertation, Temple University, Philadelphia, PA.

Brodsky, W. (1989). Music therapy as an intervention for children with cancer in isolation rooms. *Music Therapy, 8*(1), 17–34.

Brook, E. (1984). *Soothing music during the active phase of labor: Physiologic effect on mother and infant.* Unpublished master's thesis, University of Florida, Gainesville.

Broome, M. E., Lillis, P. P., & Smith, M. C. (1989). Pain interventions with children: A meta-analysis of research. *Nursing Research, 38*(3), 154–158.

Brown, J. (1992a). Music dying. *American Journal of Hospice and Palliative Care, 9*(4), 17–20.

Brown, J. (1992b). When words fail, music speaks. *American Journal of Hospice and Palliative Care, 9*(2), 13–16.

Budzynski, T., Stoyva, J., & Adler, C. (1970). Feedback-induced muscle relaxation: Application to tension headache. *Journal of Behavior Therapy and Experimental Psychiatry, 1,* 205–211.

Burke, M., Walsh, J., Oehler, J., & Gingras, J. (1995). Music therapy following suctioning: Four case studies. *Neonatal Network, 14*(7), 41–49.

Burns, D. (2001). The effect of the Bonny Method of Guided Imagery and Music on the mood and life quality of cancer patients. *Journal of Music Therapy, 38*(1), 51.

Burns, J. L., Labbé, E., Arke, B., Capeless, K., Cooksey, B., Steadman, A., & Gonzales, C. (2002). The effects of different types of music on perceived and physiological measures of stress. *Journal of Music Therapy, 39*(2), 101.

Burt, R. K., & Korn, G. W. (1964). Audioanalgesia in obstetrics: White noise analgesia during labor. *American Journal of Obstetrics and Gynecology, 88,* 361–366.

Byers, J., & Smyth, K. (1997). Effect of a music intervention on noise annoyance, heart rate, and blood pressure in cardiac surgery patients. *American Journal of Critical Care, 6*(3), 183–191.

Caine, J. (1991). The effects of music on the selected stress behaviors, weight, caloric and formula intake, and length of hospital stay of premature and low birth weight neonates in a newborn intensive care unit. *Journal of Music Therapy, 28*(4), 180–192.

Caire, J., & Erickson, S. (1986). Reducing distress in pediatric patients undergoing cardiac catheterization. *Children's Health Care, 14*(3), 146–152.

Camp, W., Martin, R., & Chapman, L. (1962). Pain threshold and discrimination of pain intensity during brief exposure to intense noise. *Noise, 135,* 788–789.

Carlin, S., Ward, W., Gershon, A., & Ingraham, R. (1962). Sound stimulation and its effect on dental sensation threshold. *Science, 138,* 1258–1259.

Cassidy, J., & Standley, J. (1995). The effect of music listening on physiological responses of premature infants in the NICU. *Journal of Music Therapy, 32*(4), 208-227.

Cassidy, J. W., & Ditty, K. (1998). Presentation of aural stimuli to newborns and premature infants: An audiological perspective. *Journal of Music Therapy, 35*(2), 70–87.

Cepeda, M., Diaz, J., Hernandez, V., Daza, E., & Carr, D. (1998). Music does not reduce alfentanil requirement during patient-controlled analgesia (PCA) use in extracorporeal shock wave lithotripsy for renal stones. *Journal of Pain and Symptom Management, 16*(6), 382–387.

Chalmers, I., Enkin, M., & Keirse, M. (1989). *Effective care in pregnancy and childbirth.* Oxford: Oxford Medical Publications.

Chapman, J. (1975). *The relation between auditory stimulation of short gestation infants and their gross motor limb activity.* Unpublished doctoral dissertation, New York University, New York.

Cherry, H., & Pallin, I. (1948). Music as a supplement in nitrous oxide oxygen anesthesia. *Anesthesiology, 9,* 391–399.

Chesky, K. (1992). *The effects of music and music vibration using the MVT*^TM^ *on the relief of rheumatoid arthritis pain.* Dissertation Abstracts International, 9300593.

Chetta, H. D. (1980). *The effect of music therapy in reducing fear and anxiety in preoperative pediatric patients.* Unpublished master's thesis, The Florida State University, Tallahassee.

Chetta, H. D. (1981). The effect of music and desensitization on preoperative anxiety in children. *Journal of Music Therapy, 18*(2), 74–87.

Chlan, L. (1998). Effectiveness of a music therapy intervention on relaxation and anxiety for patients receiving ventilatory assistance. *Heart and Lung, 27*(3), 169–176.

Christenberry, E. (1979). The use of music therapy with burn patients. *Journal of Music Therapy, 16,* 138–148.

Clark, M., McCorkle, R., & Williams, S. (1981). Music therapy-assisted labor and delivery. *Journal of Music Therapy, 18,* 88–109.

Clinton, P. (1984). *Music as a nursing intervention for children during painful procedures.* Unpublished master's thesis, The University of Iowa, Iowa City.

Codding, P. (1982). *An exploration of the uses of music in the birthing process.* Unpublished master's thesis, The Florida State University, Tallahassee.

Cofrancesco, E. (1985). The effect of music therapy on hand grasp strength and functional task performance in stroke patients. *Journal of Music Therapy, 22*(3), 125–149.

Cohen, A. (1984). *The development and implementation of a pediatric music therapy program in a short-term medical facility.* Unpublished master's thesis, New York University, New York.

Cohen, J. (1988). *Statistical power analysis for the behavioral sciences* (2nd ed.). Hillsdale, NJ: Lawrence Erlbaum Associates.

Cohen, Z. N. (1984). *The development and implementation of a pediatric music therapy program in a short-term medical facility.* Unpublished master's thesis, New York University, New York.

Coleman, J., Pratt, R., Stoddard, R., Gerstmann, D., & Abel, H. (1997). The effects of the male and female singing and speaking voices on selected physiological and behavioral measures of premature infants in the intensive care unit. *International Journal of Arts Medicine, 5*(2), 4–11.

Colgrove, T. (1991). *The effects of music versus guided imagery and progressive muscle relaxation versus guided imagery and progressive muscle relaxation with music on the pulse rate and peripheral finger temperature of hemodialysis patients undergoing treatment.* Unpublished master's thesis, The Florida State University, Tallahassee.

Collins, S., & Kuck, K. (1991). Music therapy in the neonatal intensive care unit. *Neonatal Network, 9*(6), 23–26.

Cook, J. (1982). *The use of music to reduce anxiety in oncology patients exposed to the altered sensory environment of betaron radiation.* Unpublished master's thesis, The University of Texas, Austin.

Corah, N., Gale, E., Pace, L., & Seyrek, S. (1981). Relaxation and musical programming as means of reducing psychological stress during dental procedures. *Journal of the American Dental Association, 103,* 232–234.

Cordobés, T. (1997). Group songwriting as a method for developing group cohesion for HIV-Seropositive adult patients with depression. *Journal of Music Therapy, 34*(1), 46–67.

Crago, B. (1980). *Reducing the stress of hospitalization for open heart surgery.* Unpublished doctoral dissertation, University of Massachusetts, Amherst.

Curtis, S. (1986). The effect of music on pain relief and relaxation of the terminally ill. *Journal of Music Therapy, 23*(1), 10–24.

Davila, J., & Menendez, J. (1986). Relaxing effects of music in dentistry for mentally handicapped patients. *Special Care in Dentistry, 6*(1), 18–21.

Davis, C. (1992). The effects of music and basic relaxation instruction on pain and anxiety of women undergoing in-office gynecological procedures. *Journal of Music Therapy, 29*(4), 202–216.

Davis-Rollans, C., & Cunningham, S. (1987). Physiologic responses of coronary care patients to selected music. *Heart and Lung, 16*(4), 370–378.

Day Surgery. *The Australian Journal of Music Therapy, 4*, 19–35.

Durham, L., & Collins, M. (1986). The effect of music as a conditioning aid in prepared childbirth education. *Journal of Obstetrical, Gynecological, and Neonatal Nursing, 15*(3), 268–270.

Eagle, C., Jr. (1976). *Music Therapy Index, Vol. 1.* Lawrence, KS: National Association for Music Therapy.

Eagle, C., Jr. (1978). *Music Therapy Index, Vol. 2.* Lawrence, KS: National Association for Music Therapy.

Eagle, C., Jr., & Minter, J. J. (1984). *Music Psychology Index, Vol. 3.* Phoenix, AZ: Orynx Press.

Edwards, J. (1999). Anxiety management in pediatric music therapy. In C. Dileo (Ed.), *Music therapy and medicine: Theoretical and clinical applications* (pp. 69–76). Silver Spring, MD: American Music Therapy Association.

Eisenman, A., & Cohen, B. (1995). Music therapy for patients undergoing regional anesthesia. *AORN Journal, 62*(6), 947–950.

Elliott, D. (1994). The effects of music and muscle relaxation on patient anxiety in a coronary care unit. *Heart and Lung, 23*(1), 27–35.

Ellis, D., & Brighouse, G. (1952). Effects of music on respiration and heart rate. *American Journal of Psychology, 65*, 39–47.

Epstein, L., Hersen, M., & Hemphill, D. (1974). Music feedback in the treatment of tension headache: An experimental case study. *Journal of Behavior Therapy and Experimental Psychiatry, 5*, 59–63.

Evans, D. (2002). The effectiveness of music as an intervention for hospital patients: A systematic review. *Journal of Advanced Nursing, 37*(1), 8–18.

Ezzone, S., Baker, C., Rosselet, R., & Terepka, E. (1998). Music as an adjunct to antiemetic therapy. *Oncology Nursing Forum, 25*(9), 1551–1556.

Fagen, T. (1982). Music therapy in the treatment of anxiety and fear in terminal pediatric patients. *Music Therapy, 2*, 13–23.

Fagen, T. S. (1982). *Music therapy as a tool for the assessment and treatment of fear and anxiety in pediatric cancer patients.* Unpublished master's thesis, New York University, New York.

Falb, M. (1982). *The use of operant procedures to condition vasoconstriction in profoundly mentally retarded (PMR) infants.* Unpublished master's thesis, The Florida State University, Tallahassee.

Ferrell, D. (1984). *Music therapy case studies of patients in a regional medical center.* Unpublished research manuscript, The Florida State University, Tallahassee.

Flowers, A., McCain, A., & Hilker, K. (1999). *The effects of music listening on premature infants.* Paper presented at the Biennial Meeting, Society for Research in Child Development, April 1518, Albuquerque, NM.

Foutz, C. (1970). Routine audio-nitrous oxide analgesia simplified. *Arizona Dental Journal, 16,* 15–16.

Fowler-Kerry, S., & Lander, J. R. (1987). Management of injection pain in children. *Pain, 30*(2), 169–175.

Frank, J. (1985). The effects of music therapy and guided visual imagery on chemotherapy induced nausea and vomiting. *Oncology Nursing Forum, 12*(5), 47–52.

Fratianne, R., Presner, J., Huston, M., Super, D., Yowler, C., & Standley, J. (2001). The effect of music based imagery and musical alternate engagement on the burn debridement process. *Journal of Burn Care and Rehabilitation, 22*(1), 47–53.

Froehlich, M. (1984). A comparison of the effect of music therapy and medical play therapy on the verbalization behavior of pediatric patients. *Journal of Music Therapy, 21,* 2–15.

Froehlich, M. (Ed.). (1996). *Music therapy with hospitalized children.* Cherry Hill, NJ: Jeffery Books.

Gaberson, K. (1995). The effect of humorous and musical distraction on preoperative anxiety. *AORN Journal, 62*(5), 784–791.

Gardner, W., & Licklider, J. (1959). Auditory analgesia in dental operation. *Journal of American Dental Association, 59,* 1144–1150.

Gardner, W., Licklider, J., & Weisz, A. (1960). Suppression of pain by sound. *Science, 132,* 32–33.

Getsie, R., Langer, P., & Glass, G. (1985). Meta-analysis of the effects of type and combination of feedback on children's discrimination learning. *Review of Educational Research, 55*(1), 9–22.

Gettel, M. K. (1985). *The effect of music on anxiety in children undergoing cardiac catheterization.* Unpublished master's thesis, Hahneman University, Philadelphia, PA.

Gfeller, K., Logan, H., & Walker, J. (1988). The effect of auditory distraction and suggestion on tolerance for dental restorations in adolescents and young adults. *Journal of Music Therapy, 27*(1), 13–23.

Gilbert, J. (1977). Music therapy perspectives on death and dying. *Journal of Music Therapy, 14,* 165–171.

Glass, G., McGaw, B., & Smith, M. (1984). *Meta-analysis in social research.* Beverly Hills, CA: Sage.

Godley, C. (1987). The use of music therapy in pain clinics. *Music Therapy Perspectives, 4,* 24–28.

Goloff, M. (1981). The responses of hospitalized medical patients to music therapy. *Music Therapy, 1*(1), 51–56.

Good, M. (1995). A comparison of the effects of jaw relaxation and music on postoperative pain. *Nursing Research, 44*(1), 52–57.

Goroszeniuk, T., & Morgan, B. (1984). Music during epidural caesarean section. *The Practitioner, 228,* 441–443.

Grasso, M. C., Button, B. M., Allison, D. J., & Sawyer, S. M. (2000). Benefits of music therapy as an adjunct to chest physiotherapy in infants and toddlers with cystic fibrosis. *Pediatric Pulmonology, 29,* 371–381.

Grundy, A. (1989). *The effects of music and the Somatron on the physiological and speech responses of head injured and comatose subjects.* Unpublished master's thesis, The Florida State University, Tallahassee.

Guzzetta, C. (1989). Effects of relaxation and music therapy on patients in a coronary care unit with presumptive acute myocardial infarction. *Heart and Lung, 18,* 609–616.

Hanamoto, J., & Kajiyama, T. (1974). Some experiences in use of environmental music in pediatric roentgenography. *Radiologia Diagnostica, 15*(6), 787–794.

Haneishe, E. (2001). Effects of a music therapy voice protocol on speech intelligibility, vocal acoustic measures, and mood of individuals with Parkinson's disease. *Journal of Music Therapy, 38*(4), 273.

Hanser, S. (1985). Music therapy and stress reduction research. *Journal of Music Therapy, 22,* 193–206.

Hanser, S., Larson, S., & O'Connell, A. (1983). The effect of music on relaxation of expectant mothers during labor. *Journal of Music Therapy, 20,* 50–58.

Heiser, R., Chiles, K., Fudge, M., & Gray, S. (1997). The use of music during the immediate postoperative recovery period. *AORN Journal, 65*(4), 777–778, 781–785.

Heitz, L., Symreng, T., & Scamman, F. (1992). Effect of music therapy in the postanesthesia care unit: A nursing intervention. *Journal of Post Anesthesia Nursing, 7*(1), 22–31.

Henry, L. (1995). Music therapy: A nursing intervention for the control of pain and anxiety in the ICU: A review of the research literature. *Dimensions of Critical Care Nursing, 14*(6), 295–304.

Hilliard, R. (2001). The effects of music therapy-based bereavement groups on mood and behavior of grieving children: A pilot study. *Journal of Music Therapy, 38*(4), 291.

Hilliard, R. (2003). The effects of music therapy on the quality and length of life of people diagnosed with terminal cancer. *Journal of Music Therapy, 40*(2), 113–137.

Hirokawa, E., & Ohira, H. (2003). The effects of music listening after a stressful task on immune functions, neuroendocrine responses, and emotional states in college students. *Journal of Music Therapy, 40*(3), 189–211.

Hoffman, J. (1980). *Management of essential hypertension through relaxation training with sound.* Unpublished master's thesis, University of Kansas, Lawrence.

Hoffman, P. (1975). The use of guitar and singing in a child life program. *Journal of the Association for the Care of Children in Hospitals, 4*(1), 45–47.

Howitt, J. (1967). An evaluation of audio-analgesia effects. *Journal of Dentistry for Children, 34,* 406–411.

Howitt, J. (1972). In this intensive care unit, the downbeat helps the heartbeats. *Modern Hospital, 118,* 91.

Hurt, C., Rice, R., McIntosh, G., & Thaut, M. (1998). Rhythmic auditory stimulation in gait training for patients with traumatic brain injury. *Journal of Music Therapy, 35*(4), 228–241.

Hyde, I. (1924). Effects of music upon electrocardiograms and blood pressure. *Journal of Experimental Psychology, 7,* 213–224.

Iwaki, T., Tanaka, H., & Hori, T. (2003). The effects of Preferred Familiar Music on Falling Asleep. *Journal of Music Therapy*, *40*(1), 15–26.

Jacobson, A. (1999). Intradermal normal saline solution, self-selected music, and insertion difficulty effects on intravenous insertion pain. *Heart and Lung, 28*(2), 114–122.

Jacobson, H. (1957). The effect of sedative music on the tensions, anxiety and pain experienced by mental patients during dental procedures. In E. T. Gaston (Ed.), *Music therapy 1956: Book of proceedings of the National Association for Music Therapy, Inc.* (pp. 231–234). Lawrence, KS: National Association for Music Therapy.

Jarred, J. (2003a). *The effect of live music on anxiety levels of persons waiting in a surgical waiting room as measured by self-report.* Unpublished master's thesis, The Florida State University, Tallahassee.

Jarred, J. (2003b). Music assisted surgery: Preoperative and postoperative interventions. In S. L. Robb (Ed.), *Music therapy in pediatric healthcare research and evidence-based practice* (pp. 147–162). Silver Spring, MD: American Music Therapy Association.

Jay, S., & Elliott, C. (1986). *Observation scale of behavioral distress-revised.* (Available from Susan M. Jay, Ph.D., Psychosocial Program, Division of Hematology-Oncology, Children's Hospital of Los Angeles, California, 90027).

Jellison, J. (1975). The effect of music on autonomic stress responses and verbal reports. In C. K. Madsen, R. D. Greer, & C. H. Madsen, Jr. (Eds.), *Research in music behavior* (pp. 206–219). Teachers College Press, Columbia University, New York.

Johnson, B. (1989). *DSTAT: Software for the meta-analytic review of research literature.* Hillsdale, NJ: Lawrence Erlbaum Associates.

Johnson, G., Otto, D., & Clair, A. (2001). The effects of instrumental and vocal music on adherence to a physical rehabilitation exercise program with persons who are elderly. *Journal of Music Therapy*, *38*(2), 82.

Jones, R., Hux, K., Morton-Anderson, K., & Knepper, L. (1994). Auditory stimulation effect on a comatose survivor. *Archives of Physical Medicine and Rehabilitation, 75*(2), 164–171.

Joyce, B., Keck, J., & Gerkensmeyer, J. (2001). Evaluation of pain management interventions for neonatal circumcision pain. *Journal of Pediatric Healthcare, 15*(3), 105–114.

Judd, E. (1982). *Music therapy on a kidney dialysis unit: A pilot study.* Unpublished master's thesis, Hahnemann University, Philadelphia, PA.

Kaempf, G., & Amodei, G. (1989). The effect of music on anxiety. *AORN Journal, 50*(1), 112–118.

Kamin, A., Kamin, H., Spintge, R., & Droh, R. (1982). Endocrine effect of anxiolytic music and psychological counseling before surgery. In R. Droh & R. Spintge (Ed.), *Angst, schmerz, musik in der anasthesie* (pp. 163–166). Basel: Editiones Roche.

Kaminski, J., & Hall, W. (1996). The effect of soothing music on neonatal behavioral states in the hospital newborn nursery. *Neonatal Network, 15*(1), 45–54.

Kamps, M. (1992). *The effects of singing on the respiratory abilities of cystic fibrosis patients.* Unpublished research paper, The Florida State University, Tallahassee.

Katz, V. (1971). Auditory stimulation and developmental behavior of the premature infant. *Nursing Research, 20,* 196–201.

Keller, V. (1995). Management of nausea and vomiting in children. *Journal of Pediatric Nursing, 10*(5), 280–286.

Kendelhardt, A. (2003). *The effect of live music on exercise duration, negative verbalizations, and self-perception of pain, anxiety and rehabilitation levels of physical therapy patients.* Unpublished master's thesis, The Florida State University, Tallahassee.

King, J. (1982). *Music therapy results with pediatric patients.* Unpublished research manuscript, The Florida State University, Tallahassee.

King, J. (1984). *Five case studies: The integrative use of music therapy with hospitalized children on a pediatric ward.* Unpublished research study, The Florida State University, Tallahassee.

Kleiber, C., & Harper, D. (1999). Effects of distraction on children's pain and distress during medical procedures: A meta-analysis. *Nursing Research, 48*(1), 44–49.

Knight, W., & Rickard, N. (2001). Relaxing music prevents stress-induced increases in subjective anxiety, systolic blood pressure and heart rate in healthy males and females. *Journal of Music Therapy, 38*(4), 254.

Kopp, M. (1991). Music's affect on stress-related responses during surgery. *The Kansas Nurse, 66*(7), 4–5.

Kovacs, M. (1992). *Children's Depression Inventory.* North Tonawanda, NY: Multi-Health Systems.

Kozak, Y. (1968). Music therapy for orthopedic patients in a rehabilitative setting. In E. T. Gaston (Ed.), *Music in therapy* (pp. 166–168). New York: Macmillan.

Kuhn, D. (2002). The effects of active and passive participation in musical activity on the immune system as measured by salivary immunoglobulin A (SIgA). *Journal of Music Therapy, 39*(1), 30.

Kumar, A., Bajaj, A., Sarkar, P., & Grover, V. (1992). The effect of music on ketamine induced emergence phenomena. *Anaesthesia, 47*, 438–439.

Landreth, J., & Landreth, M. (1974). Effects of music on physiological response. *Journal of Research in Music Education, 22*, 4–12.

Lane, D. (1991a). *The effect of a single music therapy session on hospitalized children as measured by salivary Immunoglobulin A, speech pause time, and a patient opinion Likert scale.* Unpublished doctoral dissertation, Case Western Reserve University, Cleveland, OH. (UMI No. 9137062)

Lane, D. (1991b). The effect of a single music therapy session on hospitalized children as measured by salivary Immunoglobulin A, speech pause time, and a patient opinion Likert scale. *Pediatric Research, 29*(4, part 2), 11A.

Larson, K., & Ayllon, T. (1990). The effects of contingent music and differential reinforcement on infantile colic. *Behavior Research Therapy, 28*(2), 119–125.

Lavine, R., Buchsbaum, M., & Poncy, M. (1976). Auditory analgesia: Somatosensory evoked response and subjective pain rating. *Psychophysiology, 13*, 140–148.

Lehrer, P., Hochron, S., Mayne, T., Isenberg, S., Carlson, V., Lasoski, A., Gilchrist, J., Morales, D., & Rausch, L. (1994). Relaxation and music therapies for asthma among patients prestabilized on asthma medication. *Journal of Behavioral Medicine, 17*(1), 1–24.

LeLorier, J., Gregoire, G., Benhaddad, A., Lapierre, J, & Deriderian, F. (1997). Discrepancies between meta-analyses and subsequent large randomized, controlled trials. *The New England Journal of Medicine, 337*(8), 536–542.

Levine-Gross, J., & Swartz, R. (1982). The effects of music therapy on anxiety in chronically ill patients. *Music Therapy, 2*(1), 43–52.

Liebman, S., & MacLaren, A. (1991). The effects of music and relaxation on third trimester anxiety in adolescent pregnancy. *Journal of Music Therapy, 28*(2), 89–100.

Liebman, S., & MacLaren, A. (1993). The effects of music and relaxation on third trimester anxiety in adolescent pregnancy. In F. J. Bejjani (Ed.), *Current research in arts medicine* (pp. 427–430). Chicago: A Cappella Books.

Light, G., Love, D., Benson, D., & Morch, E. (1954). Music in surgery. *Current Researches in Anesthesia and Analgesia, 33,* 258–264.

Lindsay, K. (1981). The value of music for hospitalized infants. *Journal of the Association for the Care of Children in Hospitals, 9*(4), 104–107.

Lininger, L. (1987). *The effects of instrumental and vocal lullabies on the crying behavior of newborn infants.* Unpublished master's thesis, Southern Methodist University, Dallas, TX.

Livingood, A., Kiser, K., & Paige, N. (1984). *A study of families to determine the effect of sedate music on their state anxiety level while they await the out-come of surgery.* Unpublished study, Eastern Kentucky University, Richmond, KY.

Livingston, J. (1979). Music for the childbearing family. *JOGN Nursing, 8,* 363–367.

Lochner, C., & Stevenson, R. (1988). Music as a bridge to wholeness. *Death Studies, 12*(2), 173–180.

Locsin, R. (1981). The effect of music on the pain of selected post-operative patients. *Journal of Advanced Nursing, 6,* 19–25.

Loewy, J. (1999). The use of music psychotherapy in the treatment of pediatric pain. In C. Dileo (Ed.), *Music therapy and medicine: Theoretical and clinical applications* (pp. 189–206). Silver Spring, MD: American Music Therapy Association.

Loewy, J. (Ed.). (1997). *Music therapy and pediatric pain.* Cherry Hill, NJ: Jeffrey Books.

Long, L., & Johnson, J. (1978). Dental practice using music to aid relaxation and relieve pain. *Dental Survey, 54,* 35–38.

Lorch, C., Lorch, V., Diefendorf, A., & Earl, P. (1994). Effect of stimulative and sedative music on systolic blood pressure, heart rate, and respiratory rate in premature infants. *Journal of Music Therapy, 31*(2), 105–118.

Lutz, W. (1997). *The effect of music distraction on children's pain, fear, and behavior during laceration repairs.* Unpublished master's thesis, The University of Texas at Arlington.

MacClelland, D. (1979). Music in the operating room. *AORN Journal, 29*(2), 252–260.

Madsen, C., Jr., & Madsen, C. (1981). *Teaching/discipline: A positive approach for educational development.* Boston: Allyn & Bacon.

Madsen, C., Standley, J., & Gregory, D. (1991). The effect of a vibrotactile device, Somatron™, on physiological and psychological responses: Musicians versus non-musicians. *Journal of Music Therapy, 28*(1), 14–22.

Magee, W., & Davidson, J. (2002). The effect of music therapy on mood states in neurological patients: A pilot study. *Journal of Music Therapy, 39*(1), 20.

Malloy, G. (1979). The relationship between maternal and musical auditory stimulation and the developmental behavior of premature infants. *Birth Defects: Original Article Series, 15*(7), 81–98.

Malone, A. (1996). The effects of live music on the distress of pediatric patients receiving intravenous starts, venipunctures, injections, and heel sticks. *Journal of Music Therapy, 33*(1), 19–33.

Mandle, C., Domar, A., Harrington, D., Leserman, J., Bozadjian, E., Friedman, R., & Benson, H. (1990). Relaxation response in femoral angiography. *Radiology, 174*(3), 737–739.

Mann, C. (1990). Meta-analysis in the breech. *Science, 249,* 476–480.

Marchette, L., Main, R., Redick, E., & Shapiro, A. (1989). Pain reduction during neonatal circumcision. In R. Spintge & R. Droh (Eds.), *MusicMedicine* (pp. 131–136). Ann Arbor, MI: Malloy Lithographing.

Marchette, L., Main, R., Redick, E., Bagg, A., & Leatherland, J. (1991). Pain reduction interventions during neonatal circumcision. *Nursing Research, 40*(4), 241–244.

Marley, L. (1984). The use of music with hospitalized infants and toddlers: A descriptive study. *Journal of Music Therapy, 21*(3), 126–132.

Marrero, D., Fremion, A., & Golden, M. (1988). Improving compliance with exercise in adolescents with insulin-dependent diabetes mellitus: Results of a self-motivated home exercise program. *Pediatrics, 81*(4), 519–525.

Martin, M. (1987). *The influence of combining preferred music with progressive relaxation and biofeedback techniques on frontalis muscle.* Unpublished master's thesis, Southern Methodist University, Dallas, TX.

Marwick, C. (2000, January 26). Music hath charms for care of preemies. *Journal of the American Medical Association,* 468–469.

Maslar, P. (1986). The effect of music on the reduction of pain: A review of the literature. *The Arts in Psychotherapy, 13,* 215–219.

McDonnell, L. (1984). Music therapy with trauma patients and their families on a pediatric service. *Music Therapy, 4,* 55–66.

McDowell, C. (1966). Obstetrical applications of audioanalgesia. *Hospital Topics, 44,* 102–104.

McElwain, J. (1993). The effect of Somatron and music on headache. In F. J. Bejjani (Ed.), *Current research in arts medicine* (pp. 437–439). Chicago: A Cappella Books.

Megel, M., Houser, C., & Gleaves, L. (1998). Children's responses to immunizations: Lullabies as a distraction. *Issues in Comprehensive Pediatric Nursing, 21*(3), 129–145.

Melzack, R., Weisz, A., & Sprague, L. (1963). Stratagems for controlling pain: Contributions of auditory stimulation and suggestion. *Experimental Neurology, 8,* 239–247.

Menegazzi, J., Paris, P., Kersteen, C., Flynn, B., & Trautman, D. (1991). A randomized, controlled trial of the use of music during laceration repair. *Annals of Emergency Medicine, 20*(4), 348–350.

Metzler, R., & Berman, T. (1991). The effect of sedative music on the anxiety of bronchoscopy patients. In C. D. Maranto (Ed.), *Applications of music in medicine* (pp. 163–178). Washington, DC: National Association for Music Therapy.

Micci, N. (1984). The use of music therapy with pediatric patients undergoing cardiac catheterization. *The Arts in Psychotherapy, 11,* 261–266.

Miller, A., Hickman, L., & Lemasters, G. (1992). A distraction technique for control of burn pain. *The Journal of Burn Care and Rehabilitation, 13*(5), 576–580.

Miller, L. (1984). *Spontaneous music therapy sessions for hospitalized children.* Unpublished research paper, The Florida State University, Tallahassee.

Miluk-Kolasa, B., Matejek, M., & Stupnicki, R. (1996). The effects of music listening on changes in selected physiological parameters in adult pre-surgical patients. *Journal of Music Therapy, 33*(3), 208–218.

Miluk-Kolasa, B., Obminski, Z., Stupnicki, R., & Golec, L. (1994). Effects of music treatment on salivary cortisol in patients exposed to pre-surgical stress. *Experimental and Clinical Endocrinology, 102*(2), 118–120.

Monsey, H. (1960). Preliminary report of the clinical efficacy of audioanalgesia. *Journal of California State Dental Association, 36,* 432–437.

Moore, R., Gladstone, I., & Standley, J. (1994, November). *Effects of music, maternal voice, intrauterine sounds and white noise on the oxygen saturation levels of premature infants.* Unpublished paper presented at the National Conference of the National Association for Music Therapy, Orlando, FL.

Moore, W., Browne, J., & Hill, I. (1964). Effect of white sound on pain threshold. *British Journal of Anaesthesia, 36,* 268–271.

Morosko, T., & Simmons, F. (1966). The effect of audioanalgesia on pain threshold and pain tolerance. *Journal of Dental Research, 45,* 1608–1617.

Moss, V. (1987). The effect of music on anxiety in the surgical patient. *Perioperative Nursing Quarterly, 3*(1), 9–16.

Mowatt, K. (1967). Background music during radiotherapy. *Medical Journal, Australia, 1,* 185–186.

Mullooly, V., Levin, R., & Feldman, H. (1988). Music for postoperative pain and anxiety. *The Journal of the New York State Nurses Association, 19*(2), 4–7.

Munro, S. (1984). *Music therapy in palliative/hospice care.* St. Louis, MO: MMB Music.

Nguyen, J. (2003). *The effect of music therapy on end-of-life patients' quality of life, emotional state, and family satisfaction as measured by self-report.* Unpublished master's thesis, The Florida State University.

Ogenfuss, J. (2001). *Pediatric surgery and patient anxiety: Can music therapy effectively reduce stress and anxiety levels while waiting to go to surgery?* Unpublished master's thesis, The Florida State University, Tallahassee, FL.

Ohlsen, J. (1967). Audioanalgesia in podiatry. *Journal of the American Podiatry Association, 57,* 153–156.

Owens, L. (1979). The effects of music on the weight loss, crying, and physical movement of newborns. *Journal of Music Therapy, 16,* 83–90.

Oyama, T., Hatano, K., Sato, Y., Kudo, M., Spintge, R., & Droh, R. (1983). Endocrine effect of anxiolytic music in dental patients. In R. Droh & R. Spintge (Eds.), *Angst, schmerz, musik in der anasthesie* (pp. 143–146). Basel: Editiones Roche.

Oyama, T., Sato, Y., Kudo, M., Spintge, R., & Droh, R. (1983). Effect of anxiolytic music on endocrine function in surgical patients. In R. Droh & R. Spintge (Eds.). *Angst, schmerz, musik in der anasthesie* (pp. 147–152). Basel: Editiones Roche.

Pacchetti, C., Aglieri, R., Mancini, F., Martignoni, E., & Nappi, G. (1998). Active music therapy and Parkinson's disease: Methods. *Functional Neurology, 13*(1), 57–67.

Padfield, A. (1976). Letter: Music as sedation for local analgesia. *Anasthesia, 31,* 300–301.

Peretti, P., & Swenson, K. (1974). Effects of music on anxiety as determined by physiological skin responses. *Journal of Research in Music Education, 22,* 278–283.

Pfaff, V., Smith, K., & Gowan, D. (1989). The effects of music-assisted relaxation on the distress of pediatric cancer patients undergoing bone marrow aspirations. *Children's Health Care, 18*(4), 232–236.

Pfister, T., Berrol, C., & Caplan, C. (1998). Effects of music on exercise and perceived symptoms in patients with chronic obstructive pulmonary disease. *Journal of Cardiopulmonary Rehabilitation, 18*(3), 228–232.

Phillips, J. (1980). Music in the nursing of elderly persons in nursing homes. *Journal of Gerontological Nursing, 6*(1), 37–39.

Prensner, J., Fratianne, R., Yowler, C., Standley, J., Steele, A., & Smith, L. (2000, March). *The effect of music based imagery and musical alternate engagement on the burn debridement process.* Paper presented at the National Conference of the American Burn Association, Las Vegas, NV.

Rasco, C. (1992). Using music therapy as distraction during lumbar punctures. *Journal of Pediatric Oncology Nursing, 9*(1), 33–34.

Richards, K. (1998). Effect of a back massage and relaxation intervention on sleep in critically ill patients. *American Journal of Critical Care, 7*(4), 288–299.

Rickert, V., Kozlowski, K., Warren, A., Hendron, A., & Davis, P. (1994). Adolescents and colposcopy: The use of different procedures to reduce anxiety. *American Journal of Obstetrics and Gynecology, 170*(2), 504–508.

Rider, M. (1985). Entrainment mechanisms are involved in pain reduction, muscle relaxation, and music-mediated imagery. *Journal of Music Therapy, 22*(4), 183–192.

Rider, M., & Kibler, V. (1990). Treating arthritis and lupus patients with music-mediated imagery and group psychotherapy. *The Arts in Psychotherapy, 17,* 29–33.

Ridgeway, R. (1983). Another perspective: A story—and a question. *Music Therapy Perspectives, 1*(2), 2–3.

Robb, S. (1996). Techniques in song writing: Restoring emotional and physical well being in adolescents who have been traumatically injured. *Music Therapy Perspectives, 14* (1), 30–37.

Robb, S. (2000a). The effect of therapeutic music interventions on the behavior of hospitalized children in isolation: Developing a contextual support model of music therapy. *Journal of Music Therapy, 37*(2), 118–146.

Robb, S. (2000b). Music assisted progressive muscle relaxation, progressive muscle relaxation, music listening, and silence. *Journal of Music Therapy, 37*(1), 2.

Robb, S. (2003). *Music therapy in pediatric healthcare.* Silver Spring, MD: American Music Therapy Association.

Robb, S., & Ebberts, A. (2003). Songwriting and digital video production interventions for pediatric patients undergoing bone marrow transplantation part I: An analysis of depression and anxiety levels according to phase of treatment. *Journal of Pediatric Oncology Nursing, 20,* 1–14.

Robb, S., Nichols, R., Rutan, R., Bishop, B., & Parker, J. (1995). The effects of music assisted relaxation on preoperative anxiety. *Journal of Music Therapy, 32*(1), 2–21.

Roberts, C. (1986). *Music: A nursing intervention for increased intracranial pressure.* Unpublished master's thesis, Grand Valley State College, Allendale, MI.

Roberts, P. (2002). *The effect of contingent music with physical therapy in children who toe-walk.* Unpublished master's thesis, The Florida State University, Tallahassee.

Robinson, D. (1962). Music therapy in a general hospital. *Bulletin of the National Association for Music Therapy, 11*(3), 13–18.

Robson, J., & Davenport, H. (1962). The effects of white sound and music upon the superficial pain threshold. *Canadian Anaesthetists' Society Journal, 9,* 105–108.

Roter, M. (1957). *The use of music in medical reception rooms.* Unpublished master's thesis, University of Kansas, Lawrence.

Rudenberg, M., & Royka, A. (1989). Promoting psychosocial adjustment in pediatric burn patients through music therapy and child life therapy. *Music Therapy Perspectives, 7,* 40–43.

Sabo, C., & Michael, S. (1996). The influence of personal message with music on anxiety and side effects associated with chemotherapy. *Cancer Nursing, 19*(4), 283–289.

Sammons, L. (1984). The use of music by women in childbirth. *Journal of Nurse-Midwifery, 29*(4), 266–270.

Sanderson, S. (1984). *Music therapy with a terminally ill cancer patient.* Unpublished research manuscript, The Florida State University, Tallahassee.

Sanderson, S. (1986). T*he effect of music on reducing preoperative anxiety and postoperative anxiety and pain in the recovery room.* Unpublished master's thesis, The Florida State University, Tallahassee.

Scartelli, J. (1982). The effect of sedative music on electromyographic biofeedback assisted relaxation training of spastic cerebral palsied adults. *Journal of Music Therapy, 19,* 210–218.

Scartelli, J. (1984). The effect of EMG biofeedback and sedative music, EMG biofeedback only, and sedative music only on frontalis muscle relaxation ability. *Journal of Music Therapy, 21,* 67–78.

Schermer, R. (1960). Distraction analgesia using the stereogesic portable. *Military Medicine, 125,* 843–848.

Scheve, A. (2002). *The effect of music therapy intervention on preoperative anxiety of pediatric patients as measured by self-report.* Unpublished thesis, The Florida State University, Tallahassee.

Schieffelin, C. (1988, April). *A case study: Stevens–Johnson Syndrome.* Paper presented at the annual conference of the Southeastern Conference of the National Association for Music Therapy, Tallahassee, FL.

Schinner, K., Chisholm, A., Grap, M., Siva, P., Hallinan, M., & LaVoice-Hawkins, A. (1995). Effects of auditory stimuli on intracranial pressure and cerebral perfusion pressure in traumatic brain injury. *Journal of Neuroscience Nursing, 27*(6), 348–354.

Schneider, F. (1982). *Assessment and evaluation of audio-analgesic effects on the pain experience of acutely burned children during dressing changes.* Unpublished doctoral dissertation, University of Cincinnati, OH.

Schorr, J. (1993). Music and pattern change in chronic pain. *Advances in Nursing Science, 15*(4), 27–36.

Schur, J. (1986). *Alleviating behavioral distress with music or Lamaze pant-blow breathing in children undergoing bone marrow aspirations and lumbar punctures.* Unpublished doctoral dissertation, The University of Texas Health Science Center at Dallas.

Schuster, B. (1985). The effect of music listening on blood pressure fluctuations in adult hemodialysis patients. *Journal of Music Therapy, 22,* 146–153.

Schwankovsky, L., & Guthrie, P. (1982). *Music therapy for handicapped children: Other health impaired.* NAMT Monograph Series. Washington, DC: National Association for Music Therapy.

Sedei, C. (1980). *The effectiveness of music therapy on specific statements verbalized by cancer patients.* Unpublished manuscript, Colorado State University, Fort Collins.

Shapiro, A., & Cohen, H. (1983). Auxiliary pain relief during suction curettage. In R. Droh & R. Spintge (Eds.), *Angst, schmerz, musik in der anasthesia* (pp. 89–93). Basel: Editiones Roche.

Siegel, S. (1983). *The use of music as treatment in pain perception with post surgical patients in a pediatric hospital.* Unpublished master's thesis, The University of Miami, Coral Gables, FL.

Simpson, J., & Burns, D. (2003). *Music therapy reimbursement: Best practices and procedures.* Silver Spring, MD: American Music Therapy Association.

Skille, O., Wigram, T., & Weeks, L. (1989). Vibroacoustic therapy: The therapeutic effect of low frequency sound on specific physical disorders and disabilities. *Journal of British Music Therapy, 3*(2), 6–10.

Slesnick, J. (1983). *Music in medicine: A critical review.* Unpublished master's thesis, Hahnemann University, Philadelphia, PA.

Slivka, H., & Magill, L. (1986). The conjoint use of social work and music therapy in working with children of cancer patients, *Music Therapy, 6A*(1), 30–40.

Snow, W., & Fields, B. (1950). Music as an adjunct in the training of children with cerebral palsy. *Occupational Therapy, 29,* 147–156.

Spielberger, C., Gorsuch, R., & Lushene, R. (1970). *State-trait anxiety inventory test manual.* Palo Alto, CA: Consulting Psychologists Press.

Spintge, R. (1982). Psychophysiological surgery preparation with and without anxiolytic music. In R. Droh & R. Spintge (Eds.), *Angst, schmerz, music in der anasthesie* (pp. 77–88). Basel: Editiones Roche.

Spintge, R., & Droh, R. (1982). The preoperative condition of 1910 patients exposed to anxiolytic music and Rohypnol (Flurazepam) before receiving an epidural anesthetic. In R. Droh & R. Spintge (Eds.), *Angst, scherz, music in der anasthesie* (pp. 193–196). Basel: Editiones Roche.

Standley, J. (1986). Music research in medical/dental treatment: Meta-analysis and clinical applications. *Journal of Music Therapy, 23*(2), 56–122.

Standley, J. (1988). Music research in medical/dental treatment: Meta-analysis and clinical applications. In C. E. Furman (Ed.), *Effectiveness of music therapy procedures: Documentation of research and clinical practice* (pp. 9–61). Washington, DC: National Association for Music Therapy.

Standley, J. (1991a). The effect of vibrotactile and auditory stimuli on perception of comfort, heart rate, and peripheral finger temperature. *Journal of Music Therapy, 28*(3), 120–134.

Standley, J. (1991b). Long-term benefits of music intervention in the newborn intensive care unit: A pilot study. *Journal of the International Association of Music for the Handicapped, 6*(1), 12–23.

Standley, J. (1991c). The role of music in pacification/stimulation of premature infants with low birthweights. *Music Therapy Perspectives, 9,* 19–25.

Standley, J. (1992a). Clinical applications of music and chemotherapy: The effects on nausea and emesis. *Music Therapy Perspectives, 10*(1), 27–35.

Standley, J. (1992b). Meta-analysis of research in music and medical treatment: Effect size as a basis for comparison across multiple dependent and independent variables. In R. Spintge & R. Droh (Eds.), *MusicMedicine* (pp. 364–378). St. Louis, MO: MMB.

Standley, J. (1993). Music research in medical/dental treatment: Meta-analysis and clinical implications. Reprinted in C. E. Furman (Ed.), *Effectiveness of music therapy procedures: Documentation of research and clinical practice* (pp. 9-61). Washington, DC: National Association for Music Therapy.

Standley, J. (1994). Music research in medical/dental treatment: Meta-analysis and clinical implications. Reprinted in J. M. Standley & C. A. Prickett (Eds.), *Research in music therapy: A tradition in excellence* (pp. 261–292). Silver Spring, MD: National Association for Music Therapy.

Standley, J. (1995). Music as a therapeutic intervention in medical/dental treatment: Research and clinical implications. In T. Wigram, B. Saperston, & R. West (Eds.), *The art and science of music therapy: A handbook* (pp. 3–22). London: Harwood Academic.

Standley, J. (1996a). A meta-analysis on the effects of music as reinforcement for education/ therapy objectives. *Journal of Research in Music Education, 44*(2), 105–133.

Standley, J. (1996b). Music research in medical/dental treatment: an update of a prior meta-analysis. In C. Furman (Ed.), *Effectiveness of music therapy procedures: Documentation of Research and Clinical Practice* (2nd ed.; pp. 1–60). Silver Spring, MD: National Association for Music Therapy.

Standley, J. (1998a). The effect of music and multimodal stimulation on physiological and developmental responses of premature infants in neonatal intensive care. *Pediatric Nursing, 24*(6), 532–539.

Standley, J. (1998b). A meta-analysis on the effects of music as reinforcement for education/ therapy objectives. Reprinted in H. E. Price (Ed.), *Music education research: An anthology from the Journal of Music Education* (pp. 538–566). Reston, VA: Music Educators National Conference.

Standley, J. (1998c). Pre and perinatal growth and development: Implications of music benefits for premature infants. *International Journal of Music Education, 31,* 1–13.

Standley, J. (1999a). Music therapy in the NICU: Pacifier-Activated Lullabies (PAL) for reinforcement of non-nutritive sucking. *International Journal of Arts Medicine, 6*(2), 17–21.

Standley, J. (1999b). Music therapy research with premature infants: Clinical implications. In R. R. Pratt & D. E. Grocke (Eds.), *MusicMedicine 3, MusicMedicine and Music Therapy: Expanding Horizons* (pp. 131–139). Parkville, Victoria, Australia: U. of Melbourne Press.

Standley, J. (2000a). The effect of contingent music to increase non-nutritive sucking of premature infants. *Pediatric Nursing, 26*(5), 493–495, 498–499.

Standley, J. (2000b). Music research in medical treatment. In American Music Therapy Association (Ed.), *Effectiveness of music therapy procedures: Documentation of research and clinical practice* (3rd ed.; pp. 1–64). Silver Spring, MD: American Music Therapy Association.

Standley, J. (2001a). Music therapy for premature infants in neonatal intensive care: Physiological and developmental benefits. *Early Childhood Connections, 7*(2), 18–25.

Standley, J. (2001b). Music therapy for the neonate. *Newborn and Infant Nursing Reviews, 1*(4), 211–216.

Standley, J. (2001c). Musicoterapia para recien prematuros en cuidados intensivos neonatales (Music therapy for premature infants in neonatal intensive care). (Spanish translation by C. Clancy). *Acta Pediatrica Espanola, 59*(11), 623–629.

Standley, J. (2001d, Spring). The power of contingent music for infant learning. *Bulletin of the Council for Research in Music Education, 149,* 65–71.

Standley, J. (2002a). A meta-analysis of the efficacy of music therapy for premature infants. *Journal of Pediatric Nursing, 17*(2), 107–113.

Standley, J. (2002b). *Music techniques in therapy, counseling and special education* (2nd ed.). St. Louis: MMB.

Standley, J. (2002c). Music therapy in the NICU: Promoting the growth and development of premature infants. *Zero to Three, 25*(1), 23–30.

Standley, J. (2003a). The effect of music-reinforced non-nutritive sucking on feeding rate of premature infants. *Journal of Pediatric Nursing, 17*(2), 107–113.

Standley, J. (2003b). *Music therapy with premature infants: Research and developmental interventions.* Silver Spring, MD: American Music Therapy Association.

Standley, J. M., & Hanser, S. B. (1995). Music therapy research and applications in pediatric oncology treatment. *Journal of Pediatric Oncology Nursing, 12*(1), 3–8.

Standley, J. M., & Hughes, J. E. (1996). Documenting developmentally appropriate objectives and benefits of a music therapy program for early intervention: A behavioral analysis. *Music Therapy Perspectives, 14*(2), 87–94.

Standley, J., & Madsen, C. (1990). Comparison of infant preferences and responses to auditory stimuli: Music, mother, and other female voice. *Journal of Music Therapy, 27*(2), 54–97.

Standley, J., & Madsen, C. (1994). Comparison of infant preferences and responses to auditory stimuli: Music, mother, and other female voice. Reprinted in J. M. Standley and C. A. Prickett (Eds.), *Research in music therapy: A tradition in excellence* (pp. 680–713). Silver Spring, MD: National Association for Music Therapy.

Standley, J., & Moore, R. (1995). Therapeutic effects of music and mother's voice on premature infants. *Pediatric Nursing, 21*(6), 509–512.

Standley, J., & Moore, R. (1996). Therapeutic effects of music and mother's voice on premature infants. Abstracted in M. Broome (Ed.), *Capsules and comments in pediatric nursing.* Chicago: Mosby-Year Book.

Standley, J., & Prickett, C. (Eds.). (1994). *Research in music therapy: A tradition of excellence.* Silver Spring, MD: National Association for Music Therapy.

Standley, J., & Whipple, J. (2003a). Pediatric music therapy: A meta-analysis. In S. Robb (Ed.), *Music therapy in pediatric healthcare: Research and best practice* (pp.1–18). Silver Spring, MD: American Music Therapy Association.

Standley, J., & Whipple, J. (2003b). Music therapy for premature infants in the Neonatal Intensive Care Unit: Health and developmental benefits. In S. Robb (Ed.), *Music therapy in pediatric healthcare: Research and best practice* (pp.19–30). Silver Spring, MD: American Music Therapy Association.

Staum, M. (1983). Music and rhythmic stimuli in the rehabilitation of gait disorders. *Journal of Music Therapy, 20,* 69–87.

Steelman, V. (1990). Intraoperative music therapy. *AORN Journal, 52*(5), 1026–1034.

Stein, A. (1991). Music to reduce anxiety during Caesarean births. In C. D. Maranto (Ed.), *Applications of music in medicine* (pp. 179–190). Washington, DC: National Association for Music Therapy.

Steinke, W. (1991). The use of music, relaxation, and imagery in the management of postsurgical pain for scoliosis. In C. D. Maranto (Ed.), *Applications of music in medicine* (pp. 141–162). Washington, DC: National Association for Music Therapy.

Stevens, K. (1990). Patients' perceptions of music during surgery. *Journal of Advanced Nursing, 15,* 1045–1051.

Stice, K., & Mornhinweg, G. (1995). Effect of imagery with music on anxiety and dyspnea in patients with chronic obstructive pulmonary disease. *Kentucky Nurse, 43*(3), 37.

Strauser, J. (1997). The effects of music versus silence on measures of state anxiety, perceived relaxation, and physiological responses of patients receiving chiropractic interventions. *Journal of Music Therapy, 34*(2), 88–105.

Tanioka, F., Takazawa, T., Kamata, S., Kudo, M., Matsuki, A., & Oyama, T. (1985). Hormonal effect of anxiolytic music in patients during surgical operations under epidural anaesthesia. In R. Spintge & R. Droh, (Eds.), *Music in medicine* (pp. 285–290). Basel: Editiones Roche.

Taylor, D. (1981). Music in general hospital treatment from 1900 to 1950. *Journal of Music Therapy, 18,* 62–73.

Taylor, L., Kuttler, K., Parks, T., & Milton, D. (1998). The effect of music in the postanesthesia care unit on pain levels in women who have had abdominal hysterectomies. *Journal of PeriAnesthesia Nursing, 13*(2), 88–94.

Thornby, M., Haas, F., & Axen, K. (1995). Effect of distractive auditory stimuli on exercise tolerance in patients with COPD. *Chest, 107*(5), 1213–1217.

Tsao, C., Gordon, T., Maranto, C., Lerman, C., & Murasko, D. (1991). The effects of music and directed biological imagery on immune response (S-IgA). In C. D. Maranto (Ed.),

Applications of music in medicine (pp. 85–121). Washington, DC: National Association for Music Therapy.

Tusek, D., Church, J., & Fazio, V. (1997). Guided imagery as a coping strategy for perioperative patients. *AORN Journal, 66*(4), 644–649.

Updike, P. (1990). Music therapy results for ICU patients. *Dimensions of Critical Care Nursing, 9*(1), 39–45.

Updike, P., & Charles, D. (1987). Music Rx: Physiological and emotional responses to taped music programs of preoperative patients awaiting plastic surgery. *Annals of Plastic Surgery, 19*(1), 29–33.

Vincent, S., & Thompson, J. (1929). The effects of music upon the human blood pressure. *The Lancet, 1,* 534–537.

Wade, L. (2002). A comparison of the effects of vocal exercises/singing versus music-assisted relaxation on peak expiratory flow rates of children with asthma. *Music Therapy Perspectives, 20*(1), 31–37.

Wagner, M. (1975). Brainwaves and biofeedback: A brief history. *Journal of Music Therapy, 12,* 46–58.

Waldon, E. (2001). The effects of group music therapy on mood states and cohesiveness in adult oncology patients. *Journal of Music Therapy, 38*(3), 212.

Walters, C. (1996). The psychological and physiological effects of vibrotactile stimulation, via a Somatron, on patients awaiting scheduled gynecological surgery. *Journal of Music Therapy, 33*(4), 261–287.

Walther-Larsen, S., Diemar, V., & Valentin, N. (1988, April–June). Music during regional anesthesia: A reduced need of sedatives. *Regional Anesthesia, 13,* 69–71.

Walworth, D. (2002, November). *Music therapy as procedural support: Benefits for patients and staff.* Research paper presented at National Conference of the American Music Therapy Association, Atlanta, GA.

Walworth, D. (2003). Procedural support: Music therapy assisted CT, EKG, EEG, X-ray, IV, ventilator, and emergency services. In S. L. Robb (Ed.), *Music therapy in pediatric healthcare research and evidence-based practice* (pp. 147–162). Silver Spring, MD: American Music Therapy Association.

Weisbrod, R. (1969, January). Audio analgesia revisited. *Anesthesia Progress,* 8–15.

Whipple, J. (2000). The effect of parent training in music and multimodal stimulation on parent-neonate interactions in the neonatal intensive care unit. *Journal of Music Therapy, 37*(4), 250–268.

Whipple, J. (2003). Surgery Buddies: A music therapy program for pediatric surgical patients. *Music Therapy Perspectives, 21*(2), 77–83.

Whipple, J. (in press). Music and multimodal stimulation as developmental intervention in neonatal intensive care. *Music Therapy Perspectives.*

White, J. (1992). Music therapy: An intervention to reduce anxiety in the myocardial infarction patient. *Clinical Nurse Specialist, 6*(2), 58–63.

Wiand, N. (1997). Relaxation levels achieved by Lamaze-trained pregnant women listening to music and ocean sound tapes. *The Journal of Perinatal Education, 6*(4), 1–8.

Winokur, M. (1984). *The use of music as an audio-analgesia during childbirth.* Unpublished master's thesis, The Florida State University, Tallahassee.

Wolfe, D. (1978). Pain rehabilitation and music therapy. *Journal of Music Therapy, 15*(4), 184–206.

Wolfe, D. (1980). The effect of automated interrupted music on head posturing of cerebral palsied individuals. *Journal of Music Therapy, 17,* 184–206.

Wong, E. (2003). *Clinical guide to music therapy in physical rehabilitation settings.* Silver Spring, MD: American Music Therapy Association.

Wylie, M., & Blom, R. (1986). Guided imagery and music with hospice patients. *Music Therapy Perspectives, 3,* 25–29.

Zelazny, C. (2001). Therapeutic instrumental playing in hand rehabilitation for older adults with Osteoarthritis: Four case studies. *Journal of Music Therapy, 38*(2), 97.

Zimmerman, L., Pierson, M., & Marker, J. (1988). Effects of music on patient anxiety in coronary care units. *Heart and Lung, 17*(5), 560–566.

Zimmerman, L., Pozehl, B., Duncan, K., & Schmitz, R. (1989). Effects of music in patients who had chronic cancer pain. *Western Journal of Nursing Research, 11*(3), 298–309.

Zimny, G., & Weidenfeller, E. (1963). Effects of music upon GSR and heart rate. *American Journal of Psychology, 76,* 311–314.

Glossaries
and Indexes

GLOSSARY OF COMMONLY USED
MEDICAL ABBREVIATIONS

@	at
A/B	apnea/bradycardia
ab	abortion
ad lib	ad libitum (freely)
ADL	activities of daily living
aeb	as evidenced by
AGA	adjusted gestational age
AIDS	acquired immunodeficiency syndrome
ALF	assisted living facility
ante-	before
ARNP	advanced registered nurse practitioner
ANS	autonomic nervous system
B/C	because
BCBS	Blue Cross Blue Shield
BHC	Behavioral Health Center
BID	bis in die (twice a day)
bilat	bilateral
bili	bilirubin
BMI	body mass index
BO	bottle (feeding)
BP	blood pressure
BR	breast (feeding)
BUN	blood urea nitrogen
c̄	cum (with)
cc	cubic centimetre
CABG	coronary artery bypass surgery/grafting
CAD	coronary artery disease
CAT	computed axial tomography
CBC	complete blood count
CCLS	certified child life specialist
CGA	corrected gestational age
CHF	congestive heart failure
CHI	closed head injury
CHP	Capitol Health Plan
CICU	Cardiac Intensive Care Unit
cm	centimeter
CNA	Clinical Nursing Assistant

CNS	central nervous system; Clinical Nurse Specialist
c/o	complained of
Code Bravo	bomb threat
Code Pink	infant/child abduction
COPD	chronic obstructive pulmonary disease
CP	cerebral palsy
CPAP	continuous positive airway pressure (breathing)
CPR	cardiopulmonary resuscitation
CRT	Cardiac Response Team (no CRT = DNR = no code)
CT or CAT scan	Computed Tomography Imaging
CTD	clinical training director
CVA	cerebral vascular accident
CVSICU	Cardiovascular/Surgical Intensive Care Unit
D/C	discharge; discontinue
DD	developmental disability
DNR (no code)	do not resuscitate
D/O	disorder
DOB	date of birth
DOW	day of week
DVT	deep venous thrombosis
Dx	diagnosis
ECU	Extended Care Unit
EEG	electroencephalogram
EKG/ECG	electrocardiogram
EMS	Emergency Medical Services
ETOH abuse	alcohol abuse
ⓕ	female
Foley	catheter
FP	for profit
FY	fiscal year
Fx	fracture
g	gram
GA	gestational age
GERD	gastroesophageal reflux disease
GI	gastrointestinal
gravida	number of pregnancies
G-tube	gastric-tube (surgically placed feeding tube)

H/A	headache(s)
HIV	human immunodeficiency virus
HMO	health maintenance organization
HN	head nurse
HOH	hard of hearing
HPSE	Health Plan Southeast
HR	heart rate
HS	hour of sleep (bedtime)
HTN	hypertension (high blood pressure)
Hx	history
H&P	history and physical
ICF	intermediate care facility
ICF/MR	intermediate care facility for the mentally retarded
ICU	intensive care unit
IDDM	insulin-dependent diabetes mellitus
IM	intra-muscular (injection)
IMCU	Intermediate Care Unit
in	inch
IPPB	intermittent positive pressure breathing (respiratory exercise equipment)
IUGR	intrauterine growth retardation
IV	intravenous
IVH	intraventricular hemorrhage
IVT	intravenous therapy; intravenous therapist
kg	kilogram
Ⓛ	left
LCSW	licensed clinical social worker
L&D	Labor and Delivery
LE	lower extremity
LOS	length of stay
LPN	Licensed practical nurse
LTC	Long Term Care
ⓜ	male
MAR	medication administration record
max	maximum, maximal, maximally
MD	medical doctor
min	minimum, minimal, minimally
MIS	Management Information Systems
mod	moderate, moderately
MR	mental retardation

MRI	magnetic resonance imaging
MRSA	methicillin-resistant *Staphylococcus aureus* (Staph infection)
MRSE	methicillin-resistant *Staphylococcus epidermis*
MS	multiple sclerosis
MSICU	Medical/Surgical Intensive Care Unit
MSW	master of social work
MT	music therapy; music therapist
MT-BC	music therapist-board certified
MTI	music therapy intern
MVA/MVC	motor vehicle accident/crash
NBICU	Newborn Intensive Care Unit
NBIMCU	Newborn Intermediate Care Unit
NC	nasal canula
neo-	new
neopl	neoplasm
NG	naso-gastric (feeding tube)
NH	nursing home
NICU	Neurologic Intensive Care Unit or Neonatal Intensive Care Unit
NFP	not-for-profit
NKA	no known allergies
NKDA	no known drug allergies
NNS	non-nutritive sucking
NOS	not otherwise specified; no other symptoms
NPO	nothing by mouth
NSAIDs	nonsteroidal anti-inflammatory drugs
OBS	observation
OD	overdose
OG	oral-gastric (feeding tube)
OT	occupational therapy/therapist
p̄	after
PA	physician assistant
PACU	post anesthesia care unit
PAL	pacifier-activated lullabies
para, parity	number of children
PCN	penicillin
PE	physical exam
Peds	pediatric unit
PEG tube	surgically placed gastric feeding tube
peri-	around
PERP	Psychiatric Emergency Response Program

PET	positron emission tomography
PICU	Pediatric Intensive Care Unit
Plan A	disaster (hurricane, tornado, riot, ...)
Plan B	fire
PRN	as needed
PO	per os (by mouth, as in feeding by mouth)
Pt or pt	patient
PT	physical therapy/therapist
Q	quaque (every)
Q15 (30, ...)	every 15 (or 30 or ...) minute ...hour ...
QD	quaque dies (every day)
QID	quarter in die (four times a day)
QOL	quality of life
Ⓡ	right
RAD	Reactive Airway Disease
RN	registered nurse
RO	reality orientation
R/O	rule out
ROI	release of information
RR	respiratory rate
RT	respiratory therapy/therapist; recreation therapy/therapist
Rx	prescription
s̄	sine (without)
SaO2	oxygen saturation
SE	side effects
SIDS	sudden infant death syndrome
SLP	speech and language pathologist
SNF	skilled nursing facility
SSN	social security number
ST	speech therapy/therapist
SVD	spontaneous vaginal delivery
SW	social work/worker
Sx	symptoms
TB	tuberculosis
TBI	traumatic brain injury
TIA	transient ischemic attack
TID	ter in die (three times a day)
TMH	Tallahassee Memorial HealthCare/Hospital
TPA	tissue plasminogen activator (Tx for CVA)

TPN (and Lipids)	total parenteral nutrition
Tx	therapy; treatment
UE	upper extremity
VA	Veterans Affairs
VRE	vancomycin resistant enterococcus (infection)
VS	vital signs
WNL	within normal limits
XR	extended release
~	approximately
&; +	and
@	at
↑	increase
↓	decrease
⊕	positive
⊖	negative
#	pound
°	hour(s)
Δ	change
φ	no; not; none

GLOSSARY OF COMMONLY USED
MEDICAL TERMS

Abcess – a collection of dead white blood cells (pus) usually caused by bacterial infection

Alzheimer's disease – degeneration of brain cells resulting in dementia

Anemia – condition defined by less than normal amount of red blood cells

Aneurysm – a weak blood vessel with thin walls that can easily rupture and cause hemorrhaging

Angina – chest pain resulting from the heart not receiving enough oxygen

Ankylosis – abnormal adhesion and rigidity of the bones of a joint

Aphasia – inability to utilize language due to brain injury/damage to left temporal and/or frontal lobes

Apgar score – given at 1 and 5 minutes (and additional intervals as needed) after birth, revealing the infant's condition measured by color, heart rate, respiratory rate, responsiveness, and muscle tone

Apnea – cessation of breath

Apraxia – inability to remember patterns or sequences required to complete a task due to brain damage to frontal or parietal lobes

Arrhythmia – abnormal heart rhythm

Asphyxia – lack of oxygen in the body caused by interruption in breathing that can result in loss of consciousness

Aspiration – breathing foreign matter into the lungs

Ataxia – inability to voluntary control muscle coordination

Benign – not cancerous (as in *benign tumor*)

Bilirubin – bile pigment, yellowish in color that can cause jaundice

Biopsy – tissue removal for examination

Bolus – a bulbous mass, as in *bolus feeding*

Bradycardia – when the heart slows to an abnormally low rate

Breech – infant's position of buttocks first during vaginal delivery

Cardiac arrest – cessation of heart beat

Catheter – a medical tube inserted into a vessel, canal, or body cavity, used to extract or insert fluids

Cesarean section – surgical delivery of an infant through an abdominal incision in the mother

Chemotherapy – treatment of cancer with anticancer drugs

Coma – state of deep sleep or unconsciousness in which a person cannot be aroused, even with painful stimuli

Computed tomography (CT scan) – type of x-ray used to detect structural abnormalities

Congestive heart failure (CHF) – a condition in which the heart pumps out an inadequate amount of blood throughout the body

Contusion – bruise or injury to tissue, not including laceration

Cyst – a fluid-filled sac that develops abnormally on body cavities or structures

Cystic fibrosis – hereditary functional disorder of exocrine glands, resulting in severe effects on the digestive tract and lungs

Debridement – surgical removal of dead or lacerated tissue

Dehydration – deficiency of fluids in the body, specifically water

Delirium – a state of confusion and diminished mental ability, usually temporary, with various causes such as dehydration, drug intoxication, stroke, and severe infections

Dementia – declined mental ability that usually develops slowly and impairs memory, judgement, language, learning, attention, and occasionally personality

Depression – a mood disorder manifesting in disproportionate feelings of intense sadness and helplessness

Diabetes insipidus – disorder of the pituitary gland in which depleted levels of antidiuretic hormone causing excessive production of urine and thirst

Diabetes mellitus – disorder in which blood sugar levels are excessively high due to inadequate release of insulin from the pancreas, causing excessive production of urine and thirst

Dialysis – process of separating and removing toxic substances and excess fluids from the body

Dubowitz – assessment to estimate an infant's gestational age and development

Dysarthria – impaired articulation in speech due to brain injury

Dysphasia – impaired speech due to brain injury

Dysphagia – feeling or sensation that food is lodged in the throat or that food is not progressing down the esophagus normally, resulting in difficulty swallowing

Echocardiogram – diagnostic procedure studying the heart's structure and function using sound waves

Echoencephelogram (EEG) – diagnostic procedure studying the brain's electrical function

Echolalia – pathological echoing of another's verbalizations

Edema – excessive accumulation of fluid in tissue; swelling

Electrocardiogram (EKG or ECG) – diagnostic procedure studying the heart's electrical activity

Endoscopy – diagnostic procedure studying internal structures using a fiber-optic tube

Etiology – causes of an abnormal condition or disease

Extubation – removal of tube from a hollow organ (as in *ventilator extubation*)

Febrile – feverish

Hematoma – mass of collected blood formed in tissue or an organ, usually as result of ruptured blood vessel

Hemiparesis – partial paralysis or muscle weakness on one side of the body

Hemorrhage/hemorrhagic – excessive bleeding

Homeostatsis – a state of physiological stability (vital signs within normal ranges and no signs of distress)

Human immunodeficiency virus (HIV) – virus that destroys white blood cells, causing a weakened immune system and AIDS. HIV has two strands: HIV-1 (most prevalent in the western hemisphere, Europe, Asia, and central, south, and east Africa) and HIV-2 (most prevalent in West Africa)

Hydrocephalus – accumulation of water or cerebrospinal fluid around the brain resulting in ventricle enlargement and swelling of the skull

Hypertension – high blood pressure that can increase probability of stroke, heart attack, heart failure, kidney damage, and aneurysm

Hypotension – low blood pressure that can cause dizziness and fainting

Incontinence – loss of voluntary control over bowel and/or bladder functions

Intubation – insertion of a tube into a hollow organ to keep it open

Ischemia – localized tissue anemia caused by inadequate blood flow

Juvenile osteochondrosis – necrosis of the femur head occurring in children, primarily male

Lumbar puncture – diagnostic procedure removing a small amount of spinal fluid for examination (also known as *spinal tap*)

Nasal canula – prolonged tube that increases the flow of oxygen into the nostrils

Neuropathy – an abnormal state of the nerves or nervous system, usually degenerative

Malignant – cancerous (as in *malignant tumor*)

Metastisize – spread of disease from one location of the body to another, common phenomenon in cancer

Myocardial infarction – heart attack

Paralysis – partial or total loss of sensation, motion, or function in any part of the body

Phantom pain – the feeling or sensation of pain in an amputated or missing limb, caused by the nerves near the amputation site

Phototherapy – treatment that increases bilirubin levels by placing the patient under bilirubin lights

Radiation therapy – treatment that destroys rapidly dividing cells by targeting cells with x-rays; most commonly used to treat cancer

Reflux – backflow; regurgitation (as in acid reflux or GERD)

Sarcoma – a malignant tumor that grows on a bodily structure

Sedate – induction of relaxed or unconscious state with the use of sedative drugs (tranquilizers)

Sepsis – infection or toxic substance in the bloodstream

Shunt – a tube surgically inserted to provide passage of bodily fluid (such as blood) from one part to another

Stenosis – constriction or narrowing of a valve or other bodily passage

Stroke (CVA) – destruction of brain tissue caused by inadequate blood flow and insufficient oxygen to the brain

Tardive dyskinesia – disorder of the central nervous system usually caused by extended use of anti-psychotic drugs, resulting in twitching and other involuntary motor movement

Toxemia – condition caused by the presence of toxic substances in the blood

Tracheostomy – insertion of a tube into the trachea to allow air flow to the lungs

Transient ischemic attack (TIA) – temporary disruption of brain function, caused by an insufficient blood supply to the brain; also known as a mini-stroke

Tumor – an abnormal growth or mass of tissue, either benign or malignant

Venipuncture – surgical puncture of a vein, usually insertion of an IV

Ventilator – a device used for mechanical breathing; also known as a respirator

Vertigo – sensation of dizziness or spinning, often coupled with nausea and loss of balance

References

Berkow, R. (Ed.). (1997). *The Merck manual of medical information.* New York: Pocket Books.

Merriam-Webster's medical dictionary. (1995). Springfield, MA: Merriam-Webster.

PHARMACOLOGY INDEX BY TRADE NAME
OF COMMONLY USED DRUGS

KEY: **Trade name**; *generic name*: use (definition)

Accolate; *Zafirlukast*: treats asthma (leukotriene receptor antagonist)

Achromycin; *Tetracycline HCl*: broad spectrum antibiotic

Adalat, Adalat CC; *Nefedipine*: calcium-channel blocker

Adderall; *Extroamphetamine salts*: treats attention deficit disorder and obesity

Alesse-21; *Levonorgestrel + ethinyl estradiol*: oral contraceptive

Altace; *Ramipril*: antihypertensive (ACE inhibitor)

Alupent; *Metaproterenol*: bronchodilator

Amaryl; *Glimepiride*: antidiabetic

Ambien; *Zolpidem*: non-benzodiazepine hypnotic, sedative, tranquilizer

Amoxil; *Amoxicillin*: antibiotic

Arthrotec; *Diclofenac Sod. + Misoprostol*: analgesic

Ativan; *Lorazepam*: antianxiety agent

Atrovent; *Ipratropium Br*: bronchodilator

Avapro; *Irbesartan*: antihypertensive

Axid; *Nizatidine*: treats duodenal ulcers

Azmacort; *Triamcinolone Acetonide*: anti-inflammatory, treats asthma

Bactroban; *Mupirocin*: treats impetigo

Beepen VK; *Penicillin C Pot.* (Potassium Phynoxymethyle Penicillin): antibiotic for gram-positive microbes

Betapen VK; *Penicillin C Pot.* (Potassium Phynoxymethyle Penicillin): antibiotic for gram-positive microbes

Betimol; *Timolol Maleate*: treats glaucoma

Biaxin; *Clarithromycin*: macrolide antibiotic

BuSpar; *Bupropion HCl*: antianxiety

Calan; *Verapamil*: treats angina, antiarrhythmic (calcium channel blocker)

Cardizem; *Diltiazem*: antianginal agent

Cardura; *Doxazosin*: antihypertensive

Catapres; *Clonidine HCl*: antihypertensive transdermal patches

Cefzil; *Cefprozil*: antibiotic

Climara; *Estradiol*: moderate symptoms of menopause

Cipro; *Ciprofloxacin*: antibiotic

Claritin; *Loratadine*: long-acting antihistamine

Claritin-D 12hr; *Loratadine*: long-acting antihistamine

Compazine; *Prochlorperazine*: antianxiety, antiemetic

Cortisporin; *Hydrocortisone + Polymyxin & Neomycin*: antibacterial, anti-inflammatory

Cortisporin; *Polymyxin B; Neomysin; Gramcidin; & Hydrocort*: broad spectrum antibiotic

Coumadin; *Warfarin*: anticoagulant

Cozaar; *Losartan Potassium*: antihypertensive (angiotensin II atagonist)

Cycrin; *Medroxyprogesterone*: progestin

Cytotec; *Misoprostol*: prevents gastric ulcers in NSAID users

Darvocet; *Propoxyphene Napsylate + APAP*: analgesic

Daypro; *Oxaprozin*: NSAID for osteoarthritis and rheumatoid arthritis

Deltasone + generic; *Prednisone*: corticosteroid

Demulen; *Estrogen combination*: oral contraceptive

Depakene; *Valproic Acid*: anticonvulsant

Depakote; *Valproic Acid*: anticonvulsant

Desogen; *Ethinyl Estradiol + Desogestrel*: oral contraceptive

DiaBeta; *Glyburide*: antidiabetic

Dilacor XR; *Diltiazem*: antianginal agent

Dilantin; *Phenytoin*: aniconvulsant

Diovan; *Valsartan*: antihypertensive

Duragesic; *Fentanyl*: narcotic analgesic

Dyazide; *Triamterene + HCTZ*: antihypertensive, diuretic

Effexor; *Venlafaxine*: antidepressant

Elavil; *Amitriptyline HCl*: antidepressant

Eldepryl; *Selegiline*: MAO-A inhibitor/antiparkinson

Elixophyline; *Theophylline*: treats bronchial asthma and reversible bronchospasm

Elocon; *Mometasone Furoate*: corticosteroid

Eltroxin; *Levothyroxine*: manages hypothyroidism

Endocet; *Oxycodone HCl + Acetaminophen*: analgesic, antipyretic

E-Mycin, Erythrocin; *Erythromycin*: broad spectrum antibiotic

ERY-TAB, ERYC; *Erythromycin*: broad spectrum antibiotic

Esidrex; *Hydrochlorothiazide*: antihypertensive diuretic

Eskalith; *Lithium Carbonate*: treats manic depression

Estrace + generic; *Estradiol*: moderate symptoms of menopause, treats atrophic vaginitis

Estraderm; *Estradiol*: moderate symptoms of menopause

Evista; *Raloxifene HCl*: prevents osteoperosis, SERM

Feldene; *Piroxicam*: NSAID

Flagyl; *Metronidazole*: trichomonacide

Flexeril; *Cyclobenzaprine*: skeletal muscle relaxant

Flonase; *Fluticasone*: seasonal and perennial allergic rhinitis

Flovent; *Fluticasone*: seasonal and perennial allergic rhinitis

Floxin; *Ofloxacin*: fluoroquinolone antibiotic

Fosamax; *Alendronat Sodium*: treats and prevents Paget's Disease and Osteoporosis

Garamycin + generic; *Gentamicin HCl*: broad spectrum antibiotic

Glucophage; *Metformin HCl*: antidiabetic

Glucotrol; *Glipizide*: antidiabetic

Glynase + generic; *Glyburide*: antidiabetic

Haldol; *Haloperidol*: antipsychotic

HydroDiuril + generic; *Hydrochlorothiazide*: antihypertensive diuretic

Humulin; *Insulin*: controls diabetes

Hytrin; *Terazosin*: antihypertensive

Imitrex; *Sumatriptan*: treats migraine

Isoptin; *Verapamil*: treats angina, antiarrhythmic (calcium channel blocker)

Isordil, Isordil Tembids Titradose; *Isosorbide Dinitrate*: treats angina pectoris

K Lyte; *Triamcinolone Acetonide*: anti-inflammatory, treats asthma

Klonopin; *Clonazepam*: treats absence seizures

Klotrix; *Potassium Chloride*: potassium supplement

'Klor-Con,' 'K-Dur;' *Potassium Chloride*: potassium supplement

K-Tab; *Potassium Chloride*: potassium supplement

Kytril; *Granisetron*: prevents nausea and vomiting

Lamisil; *Terbinafine HCl*: antifungal

Lanoxicaps; *Digoxin*: cardiovascular agent

Lanoxin; *Digoxin*: cardiovascular agent

Larotid; *Amoxicillin*: antibiotic

Lasix + generic; *Furosemide*: diuretic

Ledercillin VK; *Penicillin C Pot.* (Potassium Phynoxymethyle Penicillin): antibiotic for gram-positive microbes

Lescol; *Fluvastatin*: antihyperlipidemic

Levoxyl; *Levothyroxine*: manages hypothyroidism

Levaquin; *Levofloxacin*: fluoroquinolone antibiotic

Lipitor*; Atorvastatin Calcium*: antihyperlipidemic

Loestrin 21, Loestrin Fe1/20; *Ethinyl Estradiol + Norethindrone*: monophasic oral contraceptive

Lomotil; *Diphenoxylate HCl + Atropine*: antidiarrheal

LoOvral 28; *Ethinyl Estradiol + Norgestrel*: oral contraceptive

Lopressor, Toprol XL; Metoprolol: antihypertensive (adrenergic blocking agent)

Lorabid; Loracarbef: cephalosporin

Lorcet Plus + generic Zydone; *Hydrocodone bitartrate + APAP*: narcotic, analgesic antitussive

Lortab; *Hydrocodone bitartrate + APAP*: narcotic, analgesic antitussive

Lotensin; *Benazepril HCl*: antihypertensive, ACE inhibitor

Lotrisone; *Clotrimazole + Betamethasone*: antifungal, anti-inflammatory

Macrobid; *Nitrolfurantoin macrocrystals*: urinary tract anti-infective

Macrodantin; *Nitrolfurantoin macrocrystals*: urinary tract anti-infective

Maxzide, Maxzide-25; *Triamterene + HCTZ*: antihypertensive, diuretic

Medrol; *Methylprednisolone*: anti-infammatory

Mevacor; *Lovastatin*: antihyperlipidemic

Miacalcin; *Calcitonin Salmon*: treats postmenopausal osteoporosis

Micro-K; *Potassium Chloride*: potassium supplement

Micronase; *Glyburide*: antidiabetic

Monistat-3, Monistat-7; *Miconazole*: treats vulvovaginal candidiasis

Monopril; *Fosinopril*: antihypertensive (ACE inhibitor)

Monurol; *Fostomycin*: single dose treatment for urinary tract infection

Naprelan, Naprosyn; *Naproxen*: antirheumatic

Nasacort; *Triamcinolone Acetonide*: anti-inflammatory, treats asthma

Nasonex; *Mometasone Furoate*: corticosteroid

Neosporin; *Neomysin, Polymyxin B, & Bacitracin*: antibiotic combination

Neurontin; *Gabapentin*: anticonvulsant

Nitroglycerin, NitroBid, Nitrostat, NitroDur II; *Nitroglycerin*: treats angina

Nolvadex; *Tamoxifen*: antiestrogen, reduces incidence of breast cancer

Nordette; *Estrogen combination*: oral contraceptive

Norlestrin; *Norethindrone*: oral contraceptive

Norvasc; *Amlodipine*: antihypertensive

Omnipen; *Ampicillin*: antibiotic

Ortho-Cept; *Ethinyl Estradiol + Desogestrel*: oral contraceptive

Ortho-Cyclen, Ortho-Tricyclen; *Norgestimate + ethinyl estradiol*: oral contraceptive

Ortho-Novum; *Norethindrone + ethinyl estradiol*: oral contraceptive

Ovcon 35;50; *Ethinyl Estradiol + Norethindrone*: monophasic oral contraceptive

Ovral & Ovral 28; *Estrogen combinations*: oral contraceptives

Panwarfin; *Warfarin*: anticoagulant

Paxil; *Paroxetine*: antidepressant

PCE; *Erythromycin*: broad spectrum antibiotic

Pen-Vee K; *Penicillin C Pot.* (Potassium Phynoxymethyle Penicillin): antibiotic for gram-positive microbes

Pepcid; *Famotidine*: treatment of peptic ulcers

Percocet-5; *Oxycodone HCl + Acetaminophen*: analgesic, antipyretic

Percodan; *Oxycodone HCl + O, Terephthalate + ASA*: analgesic, antipyretic

Peridex; *Chlorhexidine Gluconate*: microbicide

Phenergant generic; *Promethazine HCl*: treats angina, hypertension, arrhythmias, etc.

Plendil; *Felodipine*: antihypertensive

Polycillin; *Ampicillin*: antibiotic

Polymox; *Amoxicillin*: antibiotic

Pravachol; *Pravastatin Sodium*: antihyperlipidemic

Premarin; *Estrogens mixed*: replacement therapy during menopause and post-menopause

Premphase; *Estrogens + Medroxyprogesteron*: prevents and manages osteoporosis and meopausal symptoms

Prempro; *Estrogens + Medroxyprogesteron*: prevents and manages osteoporosis and meopausal symptoms

Prevacid; *Lansoprazole*: proton pump inhibitor

Prilosec; *Omeprazole*: proton pump inhibitor

Principen; *Ampicillin*: antibiotic

Prinivil; *Lisinopril*: antihypertensive

Procardia, Procardia XL; *Nefedipine*: calcium-channel blocker

Pronestyl; *Procainamide HCl*: anti-arrhythmic

Propacet; *Propoxyphene Napsylate + APAP*: analgesic

Proventil; *Albuterol*: bronchodilator

Provera; *Medroxyprogesterone*: progestin

Prozac; *Fluoxetine*: antidepressant

Questran; *Cholestryamine*: hyperlipidemic

Reglan; *Metoclopramide*: antinauseant, stimulates GI tract motility

Relafen; *Nabumetone*: NSAID

Restoril; *Temazepam*: sedative, hypnotic

Retin-A; *Tretinoin*: treats acne vulgaris

Rhinocort; *Budesonide*: intranasal steroid (anti-inflammatory)

Risperdal; *Risperidone*: antipsychotic

Ritalin; *Methylphendate*: cortical stimulant, treats ADHD

Robitet; *Tetracycline HCl*: broad spectrum antibiotic

Rogaine; *Minoxidil*: stimulates hair growth

Roxicet; *Oxycodone HCl + Acetaminophen*: analgesic, antipyretic

Serax; *Oxapam*: antianxiety

Serevent; *Salmeterol*: bronchodilator

Seroquel; *Quetiapine Fumarate*: antipsychotic

Serzone; *Netazodone HCl*: antidepressant

Skelaxin; *Metaxalone*: skeletal muscle relaxant

Slo-Phyllin; *Theophylline*: treats bronchial asthma and reversible bronchospasm

Slow-K; *Potassium Chloride*: potassium supplement

Sofarin + generic; *Warfarin*: anticoagulant

Soma; *Carisoprodol*: skeletal muscle relaxant

Sporanox; *Itraconazole*: antifungal oral and esophageal candidiasis

Sublimaze; *Fentanyl*: narcotic analgesic

Sumycin; *Tetracycline Phosphate*: broad spectrum antibiotic

Synthroid; *Levothyroxine*: manages hypothyroidism

Tagamet; *Cimetidine*: prevents and treats peptic ulcers

Tamoxifen; *Nolvadex*: treats breast cancer

Tegretol; *Carbamazepine*: anticonvulsant

Tenormin; *Atenolol*: antihypertensive, beta adrenergic blocking agent

Terazol-3, **Terazol-7**; *Terconazole*: vaginal antifungal

Theo-Dur; *Theophylline*: treats bronchial asthma and reversible bronchospasm

Tiazac; *Diltiazem*: antianginal agent

Tigan; *Trimethobenzamide*: antiemetic

Tilade; *Nedocromil*: prevents mast cell degranulation

Timoptic; *Timolol Maleate*: treats glaucoma

TobraDex; *Dexamethasone + Tobramycin*: ophthalmic steroid and antibiotic

Toprol XL; *Metoprolol*: antihypertensive (adrenergic blocking agent)

Totacillin; *Ampicillin*: antibiotic

Transdermal; *Estradiol*: moderate symptoms of menopause

Traphasil; *Estrogen combinations*: oral contraceptive

Trental; *Pentoxifyline*: treats intermittent claudication

Tri-Levlen; *Estrogen combinations*: oral contraceptive

Trimax; *Amoxicillin*: antibiotic

TruSopt; *Dorzolamide*: antiglaucoma

Tylenol with Codeine; *Acetapminophen + Codeine*: analgesic

Tylox; *Oxycodone HCl + Acetaminophen*: analgesic, antipyretic

Ultram; *Tramadol*: central analgesic

Uni-Dur; *Theophylline*: treats bronchial asthma and reversible bronchospasm

Valium; *Diazepam*: antianxiety

Valtrex; *Valacyclovir HCl*: antiherpes virus agent

Vanceril; *Beclomethansone dipropionate*: corticosteroid (treats rhinitis)

Vaseretic; *Enalapril Maleate*: antihypertensive

Vasotec; *Enalapril Maleate*: antihypertensive

Veetids; *Penicillin C Pot.* (Potassium Phynoxymethyle Penicillin): antibiotic for gram-positive microbes

Ventolin; *Albuterol*: bronchodilator

Verelan + generic; *Verapamil*: treats angina, antiarrhythmic (calcium channel blocker)

Viagra; *Sildenafil*: treats erectile dysfunction

Vicodin; *Hydrocodone bitartrate + APAP*: narcotic, analgesic antitussive

Vioxx; *Rofecoxib*: NSAID

Vivelle; *Estradiol*: moderate symptoms of menopause

Wellbutrin; *Bupropion HCl*: antidepressant

Xalatan; *Latanoprost*: Prostaglandin agonist for glaucoma

Wymox; *Amoxicillin*: antibiotic

Xanax; *Alprasolam*: treats anxiety

Zantac; *Ranitidine HCl*: histamine H_2 antagonist

Zestril; *Lisinopril*: antihypertensive

Ziac; *Bisoprolol Fumarate + HCTZ*: antihypertensive combination

Zithromax; *Azithromycin*: antibiotic

Zocor; *Simvastatin*: antihyperlipidemic

Zofran; *Ondansetron*: antiemetic

Zoloft; *Sertraline*: antidepressant

Zovirax; *Acyclovir Sodium*: treats herpes

Zyban; *Bupropion HCl*: aids in smoke cessation*

Zyloprim; *Allopurinol*: treats gout, hyperuricemia

Zyprexa; *Olanzapine*: antipsychotic

Zyrtec; *Cetirizine*: antihistamine

Material for this pharmacology index was adapted from Hall, G. D., & Reiss, B. S. (1997). *Appleton and Lange's Review of Pharmacy* (7th ed.). New York: McGraw-Hill Medical Publishing Division.

PHARMACOLOGY INDEX BY USE

KEY: **Trade name**; *generic name*: use (definition)

Acne treatment – drugs used to treat various forms of acne
- **Retin-A**; *Tretinoin*: treats acne vulgaris

ADD/ADHD treatment – drugs used to reduce hyperactivity, especially in children
- **Adderall**; *Extroamphetamine salts*: treats attention deficit disorder and obesity
- **Ritalin**; *Methylphendate*: cortical stimulant, treats ADHD

Analgesics – drugs used to relieve pain
- **Arthrotec**; *Diclofenac Sod. + Misoprostol*
- **Darvocet**; *Propoxyphene Napsylate + APAP*
- **Endocet**; *Oxycodone HCl + Acetaminophen*: analgesic, antipyretic
- **Percocet-5**; *Oxycodone HCl + Acetaminophen*: analgesic, antipyretic
- **Percodan**; *Oxycodone HCl + O, Terephthalate + ASA*: analgesic, antipyretic
- **Propacet**; *Propoxyphene Napsylate + APAP*
- **Roxicet**; *Oxycodone HCl + Acetaminophen*: analgesic, antipyretic
- **Tylenol with Codeine**; *Acetapminophen + Codeine*
- **Tylox**; *Oxycodone HCl + Acetaminophen*: analgesic, antipyretic
- **Ultram**; *Tramadol*: central analgesic

Antianginal agents – drugs used to treat angina pain
- **Calan**; *Verapamil*: treats angina, antiarrhythmic (calcium channel blocker)
- **Cardizem**; *Diltiazem*
- **Dilacor XR**; *Diltiazem*
- **Isoptin**; *Verapamil*: treats angina, antiarrhythmic (calcium channel blocker)
- **Isordil, Isordil Tembids Titradose**; *Isosorbide Dinitrate*
- **Nitroglycerin, NitroBid, Nitrostat, NitroDur II**; *Nitroglycerin*
- **Phenergant generic**; *Promethazine HCl*: treats angina, hypertension, arrhythmias, etc.
- **Tiazac**; *Diltiazem*
- **Verelan + generic**; *Verapamil*: treats angina, antiarrhythmic

Antianxiety drugs – drugs used to treat anxiety
- **Ativan**; *Lorazepam*
- **BuSpar**; *Bupropion HCl*
- **Compazine**; *Prochlorperazine*: antianxiety, antiemetic
- **Serax**; *Oxapam*

- **Valium**; *Diazepam*
- **Xanax**; *Alprasolam*

Anti-arrhythmic drugs – drugs used to treat disorders of heart rhythm
- **Adalat, Adalat CC**; *Nefedipine*: calcium-channel blocker
- **Phenergant generic**; *Promethazine HCl*: treats angina, hypertension, arrhythmias, etc
- **Procardia, Procardia XL**; *Nefedipine*: calcium-channel blocker
- **Pronestyl**; *Procainamide HCl*
- **Verelan + generic**; *Verapamil*: treats angina, antiarrhythmic (calcium channel blocker)

Antibiotics – drugs used to treat bacterial infections
- **Achromycin**; *Tetracycline HCl*: broad spectrum antibiotic
- **Amoxil**; *Amoxicillin*
- **Beepen VK**; *Penicillin C Pot.* (Potassium Phynoxymethyle Penicillin): antibiotic for gram-positive microbes
- **Betapen VK**; *Penicillin C Pot.* (Potassium Phynoxymethyle Penicillin): antibiotic for gram-positive microbes
- **Biaxin**; *Clarithromycin*: macrolide antibiotic
- **Cefzil**; *Cefprozil*
- **Cipro**; *Ciprofloxacin*
- **Cortisporin**; *Polymyxin B; Neomysin; Gramcidin; & Hydrocort*: broad spectrum antibiotic
- **E-Mycin, Erythrocin**; *Erythromycin*: broad spectrum antibiotic
- **ERY-TAB, ERYC**; *Erythromycin*: broad spectrum antibiotic
- **Floxin**; *Ofloxacin*: fluoroquinolone antibiotic
- **Garamycin + generic**; *Gentamicin HCl*: broad spectrum antibiotic
- **Larotid**; *Amoxicillin*
- **Ledercillin VK**; *Penicillin C Pot.* (Potassium Phynoxymethyle Penicillin): antibiotic for gram-positive microbes
- **Levaquin**; *Levofloxacin*: fluoroquinolone antibiotic
- **Lorabid**; Loracarbef: cephalosporin
- **Macrobid**; *Nitrolfurantoin macrocrystals*: urinary tract anti-infective
- **Macrodantin**; *Nitrolfurantoin macrocrystals*: urinary tract anti-infective
- **Monurol**; *Fostomycin*: single dose treatment for urinary tract infection
- **Neosporin**; *Neomysin, Polymyxin B, & Bacitracin*: antibiotic combination
- **Omnipen**; *Ampicillin*
- **PCE**; *Erythromycin*: broad spectrum antibiotic
- **Polycillin**; *Ampicillin*
- **Polymox**; *Amoxicillin*
- **Principen**; *Ampicillin*
- **Robitet**; *Tetracycline HCl*: broad spectrum antibiotic

- **Sumycin**; *Tetracycline Phosphate*: broad spectrum antibiotic
- **Totacillin**; *Ampicillin*
- **Trimax**; *Amoxicillin*
- **Veetids**; *Penicillin C Pot.* (Potassium Phynoxymethyle Penicillin): antibiotic for gram-positive microbes
- **Wymox**; *Amoxicillin*
- **Zithromax**; *Azithromycin*

Anticancer drugs – drugs used to treat cancer
- **Nolvadex**; *Tamoxifen*: antiestrogen, reduces incidence of breast cancer
- **Tamoxifen**; *Nolvadex*: treats breast cancer

Anticoagulants – drugs used to prevent blood coagulation
- **Coumadin**; *Warfarin*
- **Panwarfin**; *Warfarin*
- **Sofarin + generic**; *Warfarin*

Anticonvulsants – drugs used to prevent epileptic seizures
- **Depakene**; *Valproic Acid*
- **Depakote**; *Valproic Acid*
- **Dilantin**; *Phenytoin*
- **Klonopin**; *Clonazepam*: treats absence seizures
- **Neurontin**; *Gabapentin*
- **Tegretol**; *Carbamazepine*

Antidepressants – drugs used to elevate mood
- **Effexor**; *Venlafaxine*
- **Elavil**; *Amitriptyline HCl*
- **Paxil**; *Paroxetine*
- **Prozac**; *Fluoxetine*
- **Serzone**; *Netazodone HCl*
- **Wellbutrin**; *Bupropion HCl*
- **Zoloft**; *Sertraline*

Antidiabetics – drugs used to treat lack of insulin
- **Glucotrol**; *Glipizide*
- **Amaryl**; *Glimepiride*
- **DiaBeta**; *Glyburide*
- **Glucophage**; *Metformin HCl*
- **Glynase + generic**; *Glyburide*
- **Humulin**; *Insulin*: controls diabetes
- **Micronase**; *Glyburide*

Antidiarrheals – drugs used to relieve diarrhea
- **Lomotil**; *Diphenoxylate HCl + Atropine*

Antiemetics – drugs used to treat nausea/vomiting
- **Compazine**; *Prochlorperazine*: antianxiety, antiemetic
- **Kytril**; *Granisetron*: prevents nausea and vomiting
- **Reglan**; *Metoclopramide*: antinauseant, stimulates GI tract motility
- **Tigan**; *Trimethobenzamide*
- **Zofran**; *Ondansetron*

Antifungals – drugs used to treat fungal infections
- **Flagyl**; *Metronidazole*: trichomonacide
- **Lamisil**; *Terbinafine HCl*
- **Lotrisone**; *Clotrimazole + Betamethasone*: antifungal, anti-inflammatory
- **Monistat-3, Monistat-7**; *Miconazole*: treats vulvovaginal candidiasis
- **Sporanox**; *Itraconazole*: antifungal oral and esophageal candidiasis
- **Terazol-3, Terazol-7**; *Terconazole*: vaginal antifungal

Antiglaucomas – drugs used to treat glaucoma
- **Betimol**; *Timolol Maleate*
- **Timoptic**; *Timolol Maleate*
- **TruSopt**; *Dorzolamide*
- **Xalatan**; *Latanoprost*: Prostaglandin agonist for glaucoma

Antihistamines – drugs used to counteract histamines, chemicals involved in allergic reactions
- **Claritin**; *Loratadine*: long-acting antihistamine
- **Claritin-D 12hr**; *Loratadine*: long-acting antihistamine
- **Zantac**; *Ranitidine HCl*: histamine H_2 antagonist
- **Zyrtec**; *Cetirizine*

Antihyperlipidemics – drugs used to reduce lipids (fats) in the blood
- **Lescol**; *Fluvastatin*
- **Lipitor**; *Atorvastatin Calcium*
- **Mevacor**; *Lovastatin*
- **Pravachol**; *Pravastatin Sodium*
- **Questran**; *Cholestryamine*
- **Zocor**; *Simvastatin*

Antihypertensives – drugs used to lower blood pressure
- **Altace**; *Ramipril*:   (ACE inhibitor)
- **Avapro**; *Irbesartan*
- **Cardura**; *Doxazosin*
- **Catapres**; *Clonidine HCl*:   antihypertensive transdermal patches
- **Cozaar**; *Losartan Potassium*: antihypertensive (angiotensin II atagonist)
- **Diovan**; *Valsartan*
- **Dyazide***; Triamterene + HCTZ*: antihypertensive, diuretic
- **Esidrex***; Hydrochlorothiazide*: antihypertensive diuretic
- **HydroDiuril + generic**; *Hydrochlorothiazide*: antihypertensive diuretic
- **Hytrin**; *Terazosin*
- **Lopressor, Toprol XL**; Metoprolol: antihypertensive (adrenergic blocking agent)
- **Lotensin**; *Benazepril HCl*:   antihypertensive, ACE inhibitor
- **Maxzide, Maxzide-25**; *Triamterene + HCTZ*: antihypertensive, diuretic
- **Monopril**; *Fosinopril*: antihypertensive (ACE inhibitor)
- **Norvasc**; *Amlodipine*
- **Phenergant generic**; *Promethazine HCl*: treats angina, hypertension, arrhythmias, etc
- **Plendil**; *Felodipine*
- **Prinivil**; *Lisinopril*
- **Tenormin**; *Atenolol*: antihypertensive, beta adrenergic blocking agent
- **Toprol XL**; *Metoprolol*: antihypertensive (adrenergic blocking agent)
- **Vaseretic;** *Enalapril Maleate*
- **Vasotec;** *Enalapril Maleate*
- **Zestril**; *Lisinopril*
- **Ziac**; *Bisoprolol Fumarate + HCTZ*:   antihypertensive combination

Anti-inflammatories – drugs used to reduce inflammation
- **Cortisporin***; Hydrocortisone + Polymyxin & Neomycin*: antibacterial, anti-inflammatory
- **Feldene**; *Piroxicam*: NSAID (non-steroid anti-inflammatory drug)
- **Medrol**; *Methylprednisolone*
- **Relafen**; *Nabumetone*: NSAID
- **Vioxx**; *Rofecoxib*: NSAID

Antiparkinson drugs – drugs used to treat Parkinson's disease symptoms
- **Eldepryl**; *Selegiline*: MAO-A inhibitor

Antipsycotics – drugs used to treat symptoms of severe psychotic disorders
- **Eskalith**; *Lithium Carbonate*: treats manic depression
- **Haldol**; *Haloperidol*
- **Risperdal**; *Risperidone*

- **Seroquel**; *Quetiapine Fumarate*
- **Zyprexa**; *Olanzapine*

Antipyretics – drugs used to reduce fever
- **Percocet-5**; *Oxycodone HCl + Acetaminophen*: analgesic, antipyretic
- **Percodan***; Oxycodone HCl + O, Terephthalate + ASA*: analgesic, antipyretic
- **Roxicet**; *Oxycodone HCl + Acetaminophen*: analgesic, antipyretic
- **Tylox**; *Oxycodone HCl + Acetaminophen*: analgesic, antipyretic

Antirheumatics – drugs used to treat arthritis/rheumatism
- **Daypro**; *Oxaprozin*: NSAID for osteoarthritis and rheumatoid arthritis
- **Naprelan, Naprosyn**; *Naproxen*

Antivirals – drugs used to treat viral infections
- **Valtrex**; *Valacyclovir HCl*: antiherpes virus agent
- **Zovirax**; *Acyclovir Sodium*: treats herpes

Asthma treatments – drugs used to treat asthma
- **Accolate**; *Zafirlukast* (leukotriene receptor antagonist)
- **Azmacort***; Triamcinolone Acetonide*: anti-inflammatory, treats asthma
- **K Lyte**; *Triamcinolone Acetonide*: anti-inflammatory, treats asthma
- **Nasacort**; *Triamcinolone Acetonide*: anti-inflammatory, treats asthma

Bronchial treatments – drugs used to open the bronchial tubes
- **Alupent**; *Metaproterenol*: bronchodilator
- **Atrovent**; *Ipratropium Br*: bronchodilator
- **Elixophyline**; *Theophylline*: treats bronchial asthma and reversible bronchospasm
- **Proventil**; *Albuterol*: bronchodilator
- **Serevent**; *Salmeterol*: bronchodilator
- **Slo-Phyllin**; *Theophylline*: treats bronchial asthma and reversible bronchospasm
- **Theo-Dur**; *Theophylline*: treats bronchial asthma and reversible bronchospasm
- **Uni-Dur**; *Theophylline*: treats bronchial asthma and reversible bronchospasm
- **Ventolin**; *Albuterol*: bronchodilator

Cardiovascular agents – drugs used to treat heart disease
- **Lanoxicaps**; *Digoxin*
- **Lanoxin**; *Digoxin*

Claudication treatment – drugs used to treat leg pain due to atherosclerosis
- **Trental**; *Pentoxifyline*: treats intermittent claudication

Contraceptives – drugs used to prevent pregnancy
- **Alesse-21**; *Levonorgestrel + ethinyl estradiol*: oral contraceptive

- **Demulen**; *Estrogen combination*: oral contraceptive
- **Desogen***; Ethinyl Estradiol + Desogestrel*: oral contraceptive
- **Loestrin 21**, **Loestrin Fe1/20**; *Ethinyl Estradiol + Norethindrone*: monophasic oral contraceptive
- **LoOvral 28**; *Ethinyl Estradiol + Norgestrel*: oral contraceptive
- **Nordette**; *Estrogen combination*: oral contraceptive
- **Norlestrin**; *Norethindrone*: oral contraceptive
- **Ortho-Cept**; *Ethinyl Estradiol + Desogestrel*: oral contraceptive
- **Ortho-Cyclen**, **Ortho-Tricyclen**; *Norgestimate + ethinyl estradiol*: oral contraceptive
- **Ortho-Novum***; Norethindrone + ethinyl estradiol*: oral contraceptive
- **Ovcon 35;50***; Ethinyl Estradiol + Norethindrone*: monophasic oral contraceptive
- **Ovral & Ovral 28**; *Estrogen combinations*: oral contraceptives

Corticosteroids – hormonal preparations used as anti-inflammatories or immunosuppressives
- **Deltasone + generic**; *Prednisone*
- **Elocon***; Mometasone Furoate*
- **Nasonex**; *Mometasone Furoate*
- **Vanceril**; *Beclomethansone dipropionate* (treats rhinitis)

Diuretics – drugs that increase urine production
- **Lasix + generic**; *Furosemide*
- **Esidrex***; Hydrochlorothiazide*: antihypertensive diuretic

Erectile dysfunction treatments – drugs that facilitate erection
- **Viagra**; *Sildenafil*

Female sex hormones – hormones for menstrual disorders, menopausal symptoms, contraception
- **Climara***; Estradiol*: moderate symptoms of menopause
- **Cycrin**; *Medroxyprogesterone*: progestin
- **Estrace + generic**; *Estradiol*: moderate symptoms of menopause, treats atrophic vaginitis
- **Estraderm**; *Estradiol*: moderate symptoms of menopause
- **Premarin**; *Estrogens mixed*: replacement therapy during menopause and post-menopause
- **Premphase**; *Estrogens + Medroxyprogesteron*: prevents and manages osteoporosis and meopausal symptoms
- **Prempro**; *Estrogens + Medroxyprogesteron*: prevents and manages osteoporosis and meopausal symptoms
- **Provera**; *Medroxyprogesterone*: progestin
- **Transdermal**; *Estradiol*: moderate symptoms of menopause

- **Traphasil**; *Estrogen combinations*: oral contraceptive
- **Tri-Levlen**; *Estrogen combinations*: oral contraceptive
- **Vivelle**; *Estradiol*: moderate symptoms of menopause

Gout treatment – drugs used to treat gout
- **Zyloprim**; *Allopurinol*: treats hyperuricemia

Hair growth stimulant – drugs used to stimulate hair growth
- **Rogaine**; *Minoxidil*

Hypothyroidism – drugs used to stimulate activity of the thyroid gland
- **Eltroxin**; *Levothyroxine*
- **Levoxyl**; *Levothyroxine*
- **Synthroid**; *Levothyroxine*

Impetigo treatment – drugs used to treat impetigo infections
- **Bactroban**; *Mupirocin*

Mast cell degranulation prevention
- **Tilade**; *Nedocromil*

Microbicide – agents that kill microbes (bacteria, fungi, and protozoal parasites)
- **Pen-Vee K***; Penicillin C Pot.* (Potassium Phynoxymethyle Penicillin): antibiotic for gram-positive microbes
- **Peridex**; *Chlorhexidine Gluconate*

Migraine Treatment
- **Imitrex**; *Sumatriptan*

Narcotic analgesic – narcotic used to reduce pain
- **Duragesic**; *Fentanyl*
- **Lorcet Plus + generic Zydone**; *Hydrocodone bitartrate + APAP*: narcotic, analgesic antitussive
- **Lortab**; *Hydrocodone bitartrate + APAP*: narcotic, analgesic antitussive
- **Sublimaze**; *Fentanyl*
- **Vicodin**; *Hydrocodone bitartrate + APAP*: narcotic, analgesic antitussive

Obesity treatment – drugs to treat obesity
- **Adderall**; *Extroamphetamine salts*

Opthalmic steroid – steroid used for eye treatments
- **TobraDex**; *Dexamethasone + Tobramycin*: ophthalmic steroid and antibiotic

Osteoporosis Treatment
- **Evista**; *Raloxifene HCl*: prevents osteoperosis, SERM
- **Fosamax**; *Alendronat Sodium*: treats and prevents Paget's Disease and Osteoporosis
- **Miacalcin**; *Calcitonin Salmon*: treats postmenopausal osteoporosis

Potassium supplement
- **'Klor-Con,' 'K-Dur;'** *Potassium Chloride*
- **Klotrix**; *Potassium Chloride*
- **K-Tab**; *Potassium Chloride*
- **Micro-K**; *Potassium Chloride*
- **Slow-K**; *Potassium Chloride*

Proton pump inhibitors – drugs used to treat heartburn
- **Prevacid**; *Lansoprazole*
- **Prilosec**; *Omeprazole*

Rhinitis treatment – drugs used to treat nasal irritation
- **Flonase**; *Fluticasone*: seasonal and perennial allergic rhinitis
- **Flovent**; *Fluticasone*: seasonal and perennial allergic rhinitis
- **Rhinocort**; *Budesonide*: intranasal steroid (anti-inflammatory)

Sedatives/hypnotics – drugs used to increase sleep/relaxation
- **Ambien**; *Zolpidem*: non-benzodiazepine hypnotic, sedative, tranquilizer
- **Restoril**; *Temazepam*: sedative, hypnotic

Skeletal muscle relaxant – drugs used to relax striated muscles
- **Flexeril**; *Cyclobenzaprine*
- **Skelaxin**; *Metaxalone*
- **Soma**; *Carisoprodol*

Smoking cessation – drugs used to assist those wishing to stop smoking
- **Zyban**; *Bupropion HCl*

Ulcer treatments – drugs used to treat ulcers
- **Axid**; *Nizatidine*: treats duodenal ulcers
- **Cytotec**; *Misoprostol*: prevents gastric ulcers in NSAID users
- **Pepcid**; *Famotidine*: treatment of peptic ulcers
- **Tagamet**; *Cimetidine*: prevents and treats peptic ulcers

Material for this pharmacology index was adapted from Hall, G. D., & Reiss, B. S. (1997). *Appleton and Lange's review of pharmacy* (7th ed.). New York: McGraw-Hill Medical Publishing Division.

SUBJECT AND NAME INDEX

B

C

D

E

G

N

O

S

T

ultrasound, 214
Unchained Melody, 212
Under the Boardwalk, 212
undergraduate, 6, 15, 16, 22, 29, 35, 121
underprivileged, 114
unit nurse, 7
units, 7, 17, 18, 19, 23, 47, 48, 54, 55, 57, 61, 62, 64, 69, 70, 146, 168, 191, 197, 239, 240, 244, 262
university, 5, 7, 11, 15, 16, 30, 37, 46, 47, 48, 49, 52, 53, 55, 58, 61, 77, 113, 115, 169, 170
university administrators, 7
University Affiliated Internship (UAI), 47
university/hospital partnership, 5, 37
Updike, 261
upper/lower division, 35
urology, 62
utilization manager, 168

V

Valentin, 261
validation therapy, 64
value, 13, 22, 24, 63, 113, 114, 124, 150, 197, 214, 218, 220, 252
vanco, 172
vancomycin resistant enterococcus, 270
variable credit, 36
vasoconstriction, 247
VD, 172
venipuncture, 51, 239
venipunctures, 56, 124, 150, 244, 253
Vent, 172
ventilator, 79, 174, 213, 214, 229, 261, 272
ventilator extubation trials, 213, 214
venues, 15, 216
verbal and gestural cues, 187
verbal feedback, 71
verbal interaction, 147
Vermont Oxford Network, 240
vestibular, 64, 170, 171, 173
vestibular stimulation, 170, 171
vibro-tactile acoustic couch, 134
videotaped, 144
Villarruel, 244
Vincent, 261
visitation time in the NICU, 197
visitors, 15, 25, 28, 29, 46, 79, 91, 234
visits, 18, 33, 117, 136, 161
visual, 9, 15, 64, 79, 155, 170, 171, 173, 183, 194, 229, 248
visual analog scale, 155, 183
visual arts, 9, 15
visual impairments, 229
vital signs, 123, 270, 272
vocal intensity, 192
vocal range, 67

volunteerism, 15, 22, 24
volunteers, 7, 8, 9, 16, 17, 18, 19, 22, 23, 24, 25, 29, 33, 46, 49, 65, 91, 226
vomiting, 147, 216, 248, 251, 278, 288
von Hermann, 13
vowels, 198

W

Wade, 261
Wagner, 261
waiting room, 8, 137, 176, 177, 213
Waldon, 261
Walker, 248
Walsh, 245
Walther-Larsen, 261
Walworth, 3, 6, 31, 36, 37, 40, 54, 155, 165, 174, 182, 223, 229, 261, 320
Ward, 155, 245
Warren, 255
Watanabe, 156
web sites, 17, 23
web-based community service course, 8
weekly reports, 15, 19, 22, 24
Weeks, 257
Weidenfeller, 262
weight, 5, 64, 123, 126, 127, 142, 147, 150, 151, 152, 157, 195, 197, 198, 199, 200, 210, 245, 254
weight gain, 5, 64, 127, 151, 157, 197
Weisbrod, 261
Weisz, 248, 253
well-being, 5, 7, 29, 125, 136, 142, 161
West, 258
Wharrad, 200, 210
What a Wonderful World, 212
Whipple, 5, 10, 17, 30, 40, 43, 149, 157, 158, 229, 260, 261, 320
White, 245, 261
white noise, 198, 254
Wiand, 261
Wigram, 257, 258
Wilcoxon Matched-Pair Signed Rank Test of Differences, 156
Williams, 157, 160, 246
Willoughby, Wallaby, 204
Winokur, 160, 262
Wlodarczyk, 161
Wolfe, 262
Wong, 262
work space, 45, 50, 52
workshop attendees, 231
workshops, 70, 90, 238
womb, 197
Wonderful Tonight, 212
Woods, 201, 210
World Federation of Music Therapy, 240

X

Y

Z

Author Profiles

Jayne M. Standley, Ph.D., MT-BC, is the Robert O. Lawton Distinguished Professor and a Distinguished Research Professor at Florida State University with research emphasis on music therapy in the Neonatal Intensive Care Unit. Standley is recipient of numerous awards and honors including the Publication and Merit Awards from the American Music Therapy Association. She holds three degrees from The Florida State University: Bachelor's and Master's degrees in Music Therapy and Ph.D. in Special Education.

Dianne Gregory, MM, MT-BC, is an Associate Professor of Music at Florida State University. She completed a Bachelor's degree in Music Education at Huntingdon College and the equivalency/Master's degree in Music Therapy at FSU. She is a prolific researcher with emphasis on technology and the development of therapy competencies. She developed the Arts in Medicine course concept and is the recipient of the SER-AMTA Research Award.

Jennifer Whipple, Ph.D., MT-BC, completed a Bachelor's degree in Music Education at the University of Richmond, the equivalency/Master's degree in Music Therapy at FSU, and the doctoral degree at FSU. She is the original coordinator of the TMH clinical MT program. She has completed research projects with premature infants and their families and with a variety of clients in clinical settings including battered women and children with autism. She is the recipient of the Mary J. Hilliard Music Therapy Scholarship for 2003–04.

Darcy DeLoach Walworth, MM, MT-BC, is a doctoral student at the Florida State University. She holds Bachelor's and Master's degrees in Music Therapy from FSU and interned at TMH. She is a past coordinator of the TMH clinical MT program and developed the pediatric procedural support music therapy practice. She received funding from the National Brain Tumor foundation for research. She has completed other research projects on the effects of music and stress and on pediatric patients' response to procedural support MT.

Judy Nguyen, MM, MT-BC, is the current Coordinator of the Medical MT and Arts in Medicine Programs at TMH. She completed both Bachelor's and Master's degrees in Music Therapy at FSU and interned at TMH. She is currently a staff member in the School of Music at Florida State University and has conducted research with use of MT with eminent hospice patients. She continues to be engaged in research in MT for brain surgery patients and as a preoperative anxiolytic.

Jennifer Jarred, MM, MT-BC, completed a Bachelor's degree in Music Education at Louisana State University and an equivalency/Master's degree in Music Therapy at FSU. She interned at TMH and was funded by the TMH Foundation to direct the National Institute for Allied Health Professionals on Music Therapy for Infants and Children. Her thesis research involved the use of live music in the surgical waiting room to reduce anxiety of patient families.

Kristen Adams, MM, MT-BC, completed a Bachelor's degree and Master's degree in Music Therapy at FSU, interned at TMH, and held the assistantship for one year assigned to the TMH medical MT program. Her thesis research involved the use of live MT for gynecological surgery patients.

Danielle Procelli, MM, MT-BC, completed Bachelor's and Master's degrees in Music Therapy at Florida State University. She interned at TMH and held the assistantship assigned to the TMH medical MT program. Her thesis research involved the use of live MT for breastfeeding newborns.

Andrea Cevasco, MM, MT-BC, is a doctoral student at Florida State University. She holds the Bachelor's degree in Music Therapy from the University of Alabama and the Master's degree in Music Therapy from the University of Georgia. She is a former instructor at the University of Georgia and has completed research with premature infants, children with developmental disabilities, and patients with Alzheimer's disease. She is the recipient of the Mary J. Hilliard Music Therapy Scholarship for 2004–05.